Praise for *Fugitive Dreams*

"You're going to want to read this book from beginning to end. I would put it down, then pick it back up, then reread many of the stories, because they are stunning testaments to 'sumud'. Ultimately, *Fugitive Dreams* is a story of "exiles, displaced persons, refugees, migrant workers, nomads, emigrants and wanderers – those who left their homes at gunpoint"…as well as a book of hope, determination, and forgiveness."
– Greta Berlin, Co-Founder, the Free Gaza movement

"A profound fictional portrayal of Palestinian life and struggle."
– Sam Bahour, *ePalestine*

"*Fugitive Dreams* whisks us along the streets and hills of Palestine, giving a glimpse of an occupied childhood witnessing an Intifada against a military power. The knock on the door, in the middle of the night, is all too familiar. The Nakba's inherited trauma, the dislocation of statelessness and exile, the suspended evanescence of interim periods, and never-ending processes of "peace" are all there."
– *This Week in Palestine*

"An intensely personal journey of the protagonist … that explores every facet of life — heritage, birth, childhood, love, livelihood, friendships, dreams, neighborhoods, memories, and aspirations."
– Ashok Subramanian, Author

"I was engaged from the start of the book and had to see how it would end, even in a world where there is no end in sight. Hanhan's suggestions toward the end would serve all of us, no matter what your challenges may be. I recommend this read to all who want to understand and honor all of the 'others' who people this Earth."
– Ned Tillman, Author of *Good Endeavour, The Big Melt* and *Saving the Places We Love*

"*Fugitive Dreams* is one of the few books that would make a compelling read even for those of us very familiar with the question of Palestine. ... I highly recommend Hanhan's debut literary project."
– Jareer Kassis, *Mondoweiss*

"A scream that comes from the mouths of an entire generation. ... This book is full of shocking, poignant, and sublime moments, and it is delightfully fascinating, vividly evocative, and emotionally honest throughout."
– *The Bookish Elf*

FUGITIVE DREAMS

Chronicles of Occupation and Resistance

Ramsey Hanhan

Fomite
Burlington, VT

Copyright © 2022 Ramsey Hanhan
Chapter 15 is adapted from a multi-part article that first appeared on
ElectronicIntifada.net, 2004
Cover Image: The Wall near Bir Nabala, Ramsey Hanhan
All rights reserved. No part of this book may be reproduced in any form or by any means
without the prior written consent of the publisher, except in the case of brief quotations used in
reviews and certain other noncommercial uses permitted by copyright law.

ISBN-13: 978-1-953236-71-5
Library of Congress Control Number: 2022934519

Fomite
58 Peru Street
Burlington, VT 05401
www.fomitepress.com
12-06-2024

to
Z
may she inherit
a better world
and may her generation
be freed from the burden

Acknowledgments

I am deeply grateful to my publishers from Fomite Press. Marc Estrin's thoughtful edits and perceptive comments helped this become a better book, and Donna Bister made the publication process feel smooth and effortless. The countless people who inspired the stories and characters herein deserve a special thanks. To protect their identities, I refrain from listing them here, but I trust they will recognize their stories among these pages. I appreciate the valuable comments and readings of Raja Shehadeh, Charles Butterworth, Edward Dworkin, Nizar Habash, Eric Linder, and Ghada al-Madbouh. I thank Maribel Rivera-Ortiz for encouraging me to write. My eldest brother's reading of an early version of this manuscript was an enormous inspiration. My thanks as well to my nieces and nephews for their enthusiasm. Most of all, I am grateful to my daughter, to whom this book is dedicated.

A particular difficulty in writing about Palestine is the confusion of competing names and identities. Arab, Jew, Muslim, Christian, Israel, Palestine, The Holy Land, Canaan, Galilee, Samaria, the West Bank, Yerushalayim, al-Quds, … Code words imposed by the accidents of history and inventions of ideology. Amidst this linguistic tornado, the narrator's evolving ideas can be traced in the names he adopts, those he capitalizes, and yet others that he tiptoes around or encloses in quotation marks. He ultimately champions the cause of the Land – the endangered physical landscape, disfigured while being fought over. In that spirit, he favors pristine physical names untainted by human "isms": the Coast and the North, or the Hills with the Faces – creations of Nature that align the true compass for an over-mapped land. He capitalizes the names of natural features when they assume such significance. He capitalizes, as well, the unnatural features he cannot escape: for instance, the Occupation, the present regime of Israeli military control reigning since 1967; or Occupied Palestine, a country with suspended sovereignty, its people enduring a lifetime of stateless existence.

Contents

I

1. Under the Desk — 3
2. First Glimpse — 7
3. The Car — 32
4. Inherited Memories — 39
5. Stateless — 52
6. School Years — 68
7. Intifada — 97
8. Resistance Through Existence — 123
9. Transplant — 137
10. Settlement — 157

II

11. Hopes Of Peace — 187
12. Process Over Peace — 209
13. Aftermath — 235
14. Body Counts — 252
15. Stranger — 268
16. Unmuzzled — 290
17. Wall — 306
18. Nature Enchained — 323

Memories of Palestine — 337

III

19. Full Circle — 343
20. Olives and Cacti — 369
21. Gaining Altitude — 377

About the Author — 393

Physical map of the area

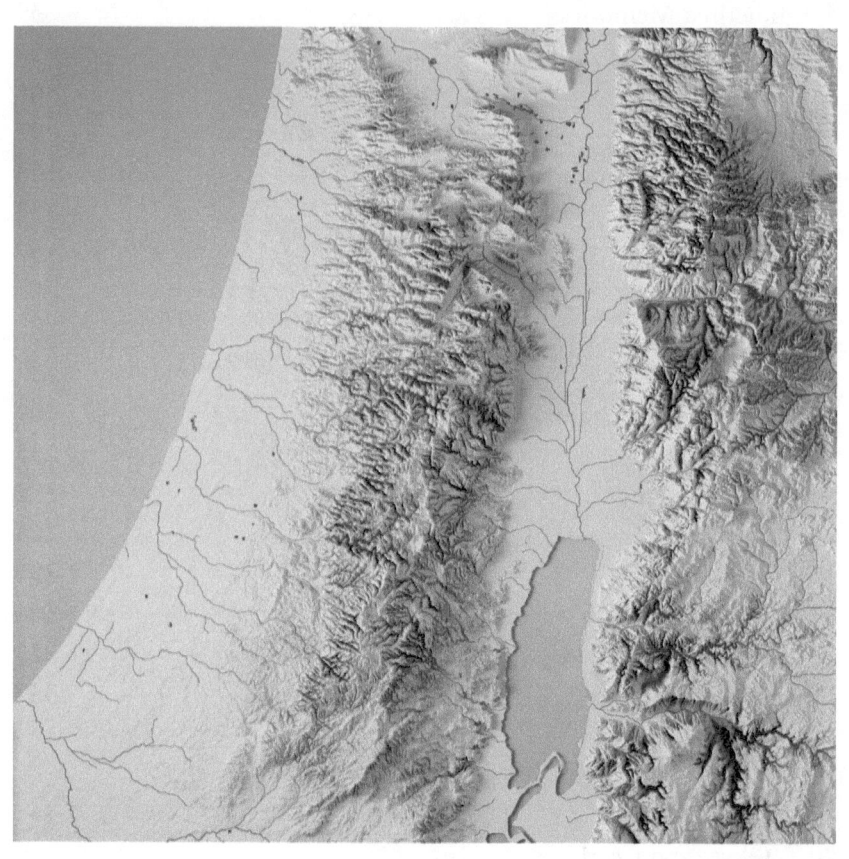

Locations mentioned in the book

"...
because ,
the trees know me,
the songs of the rain
recognize me.
...

The birds that chased my palm
at the distant airport gate,
all the fields of wheat,
all the prisons,
the white tombstones
the borders,
the handkerchiefs that waved,
all the eyes –
were with me, but they
dropped them from my travel permit!
..."

— Mahmoud Darwish, 'Travel Permit'

I

1

Under the Desk

MID-1970S. THREE YEARS OLD. My house was my castle, where I played under the loving, caring eyes of my mom and grandma.

"Stay away from the windows, or you may get a stray bullet," Mom's voice anxiously pealed, delivering one of my earliest lessons in life.

Outside, the streets were in turmoil, spilling the sound of gunfire and the smell of burning tires and tear gas into the house. A world of borders, and I was born on the "wrong" side.

Of course, I peeked when I could, wondering what a stray bullet looked like. Schoolchildren, of the same ages as my siblings, poured out of the school across the hill, packing the streets. I could hear them chanting slogans, while soldiers fired tear gas and warning shots.

All of a sudden, the tone changed. For the first time in my life, I heard the sound of a loudspeaker. Army Jeeps roamed the town, blurting orders to stay indoors or risk getting shot. My parents hurried to close the window shades. We stayed indoors for several days.

Then came the banging on the door. Loud, continuous banging with the butt of a rifle. I thought the door would break. Through the cracks in the blinds, I saw the soldiers strutting on our patio. What do they want from us? Will they search the house? Are they looking for children? Soldiers don't like children. I see them shooting at the older kids every day. Now they are right outside our house, so they must be here to get me. With this incontrovertible logic of a three-year old, I quickly scampered and hid between my dad's desk and the wall – a narrow crack into which I could barely squeeze myself. There, I would be safe from those big, monstrous soldiers. Breathless, I stayed, as long as I could hear the thuds of their boots and the jangles of their guns.

Under the desk I hid again when I was eight. I was sipping a soda in the family store when I heard a loud smash from shattering glass. A masked man was at the door with an Uzi submachine gun pointed right at me. He looked terrifying wearing a black ski mask backwards, with narrow cut-outs for eyes and mouth. I don't recall how, but in no time I was in the inside room, hiding under Dad's desk, as if bullets could not penetrate that space. Thinking back, the robber was probably stunned at my disappearance, in less time than he could blink. I cared less what he thought. I don't recall how much time elapsed before my older brother found me and walked me out of the store.

1985, twelve years of age. My dad had left on a business trip to Jordan the day before. Woke up early the next day on the sound of people talking. Found the house full of over a dozen people – Israeli tax collectors searching it from top to bottom, and bottom to top. They started at 6 AM and continued until evening, when they left carrying boxes of paperwork and accounts. My father came back from Jordan days later to find an order to detain him at the border. Israel had imposed a new sales tax that no one in the occupied West Bank paid. So I guess the Israelis needed to set a few examples.

A couple of years later, in December 1987, the Intifada, or uprising, began. Soldiers were shooting at children again, with lethal consequences, except this time the disturbances were to last more than a few days. The protests, civil disobedience and rebellious mood continued through the early 1990s. The occasional knock on the door became more frequent, usually in the middle of the night. Sometimes it was to search for wanted people, more often it was to draft us into forced labor: clearing roadblocks and erasing national slogans from the walls. *The security of the home was violable to anyone with a gun.*

Coexistent with those outside threats was the insecurity within the home. The insecurity of relying on someone else, namely my dad, to provide. The insecurity of dealing with his unpredictable moods and tempers, and with his methods of discipline. I could never figure out whether something I'd do would please or anger him, so my best strategy was to avoid him altogether. I dragged my feet coming home from school, in the hope that he was done with his lunch and back at work. Now that I'm older I realize he loved me, in his own way. I even grew to pity his old age and frailty.

But back then, I feared him, and needed places to hide, other than his desk. My favorite was outside, in the back garden, out of his sight. The ground level of the house was unfinished. Its covered patio, where no one could see me looking down from the third floor, became my hideout. Next to it was an almond tree that was my friend, who knew all my secrets and heard my grievances. Sometimes I took to the hills. Ramallah was then only lightly built, with plenty of empty lots, hills, and fields surrounding us. (This green space was to evaporate within my lifetime.)

For decades after, these insecurities of childhood continued to haunt me. I developed a mistrust, and sometimes resentment, of authority figures: tough bosses, policemen, airport security and border control – in fact anyone with a uniform, people who yell or bang loudly on doors, and people who control the purse.

When my child's birth was almost due, I yearned to spare her my experience and to ensure the security she needed to flourish. A home free from arbitrary searches, midnight banging on doors, gunshots and wars, or controlling fathers. But I know, from my own experiences, that real security does not exist. Everything can change. I have no control over outside events. The only thing I can do is be a different kind of parent than my father has been, and that path I have diligently followed, pledging at a minimum to do no harm.

Moving to America did not bring security. I spent eight years a student nomad in college and graduate school, moving from one dorm room to another, to a subletted apartment in the summer, to my brother's place for the holidays.

My periodic visits to my childhood home in Ramallah, because of mounting commitments and responsibilities, became shorter and less frequent. Each visit confronted me with more changes, to the point where

I hardly recognized the place. Stability, security, a solid foundation – so elusive in this fast-changing world.

Often I wondered how my own parents felt, having lost their homes and everything they had in 1948. Living in the coastal areas of Yafa (Jaffa) and Ramleh, they had to escape for their lives to make room for the Jewish state. In the West Bank, they started their lives anew. Until Israel occupied the West Bank two decades later, it was impossible for them to even visit their hometowns. Then, with the border down, they went back to find their places in ruins. My grandfather died in 1967 shortly after seeing the lands he owned fenced off and confiscated. I still recall my mother in tears at the empty lot that used to be her childhood home.

I document this, because it is a story not restricted to Palestine, but a human one as long as history, spanning the globe. It is the story of exiles, displaced persons, refugees, migrant workers, nomads, emigrants, and wanderers – those who left their homes at gunpoint, and those who left willingly in search of better prospects, those who were squeezed out for not being able to pay the rent, and those whose jobs required them to wander. Mine is the story of a plant with many roots, but no foothold, many places to spend the night, but no real home.

2

First Glimpse

JERUSALEM WAS ALWAYS AN EXCITING PLACE: the center of our religions, the center of our commerce, steeped in history. When we were young, going to Jerusalem was an adventure. It still is, though the adventure has taken a different form. Jerusalem to us was like Beijing, or London, or Cairo, yet older than any of them. Washington, DC's existence is a speck in Jerusalem's weighty history. "Weighty" is the operative word. Oppressing us, pushing us back from progress, attracting every invader, Jerusalem's history was to our disadvantage as oil was to Iraq's. The Promised Land that miscarried her people over and over, that is where I came into being. Jerusalem, 1973.

My name is Sameer, but you can call me Sam. I was the youngest of five siblings. My earliest memories are of my maternal grandmother, Olena, who lived with us: wrinkled, gray-haired, and mostly in bed. She told me stories while she spoon-fed me, and later taught me how to read. I liked her fairy tales more than my mother's. Distracted by housework and chores, Mom raced through her stories. Grandma took her time instead, juicing up details, and pausing often to "remember". I had no doubt she was an eyewitness to the tales' happenings. She possessed endless patience, spending her time doing intricate, painstaking artwork – vases and paintings decorated with fruit seeds and pits arranged in floral patterns. Her most cherished possessions were her cane, and her magnifying glass, which she used to read and re-read the thick Arabic copy of the

Bible installed by her bedside. By the age of three, I knew all the stories about Joseph and Moses and Jesus. The Bible contained a mythical world that I enjoyed and believed, for how can one not believe his grandma? Jesus was as real as she. He was also as real as Jack and the Beanstalk.

We lived in Ramallah, about 10 miles north of Jerusalem, in a three-story building on one of the slopes, about a five minute walk from the town center. We lived in the top floor, which was level with the street. Aunt Andrea and my paternal grandmother inhabited the middle floor, which had its own entrance from the side. Like most buildings in Palestine, the house was constructed of the local limestone, with thick outer walls. It had a flat roof in the contemporary style popular in the 1960s, unlike the older houses in Ramallah, which had red-tiled roofs. I did not have a room of my own until I was ten. Before that, I was a vagabond. From the pram in my parents' room when I was a baby, I moved practically everywhere. Once, my crib was set up in a corner of the dining room; another time, I stayed in Grandma Olena's room; and during the summers, when my second brother Adnan visited from Egypt, I was moved to a couch in the sunroom.

Aunt Andrea was a divorcee. She was too proud and independent to put up with an unhappy marriage, despite the bad reputation of divorce in those times. She lived for her art. Her oil paintings decorated our house, with a huge one of St. George slaying the dragon hanging near my bed. She was also a poet, versatile in the popular Arabic art form known as *saja'*, a little like limericks, often improvised on the spot. She sang in the church choir, hardly missing a Sunday. When I was little, she sometimes sang me to sleep, always the same children's song that I liked.

My eldest brother, Hakeem, was almost twenty years older than I, already studying at the nearby Birzeit University when I was a toddler. Adnan was at a university in Alexandria, Egypt. He spent his summers in Ramallah painting landscapes in oils, the odor of turpentine surrounding his easel on the patio. Occasionally, he would take me to the garden of Grand Park Hotel, where he hung out with his friends, but I was always deemed "too young" to be involved in their conversations. My sister Sandra was in high school. In the afternoons, with me in a stroller, she took me for walks about our neighborhood. On Sundays, she took me to church. Summers, my older siblings frequented disco parties at the Orthodox Club. Closest to my age was Basman, only seven years older, so I followed him around. He raised birds in a cage, and liked to play with marbles, something I never caught on to.

Hakeem had a huge library, housed in several floor-to-ceiling bookcases in his room. He arranged the bookcases to divide the room into four tiny cubicles, gaining surface area for more bookcases, back-to-back. One of the roomlets had a mat for exercise, another, his bed. The innermost one contained a human-size model pyramid he constructed for meditating underneath. It was the Seventies, after all. I often hung out in his room surveying the books, borrowing one occasionally. One time, using a neat clicker gadget, I counted something like 2000 books! Locked in his room, he often stayed up all night reading, to the detriment of his classes at the university, which he did not find as interesting or important as his own self-education. He was interested in Eastern religions and general New Age topics, and practiced yoga. He was also into bodybuilding, having bought a Joe Weider course set by mail order from USA. Lacking gyms or equipment, he built his own wooden exercise bench. He also made a set of weights by pouring concrete in empty powdered milk cans, then sticking a metal pipe (bent at both ends to stay in place), before the cement dried.

I had a good amount of toys, many inherited from my brothers. I liked my toy cars, animals, and Legos. When I had nothing to do I invented imaginary friends. My favorite toy was Paddington, a small orange-yellow teddy bear that I had since I was a few months old (whose name I gave years later, after reading Paddington bear stories). It was firm and had a velvety skin that eventually wore out over the years. I kept my grandma, and later my mom, busy repairing it.

Father was a businessman. He worked with his brothers in my grandfather's store, eventually owning the business after all my uncles emigrated. He managed another business in East Jerusalem, so traveled there often. A workaholic, I rarely saw him except late at night, when he toiled in his home office into the wee hours. I liked it when he sang to me and put me to sleep. He had studied at a British boarding school in Jerusalem, and later attended the American University of Beirut (AUB), so he knew several English and American songs. My favorites were "She'll be coming round the mountain …", and "When I was a baby". He also sang me Arabic songs, including several national songs I learned by heart, like Mawtini (my country). (With lyrics written by poet Ibrahim Touqan, Mawtini became the unofficial anthem of the pan-Arab and Palestinian liberation movements.)

Mother was rarely seen idle: cooking, cleaning, taking care of us and Grandma,… Having worked as a nurse before getting married, she knew medical procedures, medicines, and treatments, and hence was the family's resident medic. She also knew a few herbal medicinal recipes, but it seemed like Grandma Olena was the expert in traditional medicine. By the time I was in school, Mom was also keeping the books for the family business.

My parents did their best to provide me with a loving home, and shield me from the outside world. But Palestine is not the most stable of places. The 1973 October war broke when I was just six months old. Once when I was little, I vaguely recall the whole family staying in the unfinished lower floor ("the Shelter") for several days, keeping the lights dimmed and windows closed. The floor was made of pebbles, and I remember Mom's warnings about scorpions and lizards hiding among the stones.

The house was surrounded by a small garden. We had roses, and cypress, pine and fruit trees. I liked to stroll there, sometimes climbing trees to pick the fruit. The almond trees were first to bloom, their blossoms appearing in February, or earlier. The two plum and one cherry tree flowered in March, then the apple tree in April. We also had grapevines that bore fruit in the summer. We liked to eat plums and almonds green, dipped in salt. The house was on a hill, surrounded by several unfenced open lands that functioned like an extended public garden. There, grew fig and olive trees. The figs ripened in July, while the olives bore a big harvest once every two years, ripening in the Fall. The figs were the last to retain their leaves; the saying goes that the last fig leaf must fall before the first snowfall.

Jerusalem and Amman were always cities, for thousands of years. When they expanded, the historic old cities were retained as an embodiment of their characters. Ramallah, until recently, was a village, with few buildings of any significance. Instead, its heart were the terraced hills, the fig and olive trees, the grapevines, and the wildflowers. Until recently, the whole area was farmed extensively, but the land near Ramallah fell out of use after a disease wiped out the grapevines. Many families emigrated in the early 1950s, whereas the village, swollen with refugees from the 1948 war, transformed into an urban center. Ramallah's hills were all terraced in the typical Palestinian style, using the local large stones to build retaining walls we called *sanasel* that followed the contours of the hill. Depending on the grade, some of these walls were as high as two adults, others no higher than a step-stool. For many centuries, these walls have ensured a tillable soil, free from large stones, and slowed erosion and water runoff, preserving vital resources in this arid clime

Those terraces were my playground. I spent hours every day meandering, climbing the slopes, examining wildflowers and insects, collecting unusual stones, chasing lizards, and exploring. Here is a six-pointed flower, looking like a star, and there is an eight-pointed one with purple color. Over here, I find a flint stone, and over there I spot a long trail of ants busy collecting food. I follow the trail until the ants disappear under a rock. Flipping it over, I discover the entrance to a whole new underground cosmos. Finally catching a lizard, I try a trick Basman had once demonstrated: cut its tail and marvel at both lizard and tail wiggling, still full life. It was a magical time.

The hillsides were crisscrossed with trails, some with stairs up the terrace walls. In some places, the walls had caved in, so I scrambled over the rubble. Hopping about the rocks became second nature. The higher walls, made by neatly stacking rocks without cement, invited me to climb. The plentiful cracks and crevices offered footholds, and the lurking danger of snakes or scorpions. I often came back home bleeding from the thorns and nettles, with soil stains on my clothes and hands, and a content smile on my face.

Ramallah enjoys a pleasant Mediterranean climate, similar to that of Southern California. Its summers are sunny and dry – June through August almost guaranteed not to rain. The town lies on the peak of hills about 900 meters above sea-level. Several valleys connect it directly to the coast, funneling a cooling breeze from the sea. Summer nights are thus often cool and foggy.

In winter, the western slopes of the West Bank hills intercept the successive storm systems that swipe the Mediterranean, bringing heavy rains. The high altitude makes it chilly at times, and it snows once a year or so. On cold winter nights, the whole family huddled around a kerosene heater, roasting chestnuts and listening to the howling wind through leaky windows. Snow was rare, so we looked forward to it. Basman and I followed the daily weather reports, hoping for news of a major storm. Usually snow began at night, when the temperatures dropped. We ran from window to window, praying enough of it stuck till morning. Because temperatures do not dip much below freezing, Ramallah's snow is wet and fluffy, with large snowflakes superb for making snowballs. An inch of snow was enough to close the town.

The rainy winters make for verdant springs – lush green grasses and colorful wildflowers carpet the hills. Ramallah has two brief hot seasons, in April when the south wind lashes hot, dry, and sandy desert air, and in August when successive heat waves with stifling air swaddle the Mediterranean. The latter were hard to endure as air conditioning was unknown. By July, the cessation of rain dries up the grasses, and the hills assume a golden glow in the bright summer sun. The only types of ground cover that survive the dry summers are thistles and thorny plants that drink the morning dew.

Ramallah's position on the peaks ensured good vistas. Our house had a pleasant view of the city and the west. I enjoyed looking out from the sunroom and observing the streets, houses, and trees in the valley below. On good days, we were able to see as far as the Coast. My parents pointed out three chimneys from a power plant in Ramleh and, at night, the lights from distant Yafa and Tel Aviv.

Until the mid-1990s, Ramallah was a quiet small town. Everything was close together, school, work, church, shopping. Where we lived, just outside the tiny center, everything was quiet, apart from a few predictable interruptions. One of our neighbors played the radio loudly outside while doing housework, usually listening to Abd-el-Halim Hafez, the famous Egyptian singer, or to Fairuz, the Lebanese diva. About ten in the morning, the braying of the milkman's donkey announced their arrival from the nearby village of Qalandia. I liked watching the donkey swish flies with its tail while the milkman poured the fresh milk into our containers. On summer afternoons, an ice cream vendor, typically a teenager, walked the streets, carrying a cooler on his back, intoning the words "ICE CREAM" at the top of his voice.

By late afternoon, the shepherd showed up, leading his flock of sheep or goats over the hills to feast on the greenery, slowing down traffic as they idyllically crossed the street, to the music of the bells tied round their necks. The one lame sheep always trailed behind. In the summer when the grass dried, the sheep ate the carob from the trees lining the street, while the goats ate the thistles. The shepherd sometimes led his flock to the fig tree in the lot next to us, eliciting a stream of loud curses from the elderly woman across the street, whom we called Ol' Granny. She was an otherwise kindly old woman who sat, in her traditional embroidered dress, all day long on her balcony watching the street, greeting everyone who greeted her. Though I hardly ever saw her picking the figs, woe unto anyone who touched that tree. Fortunately for the shepherd, she was too immobilized by old age to do more than shout insults and wave her stick.

Five times a day, the *adhan*, or Muslim call for prayer, broke the silence from the minaret of the Old City mosque. Just before dawn, at noon, mid-afternoon, sunset, and early evening, the *adhan* witnessed that *There is no God but God; Mohammad is His Prophet,* inviting worshippers to pray. Usually it lasted only a few minutes each time, except on Fridays when the noon prayer sermon was broadcast on the loudspeakers. On major Muslim holidays, the early morning adhan changed to a joyful continuous stream of *Allahu akbar, Allahu akbar* (God is Greater, God is Greater) that lasted for an hour or two.

I liked it most when I slept in the sunroom on summer nights. The night sounds enchanted me. Besides the occasional car speeding down a lone street across the hills, I could hear insects chirping, dogs barking, and roosters crowing. Some households in Ramallah raised chickens or pigeons. While some people had dogs for pets, more dogs were stray, haunting the streets at night, rummaging through trash. Stray cats, too, were abundant. We might be surprised to see one walking into the kitchen if someone left the front door ajar. Usually, the nights were cloudless and the thin mountain air made for a superb display of stars. I learned to recognize the constellations and bright stars, many of whose names – Vega, Deneb, Altair, Rigel, … – had an Arabic origin, acknowledging Arab contributions to astronomy. I read avidly on astronomy, hoping science had answers to my endless questions about the universe.

Old folks in Ramallah still wore the traditional dress. The men wore a *sirwal* (a kind of baggy pants), a loose shirt, and a `*abaya* (overcoat). On the head, they wore a *hatta*, also known as *kafiyyeh*, a square scarf folded into a triangle and tied around the head. The more popular patterns for the *hatta* were plain white, checkered black and white, and checkered red and white. The women wore a colorful embroidered dress and a scarf covering the head. The colors and designs on the dress usually indicated her village of origin. The closer people were to farming, the more they retained their traditional dress. Conversely, city people abandoned it, the women preferring European fashions, and the men suits and ties, with men in my grandfather's generation adding a *tarboosh*, the Turkish fez-like headwear. Coming from the coastal cities, my parents had long abandoned the traditional dress.

Occasionally, villagers walked door-to-door in our neighborhood selling their produce, fresh from the land. The village women gracefully balanced a basket of figs, or *sahber* (pronounced *sub-err*), the cactus pears, on their heads. The villagers peeled the thorny fruit for us. I was impressed with how they handled it painlessly with their rough hands. Sometimes, pickup trucks with loudspeakers roamed the streets advertising Jericho watermelons or guava. Fruits and vegetables were available only in season, making them all the more coveted. A rare treat was the *jummeiz*, sycamore fruits, which originated from Gaza.

On Sundays, the silence was pierced by the ringing of church bells in the mornings, and the beeping of car horns in the afternoon. Like other Mediterranean countries, weddings in Palestine are celebrated with a long procession of cars escorting the bride, all honking along the way. While the bride awaits the groom's parents to join her train, the groom gets a *zaffeh*, a festive communal song where everyone participates in roasting him. After the church ceremony, the families usually have a reception that lasts well into the night. Since marriage is a once-in-a-lifetime event in a land forbidding divorce, people stretch their means to make the party big. In the quiet of night, the music of distant wedding parties echoed over the hills. One time, we went for a wedding in Gaza, stayed through the early morning, then made the 2.5-hour drive back in time for the Islamic holiday dawn *adhan*. Needless to say, I loved the up-all-night part.

Ramallah's "old city" comprised closely-packed houses surrounding narrow streets and few gardens. The older buildings used mud and adobe instead of the pervasive limestone walls, and the roofs had shallow domes. The old city accommodated the churches and mosque, as well as small shops – grocers, a bakery, falafel stalls, barbers, and gift shops. Main Street connected it with the new town center at the *Manarah* circle up the hill. On the other side of the *Manarah* is the neighboring city of el-Bireh, a more ancient town, mentioned in the Old Testament under the name Beeroth. El-Bireh's old city has ruins of a Crusader church marking the spot where Joseph and Mary have rested on their way to Nazareth, a day's journey from Jerusalem, only to discover that the 12-year-old Jesus was missing [Luke 2:41-52]. From those old nuclei, the two cities grew to be contiguous by the time I was born. Most buildings near the *Manarah* were two to four stories high, with offices and apartments above the street-level shops and restaurants. Despite the growth, the town felt small enough for people to greet each other.

The streets near the *Manarah* were wider than the old city's, but barely wide enough for one car each way. Cars often parked on the narrow sidewalks, forcing pedestrians to walk on the street and block traffic. The city had installed rails along some curbs, isolating the sidewalks to prevent cars from parking. In the late 1970s, those rails were crowded with young men, probably unemployed, idly hanging out. The guys were rough, carried penknives, and sometimes got into fights that became the talk of the town. Thick smoke from *arghileh* water-pipes billowed out of coffeeshops, where men played backgammon while sipping Arabic coffee or tea. My parents forbade us from hanging out on those streets, or in the coffeeshops. Our recreation centered on the church's youth club, which organized sports teams, dance parties, and activities.

The rest of the city had tree-lined streets and ample open space. From afar it looked green, dotted with white buildings and red-tiled roofs. I liked the *Muntazah,* the tiny public park adjacent to the town hall. It boasted a playground and a landscaped garden with fountains, waterfalls, and interesting rocks.

(Today, so little of this small-town, idyllic Ramallah remains. Though I have been to many parts of the world, its fast pace of change astonishes me.

The city has swelled to encompass outlying villages and areas. The roomy, quiet neighborhood I grew up in is now more crowded than the downtown area was in 1990. The streets are still the same, except most are turned one-way and parking on the sidewalks is forbidden, so traffic is even more jammed and noisy. It is rare to see anyone wearing traditional dress anymore. No farmers bother to go door-to-door with their produce, or perhaps – isolated by the Wall – they cannot leave their villages. Walking ice-cream sellers are a rare sight. The *jummeiz* from Gaza is practically extinct, with Gaza after the blockade feeling farther than Australia. When the milkman died in the late 1980s, his son replaced the donkey with a pickup truck. Later, we stopped getting fresh milk altogether and started buying packaged milk from collective dairies. One shepherd still walks our street sometimes, the flocks dwindling and driven to wander farther away by the shrinkage of open lands. Ol' Granny, God rest her soul, is no longer around to watch the fig tree, and it seems only a matter of time before that tree makes way for another building.

The empty hills, my playgrounds, are mostly gone. The open field is an endangered species. The city lacks a decent-sized park to match its growing population. Trees were torn to grow 20- and 30-story skyscrapers.

The view from our house is gone, blocked by one of the new buildings. Even before then, the sky became so hazy, we could rarely see the Coast anymore, or even the three chimneys of Ramleh. That, and the light pollution at night, makes it hard to see any stars, just like urban areas in America and elsewhere in the world. Ramallah's green hue gave way to the white of stacked stone towers. Even its weather has changed. The pollution and shrinking vegetation makes the summer temperatures in the city several degrees hotter than the countryside.

The *adhan* can still be heard, in cacophony from the multiplicity of mosques that sprung over the city, that are often out of sync, if only for the difference in distance from us. The crowing of roosters is gone, but you can sometimes see a pack of stray dogs roaming the streets at dawn. The traditional coffeeshops gave way to a vibrant nightlife. Church bells are still there, but weddings now happen every day of the week, as there are not enough spaces in the churches and party halls to accommodate the burgeoning wedding industry. Few people greet each other anymore. With Ramallah so crowded, most walk by unrecognized.)

One of my first childhood friends was Kareem, about my age, who lived at the end of our street. Our sisters were friends, so we played together in the garden when they visited each other. Another friend was Tanya, a year older, who lived in a three-story building on the other side of *the* fig tree. She liked to play "house". My mom helped us put two chairs together near a window, then drew the curtains around them to make a house. We lost touch when her family moved, though only to the end of the street, by the time I was four. Later, I became good friends with her younger brother, Jawad. Across the street lived Maya, my age, and her older brother and two younger sisters. We played hide-and-seek and such games in our yard.

On the ground floor of Tanya's old house lived Daniel – Danny, for short – a little younger than myself. He was the youngest of six who all lived in one small house with their dad. His mother had died when he was little, so his sisters took care of him. He was a tough, street-smart, daredevil who spoke rough language, and for all those reasons my parents didn't like me playing with him. For the same reasons, I was drawn to him, and we became good friends anyway. Our favorite hangout was the Fig Tree Lot that separated our houses. We liked to climb trees, especially when fruit was involved. Sometimes we organized "raids" on the trees in the neighborhood when fruits were in season, the ones in the open fields being fair game. We would climb the tree, stuff as many fruit as we could into our pockets, pant cuffs, and shirt, then run down before we got caught. Somehow, the fruit was more enjoyable when we picked it ourselves, and even more so if the tree was someone else's and we risked getting caught. Danny excelled at this sport, capable of climbing even the tall pine trees to collect their cones. Pine nuts were a treat, since it took work to get even a few, and then we had to break their shells one-by-one with a stone.

We loved discarded appliance boxes. We would turn one upside-down, cut out holes for windows and a door, and instantly have our own playhouse. One time, Danny and I built a tree house by fastening a discarded sheet of wood we found to a branch, making a platform and using cardboard boxes for walls. We "lived" in it for several days, cooking our food in a fire-pit nearby.

Kite flying was popular in the summer, especially because Ramallah got a steady breeze. We made our own kites by crossing three reed stems along a hexagon's diagonals, tying them in the middle and running a hemp string around the perimeter. We covered the framework with a large piece of crepe paper (or brown wrapping paper), which served as a canvas for colorful collages. We balanced it with a long tail of paper ribbons. The key was having tons of the hemp string on hand, so as to compete with other kites in altitude. We flew it from the roof to get a good start. It was rather dangerous, and tricky with all the surrounding trees. One time, we made an oversized kite, and the wind was so strong, the string snapped. Basman and I chased it in the car, finally catching it past the airport in Qalandia, about halfway to Jerusalem!

Besides toys and board games, we invented our own entertainment, like the boys' version of "house", which we called "work". We cut scrap paper to make "money", then chose professions. I usually played banker, Kareem store owner, Danny policeman, and Nimer (another neighborhood kid) ran the restaurant. The store shelves were stocked with sticks and stones, and the restaurant served the same on its menu. We would spend all day trading and making business deals and counting money. Kareem used to irk me by depositing a bundle of money at the bank, then turning right around to demand "interest". It was pure fun.

"War" was our more sophisticated version of "cops and robbers", requiring strategies that got more involved each time we played. Assembling all the boys in the neighborhood, some eight of us, we divided into teams. Each team had a home base to defend. The idea was to surprise our enemies and shoot them before they could shoot us. Sticks being the guns of choice in this low-tech version of laser tag, we had countless arguments about who shot whom first. Later, we opted for taking prisoners, because 'killing' someone just meant they got to go back to their home base and live again to fight us. In the summer of 1986, we got together with kids from two other neighborhoods and engaged in a two-day "war". We fought from daybreak until dusk, this time using stones at long-range. We never intended for anyone to get hurt, and miraculously, no one did. It was all in the spirit of good fun, and lots of it.

Every once in a while, something happened to dispel Ramallah's blanket of quiet. Protests against the Israeli military occupation erupted periodically on designated dates, and sometimes spontaneously on ordinary dates. On such days, my mother kept me indoors. Basman would rush back from school. A muffled sound of chanting from a crowd of people far away would ultimately be followed by several rounds of gunfire. Disobeying Mom's repeated warnings against windows and stray bullets, I followed Basman in taking a peek from here or there. Sometimes, we snuck to the roof to watch, while Mom, at the sound of the roof door unlocking, hurriedly followed to drag us downstairs. Usually, the protests were concentrated near the old city of Ramallah, Main Street, and the *Manarah*. We had a good view of the old city from our house, about a km away on the peak of a hill opposite us. Clouds of black smoke rose from the burning tires, while protesters blocked the streets. The soldiers would fire to disperse the crowd. People would back off, then come back and continue to protest. Some of those protests in the 1970s lasted for hours.

A few times, protests took place right on our street. Children from the nearby high school blocked the street with stones, lit tires, and chanted slogans. They were fifteen or sixteen years old but, to me, appeared like adults. Inevitably, Israeli army Jeeps sped to the scene, sirens on, turning round corners at full speed. Screeching to a halt, the *jaysh*, or soldiers, jumped out and started shooting. The gunshots were deafening when fired from just outside. Sooner or later, the demonstrators dispersed, and the soldiers drove away. Basman would then go out and collect the empty bullet shells that fell down from the soldiers. He had quite a collection. Our older brother, Adnan, an even larger one. They each gave me some when I asked them, after which I spent the day playing with the shells.

One time, when I was about ten or twelve, Danny found a real, live, unexploded round of ammo. Naturally, we got on a mission to explode it. He had the idea to light a fire, which I thought was dangerous since we would have no control of where it shot. We did it anyway, carefully squeezing the round between two stones, piling up some sticks and lighting them on fire. We hid behind a stone fence, then, Boom!

One of my earliest memories was getting caught on the balcony with matches, about to light a pile of rubber tires I had collected from my toy cars, while parroting the slogans. The horrified look on my mother's face signaled the trouble I was in. She gently asked what was I doing?

"Starting a protest," I innocently explained.

After all, that was what the older kids outside were doing – burning tires to block the street. That was the life to which my four-year-old eyes could look forward.

Such a mock-demonstration was perhaps a natural way for a child to make sense of the craziness around him. By then, I had already experienced the three-day curfew when I hid under the desk. What did the soldiers want when they knocked on our door? I never knew. What about the protesters, what were they really protesting? I understood little, but learned words like "ID card", "gunfire", "protests", and "refugee camp" almost as soon as we learned to say *"baba"* and *"mama"*.

Children who participated in demonstrations were usually among the less fortunate *awlad il-mukhayyam*, or "children of the refugee camp". The refugee camps were set up as temporary places to house Palestinian refugees in 1948, when the founding of Israel displaced nearly a million

Palestinians from their homes. The word *mukhayyam* means something like "tent city", an apt description of the camps back then. Over the years, it became clear that those refugees had no chance to return to their homes any time soon, despite all the UN resolutions and human rights conventions. So the tents were replaced with small cement-brick shacks covered with leaky metal roofs. The camps were disheveled and slum-like, some having open sewers in the narrow alleys. Though every city in the West Bank had one or more refugee camps near it, city people rarely ventured into the camps.

Crammed into those tiny shacks at night, in daytime the refugee camp children roamed the streets. In that hell of poverty, kids grew up quickly. They were tough, got into fights, stole stuff, and cared for nothing – they had nothing to lose. Although we played with them occasionally when they wandered into our neighborhood, children banded with others from their own neighborhood. My mother collected the clothes I outgrew to send to the refugee kids. She also held up those children in discipline. A complaint about my food elicited a "Look at the children of the camps, they don't have enough to eat." If I expressed discontent with a birthday present, I heard "They have few toys and not enough clothes." Sadly, that was true.

Back then, their existence was a mystery. Why didn't all children live in nice houses? Why couldn't they have enough toys? Why did some kids live in camps and others not? Later I learned that my parents were refugees, too. They left their homes in 1948, so I could have ended up in the camps myself, had they not been lucky enough to find space in Ramallah, and work. A sobering thought that further challenged my sense of security.

Palestine is famous as the Holy Land, the land of religions. Religion continues to be one of the defining factors of a person's identity, and lineage. Conversions are rare, as are inter-religious marriages. Villages and small towns had each evolved a predominant religion, not by an active act of segregation, but as a byproduct of religion's hereditary nature. Ramallah, Bethlehem, and Nazareth were mostly Christian. El-Bireh, Nablus, and el-Khalil (Hebron) were mostly Muslim. The bigger cities like Yafa or Jerusalem were mixed.

My family is Christian. At the time of my birth, Christians formed about 10% of Palestine's population (and nowadays barely 2%). Christianity was once the official religion in the Middle East, for the last few centuries of Roman rule. The Muslim Arab armies that wrested control of Palestine from the Byzantines in the 7th century AD respected the existing religions. The caliph Omar made a treaty with the Patriarch of Jerusalem, guaranteeing the sanctity of churches and allowing Christians to practice their faith without interference. Christians in Syria and Palestine gradually adopted the Arabic language, but for centuries kept their religious practices unchanged. I once heard that Christians were the majority as late as the 19th century, when they converted to Islam in large numbers to reduce taxes and avoid persecution from an increasingly repressive Ottoman Empire. If true, that may explain the unusual reverence Palestinian Muslims I know have for Christians, our Bible, prophets, and saints. Regardless, Palestine was a haven for Christians escaping persecution in neighboring countries, as I was to discover while tracing my own family history. My father's great-great-grandfather escaped Crete in 1821, during a Christian rebellion that the Ottoman Turks quelled with large-scale massacres. Though Palestine was under the rule of the same Turks, my ancestor chose it because it made him feel welcome and safe.

Later in the USA, I had an amusing incident with an Israeli-American at a company I interned with. He had interviewed me over the phone and knew I was from the West Bank. When he saw me on my first day, he declared: "You don't look Palestinian," probably expecting some kafiyyeh-clad guy with a stone in his hand. I asserted that I was, in fact, Palestinian. Finally, when he found out I was Christian, he insisted "So, you're a *Christian*, you're *not* a Palestinian."

In reality, Christians and Muslims in Palestine were well-integrated, especially in the twin cities of Ramallah and El-Bireh. People had lived alongside each other for centuries. Christians and Muslims were almost indistinguishable. They dressed the same (in the 1970s and 80s), participated in the same activities, and frequented the same stores and restaurants. The only time you could guess someone's religion was on holidays. Christian-owned stores closed on Sunday, Muslim-owned stores closed on Friday, and each went to their own churches. Schools observed both Friday and Sunday as a "weekend". Few took the school day on Saturday seriously. With only four schooldays ahead, Mondays were less harsh, while Thursday nights felt sweet. Christian and Muslim students went to the same schools. We only separated in religion class. My friends were split about 50-50 between the two groups.

My family traces our recent ancestry to the Greek Orthodox community in Lydd, a Canaanite city mentioned in the Bible, famous for being the birthplace of St. George who slayed the legendary dragon. In reality, St. George was a Roman soldier who rebelled against orders to persecute Christians, instead leading the fight against the "dragon" of empire. Many in my extended family have first names George or one of its Arabic variants. Georgette is not uncommon for women in my family. The Eastern Orthodox church claims direct descent in teachings and ritual from the disciples of Jesus. Its doctrine is similar to the Catholic Church's, but the Orthodox churches refuse to recognize the authority of the Pope, a split aggravated by the historic fracture of the Roman Empire.

On visits to the Church of the Holy Sepulchre in Jerusalem, I became fascinated with the smaller sects, each of which had carved a corner of real estate within the shrine: the Syrian (Assyrian) church, whose members speak Aramaic, the common language of the Middle East at the time of Jesus; the Armenian Church, who along with the Syrian were condemned as heretic by the Orthodox Church in the early Councils; the Orthodox Ethiopian church; and the Coptic church. The latter is the main Christian sect in Egypt, using the same language spoken in Ancient Egypt. In Palestine, however, (and in the Holy Sepulchre's real estate map) the Greek Orthodox Church remains dominant.

My mother is a Roman Catholic, the second most popular Christian sect in Palestine. Palestinian Catholics descended from European Crusaders who invaded Palestine about 1000 years ago, though some were converted by missionaries in the 19th century. There were also several protestant denominations, the product of more recent missionary activities. Ramallah had Lutheran, Anglican, and Baptist churches, as well as a Quaker meeting house. On Sundays, you could hear the clamor of different bells from all the churches.

The Eastern churches emphasize the teachings of Jesus and following his commandments more so than the creed of "faith" promulgated by Protestant sects. Society in Palestine is closely-knit and centers on one's church. The congregation as a whole acts to enforce religious conventions, ostracism more feared than a conviction in court. The building block within each community is the family. Extended families are large and go back generations. As with Muslims and Orthodox Jews, children are considered a blessing among Palestinian Christians and people are expected to "go forth and multiply".

I found that living on the same land that Jesus has trodden was helpful in making sense of the Bible, and building an understanding grounded in the reality of the land. The parable of the fig tree assumes a palpable immediacy when you see a fig tree outside your window every day. The reference to the road from Jerusalem to Jericho – an actual road I have frequently taken – gives Jesus himself a profound realism that is hard to contest. The writings of 19th century Western travelers betray their shock at the inaccuracy of their imagined Palestines.

My siblings and I preferred to attend the Catholic Church on Sundays since their liturgy was in Arabic, whereas the Orthodox mass was mostly in Greek, a language none of us (except Aunt Andrea) understood. Although both churches had Arabic priests, most of the upper echelons of the Orthodox Church in Palestine were Greek. The Catholic Church had a more local flavor. Father Louis, born Italian, had lived in Ramallah for 50 years as the head priest of the Ramallah church, spoke perfect Arabic, and was practically one of us. Eventually, the Catholic Church appointed a Palestinian archbishop to head the local churches, something the Orthodox Church has yet to do, despite decades of promises.

Sandra, Basman, and I walked every Sunday to the Catholic Church in the old city. After the mass, they chatted with their friends in the courtyard. When I was seven, in preparation for my First Communion ceremony, I attended a class at the church every afternoon for two months. The aged nun who monitored the class, Sister Felicia, was tough and meted punishment for the slightest whisper during class. Shorter than us thanks to her stoop, she constantly yelled at one child or another.

Her favorite punching bag was an autistic child who was incapable of following the strict discipline she demanded. Thankfully, the big day arrived. We wore the ceremonial robes and walked through to receive our first communion from Father Louis. My interest in church gradually waned past that age. I cared more about sleeping late on Sunday mornings and doing other things with my time.

Until third grade, I attended a Catholic school attached to the church. It was run by the nuns, who exerted the same authoritarian discipline as they did in church. Fun was simply not allowed. Sister Felicia, dreaded by students and nuns alike, often beat us and threatened to lock us up in a dark room they called the "mice room". Others, though, were kind and compassionate. Sisters Mariana, who wore the thickest glasses I have seen on a human being, and Beatrice were of the latter category. They were also friends with my mother and visited her every once in a while. The other nuns, whose names had faded, fell between those polar extremes.

I attended the Orthodox Church only on holidays, when the whole family went together. I liked its rich atmosphere – more incense, more colorful icons, and melodic music. Their masses, however, were long and tedious, and without enough seats, I had to stand for the entire mass, fidgeting all the while. The crowd was not as disciplined. People talked and children ran around in the back. There were no nuns to keep everyone in line. My friend Kareem served the altar. An air of mystery imbued the screened room behind the altar, hidden from the congregation. The priest periodically entered it through a narrow door, his muffled voice filtering through the smoke from the censer. I peeked through the curtain covering the tiny door when I could, itching to discover what he did inside.

I enjoyed the festive holidays, which reflected the multiplicity of Christian denominations, each of which observed its own calendar. The Greek Orthodox celebrated Christmas on January 7, and New Year's Eve on January 13, following the Julian calendar. So did the Copts, Ethiopians, and Armenians. Easter sometimes coincided, but usually separated by as much as five weeks. Even the saints' festivals were duplicated.

For my family, Christmas season began on Dec. 23 when we got a fresh cypress tree into the house. I was eager to help Mom hang the ornaments. She improvised additional decorations by wrapping the small, rounded, tree cones with colorful chocolate wrappers. Underneath, she set up a nativity scene using a cavern she made herself from egg cartons and brown wrapping paper. On December 25th, hearing bells ring, we looked out the window at "fake" Santas standing in the backs of pickup trucks. Frustratingly, they only delivered presents to the Catholic kids. We attended the Christmas Eve mass at the Catholic Church to escape the agonizing thought that "the true" Orthodox Santa wasn't coming till Jan. 6!

Finally, on Orthodox Christmas Eve, the family gathered to wait for Santa. Every year we waited and waited. Dad eventually got impatient, murmuring something about being late for his evening work meeting if he stayed any longer. Invariably he left, only to just miss Santa, who suddenly appeared at our front door ringing his bell, and talking in languages. Santa scared me – he somehow knew everything I did, and always gave me the gifts with strings attached. After the gifts, we celebrated at home with a big meal and wine, and no age limits on drinking. Eventually, a Santa suit I found while rummaging through the house was evidence enough.

My school gave us a two- to three-week break for Easter. Every day during Holy Week brought a celebration of some sort. On Palm Sunday, we circled the church courtyard carrying *Sha'ninehs*, palm fronds with leaves interlaced into miniature baskets, studded with colorful springtime flowers. A few times, I participated in the Catholic Palm Sunday procession from Bethany to Jerusalem, retracing the steps of Jesus alongside pilgrims from all over the world. Joining a group from our local church, we took a bus to a church in Bethany with a large garden, crowded with people. Since local churches marched near the end, we waited several hours before our turn to leave. We then left the confines of the church in two columns along the narrow, winding, road connecting the village with Jerusalem. Worshippers carried palm fronds and sang hymns while spectators lined both sides of the road. We first climbed the eastern slope of the Mount of

Olives, then descended its western slopes through a vast Jewish cemetery into the Valley of Kidron, then ascended to the Old City. Not too many miles, but the stop-and-go pace, in the hot naked sun, made it more tiresome. By the time we left Bethany, the front of the procession would have reached Jerusalem, slowing down everyone behind as they squeezed, two-by-two, through the narrow Old City gate. In all, it took us about three hours to cover the distance.

The Orthodox Holy Saturday was my favorite. We call it *Sabt in-Nur*, or Sabbath of Light, for the supposed miracle of the flame which appears every year above the tomb of Jesus. I went to see it one time with relatives living in Jerusalem, who led me that morning to a perch on the roof of the Church of the Holy Sepulchre. Looking down through ventilation gratings above Golgotha, the site of the Crucifixion, we could see the throngs encircling Jesus' supposed tomb. The priests locked the Tomb's gates in the late morning. We waited till about noon, when a flame leapt forth from the sealed structure. So they say. I only saw the stampede of people hoping to catch the flame with candles. For the occasion, the church sold thin, long, beeswax candles bundled together so as to burn brightly for a long time. The flame quickly spread from candle to candle, with official flame-bearers rushing to all the cities in Palestine to light candles in their churches.

My friends were not shy to admit their suspicion of a magic trick on the part of the priesthood. Regardless, we were excited to watch the celebrations. In Ramallah, on *Sabt in-Nur*, the Boy and Girl Scout groups led a parade from the church in the old city over to the town center, to receive the flame from the envoy. Everyone lined Main Street to enjoy the bagpipes and drums of their marching band.

On Easter eve, we usually attended the midnight mass in the Holy Sepulchre. The city buzzed with pilgrims from Greece, Ethiopia, Russia, and other places that follow the Eastern Calendars. Since cars could not go into the old city, we usually parked outside *Bab el-Khalil* (Jaffa Gate) and walked to the Church. My legs have memorized the labyrinth of streets and alleys leading to the church. I loved walking in the Old City – its narrow, covered streets, colorful shops, the shallow steps and the sharp angles. I was fascinated at the exotic traditional clothing of the diverse pilgrims.

About 10 PM, the Patriarch of Jerusalem, wearing a giant golden crown and dressed in sparkling regalia, walked to the church amid a procession of Greek Orthodox priests. The priests uniformly wore long black gowns, long beards (typically white), and funny, black upside-down hats. Clearing the way for the procession were two guards dressed in the Ottoman military uniform, rhythmically pounding heavy walking sticks that sent onlookers scampering to either side. I was warned they stomped on anything in the way, a rumor I wasn't keen on testing with my feet. Following the procession, we squeezed inside the crowded church.

I loved exploring all the hidden corners, caverns, and chapels in this ancient church. Founded by St. Helen in the 4th century AD, it remains one of the oldest church buildings still in use. I liked to touch the gigantic stones in its walls, made smooth by centuries of pilgrims' hands. I could not see above the crowd, and had to find a higher perch. Adnan sometimes carried me on his shoulders. Other times, I climbed atop the pedestal of a column. My favorite perch, however, was the stairwell and balcony leading to Golgotha, from which the Tomb of Christ was in clear view. I loved to read the inscriptions visitors carved on the stone railing, some centuries old, and written in a variety of languages – Arabic, Greek, Russian, French, Italian, English: "1905 AD", "Χ. ΔΗΜΙΤΡΙΟΣ 1845", or, an Arabic one, "Yacoub Baramki, 1899 AD". There was even one from 1690!

The crux of the ceremony occurred at midnight when the priests continuously chanted the Easter hymn, in Greek and Arabic: *Kristos Anesti Ek Nekron, al-Maseeh Qam min bayni-l-amwat*, "Christ has risen from the dead." The painful part was having to stand all the time. The Easter ceremonies were torturous, some lasting until three in the morning. I recall seeing the crack of dawn one Easter morning as we headed back to Ramallah. It was a treat to be up at those forbidden hours. We would come home to find Mom had colored the Easter eggs.

Easter Sunday and Monday, we exchanged brief visits with relatives and friends. Guests were offered colored eggs, liquor, plus specially-made Easter pastries filled with dates or nuts. My favorite part was the Easter egg-smashing contests. We took turns, two children at a time, first smashing the pointed ends of two eggs against each other, then flipping them to smash the other ends. The one with the intact egg took the broken one for a prize. Carrying bags of eggs we won, we went door-to-door challenging other neighborhood kids to egg duels. Naturally, we became experts at selecting "strong eggs", usually by testing them against the teeth. Some kids colored wooden eggs as a cruel joke. It was heartbreaking to see someone's prize egg smashed by the wooden one.

Besides Easter and Christmas were the saints' days, observed by pilgrimages to their shrines. My family frequented the *Mar Jiries* (St. George) festival in Lydd, carrying a live lamb in the trunk of the car. There, in a special part of the church, the priests slaughtered the offering, putting a knife to its neck and letting the blood run out. Part of the offering was distributed to the poor. People usually brought an offering in fulfillment of a *nidher*, or vow, for example in return for healing a sick person. I could not stand the stench in that part of the church, and the pool of blood was sickening.

One holiday peculiar to Palestine is *Eid es-Salib*, or Holiday of the Cross (again with Catholic and Orthodox versions). Falling in September, it marks the discovery of the Cross by St. Helen, in the 4th century AD. The news of the discovery was sent from Jerusalem to Constantinople by lighting successive bonfires, hilltop to hilltop. Ramallah was likely along the way. Fascinated by the idea, I once estimated that the message could get there, if the fires were ready to be lit, in 15 to 30 minutes down this Roman internet. Neighborhoods in Ramallah and other cities still light fires to commemorate this event. Given the time of year, I'm guessing it replaced an existing pagan harvest festival, as other Christian holidays have. The local lore associates this holiday with the advent of the first rain of the season.

Eid es-Salib was great fun for children, but kept the fire department busy. Danny and I teamed up every year, using the empty land between us, one terrace level below the Fig Tree, to set up our fire. The two of us, and Jawad who later joined our efforts, aimed for the "biggest fire of the neighborhood", an unofficial self-declared title we jealously guarded. We spent a good part of summer collecting sticks and branches. Regrettably, once or twice we sawed branches from live trees, but the green wood did not burn well, so we preferred finding ones already fallen and dried. We roamed the hills far and wide to grow our stash. When the big day arrived, we built a pyre twice our height and guarded it all day long, waiting with difficulty until sunset.

Our ambition for the biggest fire once drove us to raid another group's stash. We waited until after sunset, masked our faces with *kafiyyehs*, and hurriedly dragged some of their branches away, almost doubling our pile. The next day, we struggled to hide our smiles as they told us how "masked guys" stole their firewood. We never got to enjoy it, though. In an act of divine retribution, that same summer, about a week before the holiday, a group of older boy scouts raided our stores for their campfires. By the time we discovered and stopped them, most of our wood was gone. We could not protest their un-scoutly actions, having done that ourselves.

Muslims in Palestine have equally festive holidays. The most important one is Eid el-Adha. It lasts three days and Muslim families are supposed to sacrifice an animal – usually a lamb. Those who are able, go to Mecca for the Hajj, or pilgrimage. From the West Bank, the only way to go to Mecca is through Jordan, so the "bridge" to Jordan gets crowded with pilgrims around the time of the Eid.

The most visible Islamic holiday is Ramadan, where observant Muslims fast for an entire month. From sunup to sundown, they abstain from food or drink. My parents taught us to be sensitive to those who were fasting and avoid eating in public during the day. The town became tranquil in the afternoons, as people took long naps or reduced their level of activity. At sunset, the minaret of the mosque in the old city lit, as the sundown *adhan* began, signaling the time for *iftar*, or breaking the fast. Afterwards, Ramallah would suddenly come to life – restaurants packed, streets abuzz with activity, and stores brightly lit. Joining the celebrations, my family cooked special pastries called *qatayif*, filled with either cheese or nuts, and soaked in syrup.

People stayed up late on Ramadan nights. TV channels broadcast longer than usual, offering extra Ramadan programming – game shows, comedy, or stories from the Arabian Nights. A herald walked the streets beating a drum to awaken people for a last meal before the next day's fast. Sometimes I heard him in the quietness of the pre-dawn. Once the new crescent moon made itself seen, Ramadan officially ended, and people celebrated with a big feast. One time, 1984 I think, I decided to fast Ramadan in solidarity with my Muslim friends. Surprisingly, I stuck to it. The experience taught me to appreciate our vital need for that most abundant liquid on the planet – water.

This rich cultural variety multiplied with even a short trip out of town.

3

The Car

THE AGING STATION-WAGON WAS MY TICKET out of Ramallah's small-town monotony. I never turned down an invitation to hop into what felt like a roller-coaster of speed and g-forces. I usually sat on the armrest in the back, but the real treat was sitting on the spare tire in the way back.

Our most frequent destination was al-Quds (The Holy City), the Arabic name for Jerusalem. Only ten miles away, Jerusalem's outskirts could be seen from our house, though the road to it is more convoluted. We drove through the *Manarah* to the Nablus-Jerusalem road, heading south through a dark stretch past the *'arak* distillery (a strong drink from aniseed), and past the little-used single-runway airport at Qalandia. Beyond, the road widened and was better lit. Traffic thickened through the Palestinian neighborhoods of Beit Hanina and Shu'fat, where I was exposed to traffic lights – something we lacked in Ramallah. We also passed an Israeli "settlement", Pisgat Ze'ev. Its stone high-rises looked identical, each accommodating identical apartments distinguished only by the colors of the laundry hanging to dry from balconies.

Jerusalem was two cities in one, divided roughly along the lines of the 1948 war. The Eastern part of the city, including the Old City, had a familiar look, with low-rise stone buildings and Arabic signs on stores. Salah-al-Din Street (Saladdin), the main thoroughfare, though longer, wider, and busier than Ramallah's Main street, nevertheless hosted the same type of family-owned small stores and restaurants. We usually stopped at a bakery there to grab Jerusalem's famous *ka'ek*, an elongated donut of sesame-crusted bread. The business my father ran was further away from the center, on one of the hills overlooking the city. When visiting him, I liked to sit by the window admiring Jerusalem's skyline, which was dominated by the towering high-rises of West Jerusalem.

West Jerusalem felt rather like a foreign country. A different language echoing around more organized and orderly streets lined with larger businesses alongside smaller ones. Here was my first exposure to the supermarket, the department store, and the multi-story furniture outlet. I felt more at home in the large century-old Orthodox Jewish neighborhood of Mea She'arim, which had narrower streets and stone houses with red-tiled roofs, similar to the Palestinian Arabic style. The Orthodox community was militant about enforcing the Sabbath, so the entire neighborhood was sealed by police barricades, starting Friday evening according to the Jewish calendar. Sometimes, we went to the newer neighborhoods further west to shop, as stores there had a wider variety of products than in Ramallah. The clothes were more fashionable, the furniture more modern.

The people in West Jerusalem spoke Hebrew. Though I knew that was the language of the soldiers, I was too young to connect the two. The soldiers might as well have been an entirely different species, vicious and born in uniform. Dad usually parked the car in a lot near Jaffa Street. The lot's attendant knew us well and spoke to us in Arabic. Some Israeli Jews had emigrated from Arab countries, and hence were both Arab and Jewish. One time, after a bomb had exploded in the city, the attendant volunteered to "hide" our car, identifiable as Arab from the license plate, protecting it from acts of revenge. My mother knew Hebrew well, so she conversed with the store owners. Israelis also knew English, the language my father communicated with them. There was nothing unusual about Arabs shopping in Jewish stores or vice-versa. The owners of a clothing store knew us by name, my parents bargained with them as usual, and "business was business".

The shopping part bored me. I was more excited when we went to Jerusalem's small zoo, or visited a swimming pool. Ramallah had neither swimming pool nor zoo, and few avenues for recreation. I was impressed with an underground cavern on the outskirts of Jerusalem, my first time to see stalactites and stalagmites. In Jerusalem, I saw a circus show, visited a museum, and attended a concert, and that was besides the attractions of the Old City. I liked the large English-language bookstore on Jaffa Street, *Steimatzky*, where I could find *Tintin* comic books. My brother Hakeem frequented it to build his library.

On summer Sundays, supposedly our family's "day off", we went to the beach in Tel Aviv. My mother packed our swimsuits, towels, and refreshments the night before, so we could leave by first light. The drive was two hours long. We headed west along Ramallah's Jaffa Street, through the light industrial area, down the hill to the village of Beitunia. There, we passed the "sinkhole", a seasonal marshland where Dad used to take me after a winter rain to see the flooding. Just beyond was an Israeli army camp.

Henceforth along steep grades, the road wound following the contours of the hills, for a 2000-foot descent in half an hour. A few sharp turns and steep cliffs made for a dangerous drive, and shifting vistas I relished. The hills were distinctive. Some had olive trees, some were rocky and denuded. All were contorted, as if they were the faces of giants, their striated rocks and terraces like the furrows in an elderly forehead. They were the old friends I recognized as our guides, ancient landmarks more truthful than man-made road signs that change languages and colors and names.

We passed near several Palestinian villages along the way: Al-Qubeibah, Beit Duqqu, al-Tirah, Beit 'Ur al-Fouqa (the upper), Beit 'Ur al-Tihta (the lower), and Beit Sira. Those villages are ancient, mentioned in historical census data and other texts, and possessing ruins going back thousands of years. The village lands had stone-terraced fields separated by cactus plants, which the farmers used as a natural barbed-wire fence. In al-Qubeibah, I visited a Franciscan basilica, built over one of the supposed sites of the Biblical Emmaus, where Jesus shared bread with his disciples after his resurrection. The church had a scenic spot with arrows marked on the floor indicating directions and distances to all the major cities in Palestine. My most memorable visit to al-Qubeibah, though, was the olive press. There, I watched bags of olives emptied down slides, the pregnant fruit rolling down till squeezed by a hydraulic press, liquid gold pouring out the other side. The crushed pits were bagged for use as fertilizer, animal feed, or fuel for furnaces. Onsite, we saw the ruins of an ancient press, where the thick trunk of an olive tree was used to press and turn a grindstone.

Once we reached the lower Beit 'Ur, the road straightened into a shallow descent to the coastal plain. We closed our noses from the smell of manure as we sought our next landmark, the Latrun monastery near the village of Emmaus (another candidate for its Biblical namesake). My parents sometimes stopped there to buy the distinctive sweet wine produced by the Trappist monks from the monastery's vineyards. I enjoyed strolling amid Latrun's idyllic gardens.

From there, the road to Tel Aviv originally went through Ramleh, a formerly Arab town. There, we saw the three chimneys from the power plant that we could spot from our house. Occasionally, we visited relatives of my father in Ramleh. They had an old-style house with a patio shaded by palm trees in their garden. Eventually, a freeway was opened connecting Jerusalem with Tel Aviv, passing through Ramleh's twin city, Lydd. It was wider and free of traffic lights, but Dad still liked to go through Ramleh every once in a while, as it was the city of his childhood. We opened the windows to enjoy the sweet fragrance of orange blossoms from its surrounding groves. Sometimes I heard Dad remark, "Those used to be our orange groves." Back then, I did not understand why, or how, or if it mattered.

Tel Aviv was a megalopolis compared to Ramallah, or even Jerusalem. Traffic was usually clogged, leaving us stuck in traffic lights along Dizengoff and Ben Yehuda Streets, close enough to smell the salty sea, but unable to see it. The city was jammed with drab cinderblock high-rises, some wearing partially-peeled pastel paints. Sunday was our holiday, but a business day here, and Dad took advantage of that to conduct business before taking us to the beach. We waited in the car, parked on Herzl Street, for over an hour while Dad went for a "quick transaction".

Done, we would head south to Yafa (Jaffa). Yafa appeared older and more established than Tel Aviv, its narrow streets and houses reminiscent of Jerusalem's Old City. Some of the buildings were partially destroyed, and the whole city dilapidated. It was beautiful in a way, but by that time, my mind would be on the beach. Before we got too excited, Dad often stopped at another business contact in Yafa. The rest of the family got impatient. By the time we made it to the beach at Bat Yam, we couldn't wait to jump in the sea.

Mom liked visiting Yafa. That was her city. Dad occasionally drove us around, pointing out landmarks: "that's your mother's school", and "that's the Catholic church she used to attend". It was surreal enough to imagine my own mother a little girl going to school. Yet the school was real, a building amid a grove of trees, surrounded by a high fence. The locked gate bore a sign reading "Terra Santa School for Girls". The church was also real, painted in pink, with a spire functioning as a clock tower. Mom told us how she used to walk a long distance from her house to school every day. "Show us Mom's house," one of my siblings invariably asked. The ensuing debate usually ended with our parents vetoing the idea, on the grounds that the house was "out of the way", while enticing us with the beach.

I finally got to see my mother's house, or what was left of it, one time when all us kids agreed not to be lured by the beach and stick to our request. After some trial and error driving in narrow streets, we ended up in front of an empty lot covered with stones and rubble. That used to be my mother's childhood home. I saw tears roll down her face. I didn't understand why, or what this whole experience meant. Why was the house not there? How did it get destroyed? Why didn't she still live in Yafa? One more mystery to add to the growing list: protests, slogans and songs about *Falastin*, burning tires, and our orange groves.

Bat Yam was a cluster of high-rises similar to Tel Aviv's, with a nice beach. A string of large rocks arranged in a semi-circle created a safe swimming area. We called the prominent one near the center "Adam's Rock". Legends claimed Andromeda was chained to such a rock in Yafa when Perseus found her. The view of the sun setting behind it was exquisite. When I was little, I mostly played in the sand and feared the water. Later, I totally dug the new water slides, lining up for a repeat soon as I swooshed down the chute in an endless splashing cycle of joy.

On the way back from the beach, we often stopped at the Old City of Yafa, a picturesque three-dimensional cluster of domed buildings and narrow alleyways. The Old City was partially restored and turned into a park. Basman and I liked exploring the hidden corners. We would have dinner in Aladdin restaurant, where we would get a table in a small domed room with a window open to the sea, close enough to smell it. The view was charming: an old minaret amid a thicket of palms in the foreground, with the shoreline leisurely stretching to a distant Tel Aviv, contrasted by a deep blue sea. We sometimes visited the safari zoo at Ramat Gan where we could drive our own car among ostriches, zebras, giraffes, and lions. I enjoyed it despite the trepidation I felt entering the segregated lion area. Near the zoo was "Luna Park", an amusement park with roller-coasters, a haunted house, and a labyrinthine Hall of Mirrors.

In the 1980s, the Bat Yam beach became more crowded. My parents began taking us to beaches in Herzliyya and sometimes Netanya north of Tel Aviv. The water there was shallower and we could walk deep into the sea. One street I admired in Herzliyya had the canopies on both sides joining to form a shady tree tunnel.

Leaving Tel Aviv at night, the road was pitch-dark outside the city. A few lights illuminated the Latrun monastery, and dimmer lights glowed from the houses of Beit 'Ur. We knew we neared Beit 'Ur from the smell of the *tabun*, a special oven fueled by sheep manure and used to bake a delicious flatbread with the same name. The villagers were friendly. One time we had a flat tire in Lower Beit Ur, and a resident helped us get back on track. After Beit 'Ur, the next glimmer of light came from the Israeli army camp, just before Beitunia on the outskirts of Ramallah.

A frequent destination for my family those days was Gaza, where Dad's other sister lived. Starting out on the same road to Tel Aviv, at Ramleh we branched south to Gaza, along the coastal plain, skirting Ashdod and Ashkelon. The coastal road was straight and long. It was pretty, lined with tall sycamore trees, cypresses, and, to the south, palm trees. Listening to endless tapes of Umm Kulthoum, the famous Egyptian singer, we sped past citrus groves, greenhouses, and turkey farms. Her music, and the monotony of the straight, flat road, usually put me to sleep.

Gaza itself was larger than Ramallah but fairly quiet. The main street, wide and surrounded by white low-rise buildings, extended west towards the sea. Before heading home, near sunset, my parents stopped at Gaza's beach to buy fresh catch from the fishermen. Behind the market was a pier that extended into the sea. The high tide slightly submerged it, at which times Dad drove the car on it while teasing me about driving us "into the sea", to my horror. I was also spooked by the eerie skeleton of a sunken ship near the horizon. It was tipped over, one of its two large chimneys halfway under water.

My aunt's house was close to the beach. Surrounding it within the high fence was a large garden teeming with fruit trees, including pear, citrus, and a couple of large sycamores. It was a treat to eat *jummeiz* (sycamore fruit) and dates from their trees. The house had a patio facing the garden and a small courtyard inside. The floor was made of large stone tiles, larger than what we use in Ramallah and with more decorative patterns, similar in style to the houses of Ramleh. Their proximity to the sea kept my aunt busy sweeping the floors from the sand that filled the city.

One time, my aunt invited us to go to el-Arish, an Egyptian city in the Sinai peninsula, which Israel had occupied in the 1967 war. Near 1980, it was due to return to Egypt per the peace agreement between the two countries, so it was our last chance to easily visit it. The trip was long – hours of driving along the shore, with nothing to see but the sun, sky, sea, and sand dunes. Endless sand dunes. In the end, I didn't think el-Arish had anything special to justify the long drive. All this for a picnic in the sand?

The last time I visited Gaza was in 1984. Gaza since became out of reach to people from Ramallah and other places in the West Bank. Leaving the borders of Israeli control was an entirely different story I will shortly relate. First though, I needed to quench my thirst for answers to the nagging questions.

4

Inherited Memories

THE EIGHT-YEAR-OLD ME little understood the destruction of his mom's house in Yafa, the orange groves, the cultural divide between East and West Jerusalem, the existence of refugee camps, or the frequent protests. An opportunity for answers presented itself when my mother, Basman and I were staying in England for a month with Adnan, who was now attending college there. Away from her daily routine and preoccupations, Mom finally had time to answer my incessant questions about her life – what was it like when she was young, and what about her family, and her house in Yafa? Over time, further interviews with my parents, my keen reading of history books, and my own research on the family tree filled the gaps. Here is the understanding I pieced together from those sources, largely following my mother's narrative.

She told of a different Yafa, an Arab Yafa on Palestine's Coast, its largest city and cultural capital. The "Bride of the Sea," the Yafa of her youth was free from the slums I saw on my visits. Tel Aviv, the overgrown metropolis that eventually engulfed it, was then just another recently-established Jewish settlement in a chain of settlements surrounding Yafa. Opposite, on Yafa's southern outskirts near the settlement of Bat Yam, my mother grew up in a house only a few steps from the sea, where she spent hours swimming by the rocks. Known to the Canaanites as Joppa, Yafa's history goes back to 7,500 BC. Later it became famous for the oranges exported to Europe under the label "Jaffa Oranges", from the orchards surrounding it and nearby Ramleh, where my father was born.

His paternal grandfather was one of the first exporters of Jaffa Oranges, having worked hard to buy and cultivate land at Ramleh's outskirts. Ramleh was a newer city than Yafa, founded over 1300 years ago by the Arabs. My grandfather was only ten years old when his father died, and being the eldest son, had to support the family. He opened a vegetable stall in the local market. With the advent of the British in 1917, and several currencies floating, he started a foreign exchange business. My father grew up in a large house in Ramleh's old city with his six siblings.

By the time my parents were born (around 1930), Palestine had been occupied for a decade by the British under the so-called Mandate. Like myself, they grew up under occupation, except the soldiers wore British uniforms. What were the British doing there? The geopolitics were too complicated for a child to understand. Mom explained colonialism. Palestine in 1917 was, along with Jordan and Lebanon, a part of Syria, which was a province of the Ottoman Empire. People moved freely across the Middle East. My great-grandmother came from a village in Lebanon – her move was not considered emigrating to a different country. An uncle of my mom was a soldier in the Ottoman army, and remained missing after being drafted to fight in the Balkans. The Ottoman Empire, however, was on the losing side of World War I. The Arabs in Syria helped the British by revolting against the Turks, in return for a promised free Arab state. Our independence mattered little to the British government, who was concerned with paving itself a land route to India, and securing the Suez Canal. At the end of the war, the British divided the former Ottoman lands with the French, imposing their rule against our will. This betrayal became a key factor in Arab opposition to British colonial rule.

Mom's father was a tailor. His father's family originated from Ramallah. His mother, the one from Lebanon, descended from Crusaders. Her family name, *Shuqur*, literally means "The Blonds," hence the blond hair coloring my baby photos. Her father, plus eight of her ten brothers, perished in Lebanon's sectarian wars of the 1860s, when Druze attacked their village. It was then that my great-grandfather met her. An artist, he traveled from church to church to paint frescos of religious scenes – the

Church's comic-book version of the Bible for the illiterate masses. She was taking refuge in a church when they met. They fell in love, got married, and moved to Yafa, Palestine becoming her welcoming home.

My mother was the youngest of three sisters. Upon finishing her schooling, she earned a scholarship to study medicine in Britain, but her parents feared losing her in the hectic aftermath of World War II. Life was unstable throughout the world, especially in Palestine. During the war, conditions were hard. British soldiers were everywhere, while her family, like everyone else, stood in lines to get their rations of flour and milk. When she was little, a group of soldiers stationed by her house were friendly to her, perhaps because of her British name. She was on her balcony one time when they tossed her a ball, but she promptly tossed it back and ran away.

People resented the British occupation and the brutality of the soldiers. Mom remembered a long night when the British ordered all the men of Yafa to assemble in one location for interrogations. My grandma and all the other women of the neighborhood stayed up all night at someone's house, waiting for the men to come back, worried that something might happen to them. The British frequently searched houses looking for any kind of weapon, with harsh penalties for possession of firearms. Scores were executed during the revolt of 1936 for that reason.

The strict British rules against possession of weapons applied only to Christian and Muslim Palestinians, the vast majority of Palestine's population. Meanwhile, the British turned a blind eye to Zionist arms smuggling and armed militias. Enshrined into Britain's "mandate" over Palestine was the Balfour declaration of 1917, written in the heat of World War I, committing the British to establish a "national home" for the Jews. Given this objective, in the 1930s the British actively armed and trained Jewish militias to use them against the Palestinian liberation movement. Effectively, the British confiscated weapons from us and handed them over to the Zionists. Palestine might have gained its independence at the end of World War II, like its neighbors, were it not for the Zionist dimension. Those countries had one colonizer. Palestine had two.

In the West, Zionism was portrayed romantically as a humanitarian movement for the advancement of Jewish people, concerned with creating a home for the homeless, bringing persecuted people from the slums and ghettoes of Europe "to the land". The Arabs in Palestine, whose land was the land in question, could not afford to think in such terms. The Zionist movement left no room for them. Its main pillars were acquisition of land, Jewish immigration, and Jewish governance. This program was enforced no matter that purchases of land from absentee landlords deprived tenant farmers of their livelihood and homes; no matter how rapid immigration strained resources; and no matter that a Jewish administration meant the loss of freedom, democracy, and self-determination to the indigenous Palestinians. That is the root of the conflict and remains so.

The Balfour declaration gave the backing of the leading world power to the Zionist program. People in Palestine regarded it with concern, seeing the Zionist movement as a potent extension of British colonialism. The first Prime Commissioner for the Palestine Mandate, Herbert Samuel, was a dedicated Zionist. The government for Palestine was dominated by Zionists while local Palestinians were relegated to low-level jobs. Zionists controlled sensitive departments, the police and the customs particularly, which facilitated arms-smuggling to the *Hagannah* and other militant groups. The Mandate government accepted decisive numbers of Jewish immigrants into Palestine, swelling the proportion of Jews from 10% to 40% of the population in a mere three decades.

Settlements were located strategically, spanning the most fertile areas of Palestine – the coastal plain and the plain of Marj Ben 'Amer (Jezreel Valley). Each settlement was built like a fortress, with high walls and a watchtower, its lands surrounded by barbed wire. Inside, some housed weapons factories, barracks, and fortifications. Mom grew up hearing worried talk about the chain of settlements surrounding Yafa, ready to cut it off from the rest of Palestine at a moment's notice.

Naturally, Palestine's Arab majority was alarmed at the Zionist program. Resistance was peaceful at first. In our attic, I found boxes of *Falastin* newspaper father had somehow kept from the 1940s. The front pages invariably carried pictures of demonstrators in Yafa or another city marching for a "free Palestine". Some pictures showed British soldiers shooting at protestors defending themselves with stones, a scene no different from what I experienced under Israeli occupation. As more Palestinian farmers were displaced to make room for newly arrived immigrants, the futility of peaceful resistance became apparent, and some turned to armed resistance against the British occupation and against Jewish immigration. Resistance culminated in a six-month strike in 1936, which started from the port of Yafa, shutting down the Arab cities.

Mother considers the strike a big mistake, damaging our economy for no real gain. While Arab Palestinians were idling at home, Zionist factories worked round the clock and immigrant ships arrived daily. The British forcefully crushed the 1936 revolt, disarmed us, and executed, imprisoned, or exiled our leaders. Zionist groups abroad, especially in America, raised untold millions of dollars to fund and arm settlements in Palestine. Both the donor countries and the British Mandate administration permitted the transfer of these funds for aggressive purposes. Meanwhile, Palestinians had little external support, as the neighboring Arab countries were similarly enmeshed in their own struggles for independence from their European colonizers. The net result was a better-armed and better-organized Jewish minority.

World War II did not help. The Arabs in Palestine were too scarred to support the British again. Nevertheless they stopped the revolt in 1939 in exchange for a British promise to stop Jewish immigration during the war years. The Holocaust in Europe, however, drove more Jews into Palestine. Though Palestinians had nothing to do with the Holocaust, they were somehow forced to pay the price, while the rest of the world shut its doors to Jewish refugees. The postwar years were tense. Armed attacks and terrorism increased, as both communities fought against each other and against the British. There was no security, especially for the unarmed Palestinians. Zionist terror groups like the Irgun, led by Menachem Begin, future Israeli prime minister and "peacemaker" of Israel, and Lehi, led by future prime minister Yitzhak Shamir, were assassinating people and exploding bombs, threatening the lives of innocents.

By the end of 1947, after the British gave up their empire in India, they lost interest in Palestine, and began to withdraw troops. They left the fate of Palestine to the newly-formed UN, who did a botch job of it. The UN recommended dividing Palestine into an Arab State and a Jewish State, roughly equal in areas, with Jerusalem as an international city. The "Partition Plan" was mired in iniquity. The fertile plains were allocated to the Jewish State. Concentrated in cities like Tel Aviv, Jews at the time owned only 7% of the land. Consequently, a third of Arab Palestinians lived and owned property in areas mapped to the Jewish state. The newly admitted Arab members of the UN all opposed the partition plan. Most telling, however, was the opposition by countries that had recently suffered partitions and forced population migrations of their own: India, Pakistan, Greece, and Turkey! The dissent was insufficient to stop a UN dominated by a few industrial powers from dictating injustice. The plan's inherent unfairness reflected their assessment, and exploitation, of our weakness. Perhaps our mistake was the unrealistic expectation that moral right triumphs against such overwhelming odds.

On the ground, the armed Zionist groups filled the vacuum left by the British disengagement, strengthening their military hold over Palestine. Palestinian villages were isolated and attacked one by one. Having secured the land area of the UN Jewish state, Zionist troops launched major offensives against Western Galilee and the vicinity of Jerusalem, areas assigned to the UN "Arab state". Clearing a corridor between Tel Aviv and Jerusalem was cornerstone of their strategy. Lydd, Ramleh, and numerous Arab villages stood in the way. A turning point of the conflict took place on April 9, 1948 in Deir Yassin, an Arab hamlet with a population of 600 people on the outskirts of Jerusalem. In the dark of night, Irgun and Lehi terrorists attacked the village. After encountering minimal resistance, the Zionist groups massacred from 107 to 250 Palestinians. Hand grenades were thrown into open windows, people were kidnapped and paraded naked through the streets of West Jerusalem, and afterwards, the bodies of men, women, and children were found dumped in a well. Decades later, Israel erected a memorial not far from Deir Yassin – to Jewish victims of the Holocaust.

Deir Yassin was no isolated occurrence. Select massacres of civilians were part of a program to terrorize the Arab population and induce us to evacuate the lands they coveted. Sound recordings from Deir Yassin were played on loudspeakers as Zionist forces approached other villages, so as to induce terror. Palestinians were left to fend for themselves. The British did nothing to defend the towns under their control, nor to stop the massacres and protect innocent civilians. At the same time, the neighboring countries refused to assist while the British were nominally in charge, for fear of confrontation.

By early May 1948, the Irgun terrorist group turned to Yafa, which was by then bombarded daily from the encircling ring of settlements. My grandfather worried about his family. He had no weapons, and their house lay in the remote outskirts. He took my mom and grandma for a day to Ramleh to visit mom's sister, Laura, who had just delivered their first grandson. When they called for a taxi back to Yafa, they couldn't find any. The road to Yafa was cut off. They had nothing on them, had taken no belongings. Ultimately, they thought it safest to move to the hills of Nablus. A few days after they left Yafa, the city fell to the Irgun, who again resorted to such tactics as throwing grenades inside houses. Palestinians trapped in Yafa by then had no escape but the sea, huddling in small, over-crowded fishing boats to Gaza, many perishing en route.

By May 15, the day the British Mandate formally ended and Israel declared its "independence", about 300,000 Palestinians were already displaced from their homes. Yafa, Palestine's largest Arab city, had fallen. So had Haifa, the second largest. The Arab neighborhoods of Katamon and Talbiyyeh in West Jerusalem were emptied. Scores of Arab villages lay depopulated. Akka's Arab inhabitants were expelled on May 17. In Israeli accounts, May 15, 1948 is the official start date of the "War for Independence" when "seven Arab countries attacked the new state", for seemingly no reason. In reality, the inexperienced armies of the newly-independent Arab states entered, too little too late, to stop the massacres and restrain Israel's land-grab in Palestine. Some of those armies had their own designs. The Arabs practically aided Israel with their rivalries, disorganization, and lack of leadership.

That summer, the Israeli forces turned their attention to Lydd and Ramleh, which were steadfast in their resistance. After heavy shelling, Israeli forces led by Yitzhak Rabin, future Israeli prime minister and Nobel laureate, attacked the two cities. Lydd resisted to the end, while Ramleh surrendered. Both suffered the same fate. In each city, all male residents were assembled at a school. The Israelis then opened fire on the civilians, murdering scores. Those who could, escaped for their lives over the hills, on foot, under fire. Aunt Laura's family was among them. They left Ramleh in the middle of night, climbing the hills to Ramallah, the nearest town in a safe zone. It took them a day to make the 20-mile journey eastward, arriving with nothing but the clothes they had on, their shoes threadbare. With her older husband needing a cane, my aunt carried her newborn in her arms, all the way.

My dad's family were spared the ordeal by traveling at the last minute to Beirut, where dad was attending college. In a box of collectibles dad had kept, along with the deed to his father's house and lands in Ramleh, I found grandpa's Palestinian Passport from that period. Stamped was a visa from the Lebanese Consul in Yafa, issued April 26, 1948, allowing him a maximum stay of 1 month. No one expected a permanent migration. In that box I also found a phone book of "Western Palestine", with my grandfather's name under "Ramleh".

The Israeli army won their "War of Independence" at our expense. It was an eviction more so than a war, enforced by a series of deliberate, exemplary, massacres. By its end in September 1948, Israel controlled 75% of the land of Palestine (including half the area the UN had designated for an Arab Palestinian state). Within, only 200,000 Palestinian Arabs remained, who were reluctantly granted Israeli citizenship, after enduring additional massacres and forced population movements. Over 800,000 others had become refugees, unable to return to their homes, cities, and villages.

Nearly 420 villages were completely depopulated. Within the next few years, Israel systematically destroyed evidence of their existence. The houses left behind were first robbed of valuable belongings, then stripped of any useful implements, appliances, furniture, doors, and windows. Finally, the buildings were razed and the earth turned. Few landmarks remained to tell the tales. Arable land was allocated to adjacent moshavs and kibbutzim. The villages' ruins remained off the beaten path, out of sight. Some were converted into parks, others left to be overgrown with weeds and forests. Destroyed village sites can still be identified in satellite views, the telltale sign being a road network in a wilderness area, with no buildings. Israel even tried removing the cactus plants from the village sites, but strongly rooted, the cactus kept reappearing – a natural memorial for the communities that cultivated it.

1948 became the year of the *Nakba*, or "Catastrophe", for Palestinians. The year when we were robbed of our country, our homes. The year we were transformed from self-reliant human beings into refugees, dependent on others.

Mother faced a new beginning. Her entire life was uprooted. Her belongings all gone, her memories of Yafa relegated to oblivion. She was 16 years old in the earliest photograph I saw of her. Her childhood photos were left in Yafa, to be trampled by the bulldozers that knocked down her house. In Nablus, her education helped her find nursing work with the Red Cross, administering basic medical care to the thousands of refugee children flooding the city. Father's family, meanwhile, arrived in Ramallah to find it crowded with refugees. They found a temporary room in the old city, then moved from house to house. My parents got married in the early 1950s. Mother moved from Nablus to live in the same house in el-Bireh with dad's parents and four of his brothers.

They had little money. The orange grove my grandfather had inherited was gone. The exchange business he had founded in Ramleh was also gone. Fearing looting during the fighting, he had hidden what he couldn't carry to Lebanon from the family's jewelry and his inventory of coins, hoping to dig it up when the war was over. Now it lay beyond the border. Some refugees tried returning to their lands and houses, to pick the harvest left in their fields, or to take belongings and memorabilia out of their homes. The Israelis kept tight control over the borders, shooting "infiltrators".

According to Hakeem, a chance friendship with an American aid worker my grandfather had met in Beirut ultimately helped set things right. Visiting my family in Ramallah in the early 1950s, Ronald learned of the hidden belongings in Ramleh. Without hesitation, he offered to help my grandfather retrieve his cache, taking advantage of his UN credentials to cross the border without a search. My grandfather entrusted him with a map. Ronald went to Ramleh on his motorcycle, dug up the gold and brought it straight back. Astounded, my grandfather offered him to take whatever he wanted as a reward, but Ronald refused. He not only helped my family rebuild their lives, but also inspired in them a deep admiration for Americans. I met Ronald once when he stopped at our house on a Middle East trip of his in 1980. A child at the time, I had no knowledge of the story, but was impressed at his ability to wiggle his ears.

There was no point in dwelling on the past. My family concentrated on rebuilding their business, making new contacts, and establishing themselves in the new place. Ramallah had swelled almost overnight from the influx of refugees. The stress was balanced by the opportunity arising from Ramallah's sudden expansion.

The Arab countries effectively blocked the creation of a Palestinian state. Egypt held the Gaza strip, while Jordan's King Abdullah annexed the West Bank and East Jerusalem, granting Palestinians in those areas Jordanian citizenship. A year later, he was assassinated in Jerusalem on the steps of the Aqsa mosque. Tension prevailed between Palestinians, now the majority of Jordan's population, and the Jordanian government. In spite of Jordan being the only country to grant Palestinian refugees equal rights, some saw the annexation as a hindrance to the establishment of a Palestinian state, or the return of the refugees to their homes. King Hussein, Abdullah's grandson, had to increasingly rely on his army to keep him in power.

My father became involved with the Ba'ath party, a pan-Arab movement with the ultimate goal of unification of the Arab countries. Though it eventually succeeded in establishing regimes in Syria and Iraq, it failed in achieving any unity. Since the borders between Arab countries were widely regarded as artificial lines drawn by European colonial powers, the Ba'ath movement, underground in the 1950s, attracted the young and the idealist. Dad attended secret meetings till midnight while mom worried herself at home until he returned. Once, he was tipped off that he made Jordan's wanted list for his activism, and fortunately flew out of Jerusalem's tiny Qalandia airport to Syria just before the new list reached the border points.

His youthful discontent aside, dad longingly reminisced about *Zaman al-Urdun* (Jordan's Era). For once, Palestinians were citizens of a country. They voted, they could carry guns, and they traveled on a passport. He used to take Hakeem to the hills outside Ramallah to shoot. "How can *we* carry guns?" Myself growing up under military occupation, the very thought was an absurdity. Only the soldiers carried guns. *Zaman al-Urdun* would pop up again when we traveled to Jordan. Dad would reminisce about driving his own car to Amman in less than two hours, there being no borders to detain them. I listened in disbelief, sure he was pulling my leg with tall tales.

The family fared better in the 1960s, and my parents were able to build a house of their own. It faced west, towards their beloved Ramleh and Yafa. Though I grew up in that house, I only realized the significance of that alignment decades later.

Zaman al-Urdun, this mythical bliss, was not to last long. In 1967, another war broke out, Israel won, having invaded additional lands for its insatiable Zionist scheme, including Jerusalem, the West Bank, Gaza, and parts of Egypt and Syria. This time, fewer of us escaped, most preferring Israeli occupation to leaving their homes. Our rootedness confronted Israel with a large Arab population that threatened to overwhelm Israel's Jewish majority. Israel forestalled this fate by keeping most of us in a secondary status without any rights. In 1968, Israel annexed East Jerusalem, offering its Arab residents a mildly upgraded status. In the wake of the Camp David peace agreement, Israel returned Sinai to Egypt, but annexed the Golan Heights, a part of Syria. The remaining areas – the most populous – continue to be in limbo today, more than fifty years later. The 1967 war came to be called the *Naksa*, the "Disappointment" or "Big Letdown". It was more of a *Naksa* for the Arab countries that fought the war rather than for Palestinians. Regimes were shaken. People could no longer place their hopes on the promises of charismatic leaders like Egypt's Gamal Abd-el-Nasser. The Palestine Liberation Organization, or PLO, initially emerged as the big winner on the Arab side, attracting recruits in the refugee camps and cultivating a new hope in the wake of the Arab regimes' failure.

Basman was a baby when the whole family hid in the basement for a few days during the war, just like they did during the next war, when I was a baby. For a tense night they could hear airplanes relentlessly bombing a Jordanian police station at the top of the hill. They emerged the next morning to see the neighbor, Ol' Granny, hanging a white bed sheet on her roof. The Israeli army had entered Ramallah. One of our relatives, Abu Salem, a stooped aged man who always carried a cane, walked across the hills from the other side of town to visit my family. He was hard of hearing and apparently had no idea that a war was ongoing. Lucky he wasn't shot. (He was known to have remarked, on first seeing a television set, "how did they get these people inside this box?")

Families were separated by the war. Whether attending college in Amman, or working temporarily in the Gulf, those absent from the West Bank at that arbitrary date the Occupation began could no longer return, not without a "reunification" process that could take decades. There were no phone lines and no mail services between Israel and the Arab countries, so people resorted to the radio instead. Radio shows from Jordan welcomed callers who left brief messages for their relatives in the West Bank, and vice-versa. Throughout my childhood, I heard such messages on the radio: "*Hajjeh* Sabhah sends her *salam* to her sons Tarek and Mahmoud and their children Wissam and Mohammed, and to her sister Haniyyeh and brother Hamed and tells them her daughter in Amman has just given birth;" or "so-and-so urgently come to Jordan, your father is dying;" or "so-and-so is getting married ..." People coped.

Along with separation, the Occupation brought unification. For the first time in two decades, people from the West Bank could travel to areas of Palestine that were off-limits. Some looked for their old homes. It was an emotional experience, but futile in terms of restoring what was gone. While offering citizenship to anyone of Jewish faith requesting it, Israel has consistently denied our rights to return to our homes. My grandfather died shortly after seeing his land in Ramleh.

In the 1998 Cuban movie *"Life is to Whistle,"* one character faints every time she hears a particular word pronounced. Likewise, "1967" and "1948" became magic numbers, "fainting words" ingrained on the collective psyche of any Palestinian. You could be in a cheerful mood, on vacation say, check into a hotel and get assigned room number 1948. Click! Immediately all the depressing connotations of that infamous number surfaces on your memory, spoiling your day. For anyone else, 1948 is just another number, with no meaning at all. For Palestinians, it is another poke at a wound prohibited from healing. Street addresses, phone numbers, hotel rooms, … there is no end to the possibilities. No getting away.

It took me decades to realize I must exorcise those triggers, purify my brain. Own them back. Give new meanings to those words and numbers that were taken away from us and assigned meanings we never wanted. Catharsis.

5

Stateless

Though I can purge the spell of "1948" and "1967" from my mind, their hold on my life continues. No span of time or distance, or the shield of other citizenships, protects me from their long, menacing, tentacles. The mundane act of travel inevitably reignites the pain of a Palestinian birth, particularly when crossing international borders. This is where it gets personal. Facing the guards at the border, any border, you realize their extended powers over you, simply because they have a country, while you don't.

The first time I visited USA in 1987, I marveled at something Americans took for granted. We rented a car and circled the Midwest: Pittsburgh, to Niagara Falls, Detroit, Chicago, Indiana, and back through Ohio and West Virginia. We also drove round-trip from San Francisco to Los Angeles. For spring break years later, I twice made the 24-hour road trip from Michigan to Florida. For once, we could travel anywhere we wanted, for thousands of miles, crossing state lines, with no one stopping us.

Getting stopped was a given in Occupied Palestine. It was probably on one of the 10-mile drives to Jerusalem that I encountered my first checkpoint. About halfway, we stopped at this place my dad called the "check post", after its British designation. A pair of barbed-wire barriers blocked the road from alternate sides. As the car wound its way through it, it trod over directional spikes of the kind used in rental car lots. Here, I was confronted with Israeli soldiers up close. They wore green uniforms with colored berets, carried long rifles, and serious expressions on their faces. One of them came near, took a good look inside the car, and asked us for *Hawiyyeh* (Identification). My dad presented him a handful of orange cards. After inspecting them, the soldiers mumbled a word for us to go ahead. Occasionally, they made us turn around and go back. "Jerusalem is closed today." We had no say in the matter. I used to hold my breath throughout the encounter, wary of offending those with the power to close Jerusalem.

Every once in a while, something happened in Jerusalem and we were stopped more than once. My parents assured us that the soldiers were likely looking for a specific car. We needed not worry because we did nothing wrong. It was a relief to pass through each one. The trip, ordinarily shorter than the daily commute of most Americans, was for us sometimes an expedition.

The *Hawiyyeh*, or ID card, was one of several instruments the Israeli government used to discriminate between people, divide, and control. In the 1970s and `80s, Israeli license plates were color-coded to identify origin: yellow for Israeli cars, blue for West Bankers, and white for Gazans. At a glance, soldiers at a checkpoint could tell the identity of an approaching car. Yellow license-plate holders were rarely stopped.

ID cards had a similar color-coding. Blue cards in a blue jacket indicated Israeli citizens or residents of East Jerusalem. West Bankers carried orange cards, and Gazans white ones. Jerusalem especially was heavily policed, and we were expected to show our ID cards when stopped. One of the earliest Hebrew words I learned was *kattan* (little), which I needed to get out of trouble when soldiers yelled *"Yeled!"* (Boy!) and asked for ID. This magical escape word informed them I was under the age of 16. Like cars, not everyone was stopped for ID – only people who looked Palestinian, or were heard speaking Arabic. We were accustomed to being eyed with suspicion wherever we went in Israel, and were often ID'ed: in West Jerusalem, in Tel Aviv, and sometimes even at the beach.

In addition to the name of the holder, date of birth, father's and mother's names, the Israeli ID cards listed their "religion". Not quite a Yellow Star of David, this line on the ID card identified people's religious persuasion on demand, facilitating discrimination, and violating an individual's freedom of faith. Even Palestinians living in Israel, nominally Israeli citizens who carried blue ID cards, were thus identified as non-Jewish and treated differently. The Israeli government kept files on every person, keyed by the unique ID number, a number we carried for the rest of our lives. Calling our ID numbers over their radio, soldiers stopping us promptly had our file inspected, and received relevant instructions. It was a methodical system for control, and in a gross sense, for tracking our movements.

I read an American story once about a man without a country. The story was meant to induce people to imagine an unthinkable situation. For me, the unthinkable was reality. For the first 24 years of my life, until I gained Canadian citizenship, I was technically "stateless", without a passport or an acceptable affiliation. After 1967, we were issued Jordanian passports that clearly indicated we came from the "West Bank", limiting our privileges. In practice, they were no different from the travel documents that Israel gave us to use its airports (when we could). Each had a statement stressing it was a "temporary travel document", usually valid for two years, and not a "proof of citizenship".

The Bridge

My earliest memories of going abroad involve crossing the Jordan River into Jordan. From there we traveled elsewhere, or visited our numerous relatives in the "East Bank". Jordan is our closest neighbor, with its capital Amman lying just 50 miles due east of Ramallah, on the opposite side of the Jordan River valley. Under normal circumstances, the journey can be made in about two hours by car, considering the mountainous terrain. Physically, the trip is not unlike going from Buffalo to Toronto, or Seattle to Vancouver. In Europe and America, such border crossings are commonplace, with people easily living in one country and working in another. Not in the Middle East!

A typical Jordan trip in my childhood began at 3 AM when my mother, who had stayed up to pack our bags, woke me up for a taxi ride to Jerusalem. In half an hour, we would be at the cab company office just inside Jaffa Gate, waiting for enough people to fill our shared ride. It would have been simpler to use our own car, but only designated "bridge taxis" could access the border zone. By 4 AM, the sky still dark, our filled eight-seater 1960s Mercedes was cruising down the Jericho road. Anybody could tell it was a Bridge car from the luggage bundled on the roof.

That was the sweet part of the trek, with the car winding its way down the steep eastern slopes, quickly descending the mile of elevation. I relished watching the fledgling beams of the rising sun paint the sandstone hills with rosy colors. Sometimes we saw a few Bedouins tending their flocks, with clear skies adding a postcard feel. Halfway, we passed an old ruin agreed to be the inn where the Good Samaritan entrusted the man he saved. Soon, we passed a sign reading "Sea Level", as we continued our descent towards the lowest point on Earth's surface. Our ears periodically popped, as in a landing airplane.

Near the border, the car got to a standstill behind a long queue of taxis and buses waiting for the "Allenby" Bridge to open. The border opened for only a few hours a day (usually 7 AM to 1 PM), with a fixed number of buses making the crossing. A late arrival might mean missing the "last bus", so most chose to camp outside as early as possible.

That's where hell began. First, came the agony of waiting in that car for hours without progress. Situated in a deep depression, Jericho gets sweltering hot in summer. Even at dawn, the temperatures were unbearable in that crowded taxicab, with the natural air conditioning of the open window stopped with the car. Once, I was stuck with another family whose younger children were impatient, crying and fussing. I could not sleep, read, or do anything with my time. One of the kids spilled orange juice on the long backseat, and I had to endure hours sitting on a sticky seat, pestered by flies.

Finally, the line moved, slowly, as the cars entered the checkpoint one by one. It was mid-morning, perhaps 9 AM, when the taxi dropped us off at the Israeli border building. The next hour or two were spent inside that building standing in lines. That's all I remember. One long line after another for document checks. There we temporarily surrendered the Israeli IDs, keeping our Jordanian passports and one-time "Bridge permits" for the rest of the voyage. We had to apply in advance, per trip, for the *Tasrih* (the Bridge permit), a green piece of cardboard bearing our information and photos, and plastered with postage stamps. Its large size made it superior to the passport for fanning oneself from the heat.

Next, we boarded the bus for Jordan. At the foot of the Bridge, we stopped again for a goodbye boarding and document search by the Israelis. In all those years, I paid little attention to the river flowing under the old, rattling, wooden bridge. By the time we actually crossed, I was happy merely to breathe fresh air.

The Jordanian side offered scant relief. We disembarked at what was little more than an expanded bus stop in the desert. No air conditioned buildings, just the heat and the sand as we waited, and yes, *the flies* … zillions of them. A concrete canopy offered relief from direct sun, but the fans hanging underneath only swirled the hot air about us. More lines of course, for document checks, then bags searches on folding tables. More soldiers dressed in khakis, too, this time wearing red-and-white checkered Jordanian *kafiyyehs* instead of berets. Running back and forth from one window to another – hectically and without clear procedures.

A visit to the *Mukhabarat*, or Intelligence Services, for a clearance was usually in order. It felt that their sole job description, like that of everybody else at both sides of the border, was to harass us and impede our journey. Their questions were aimed at whether we used "the enemy's airports", something the Jordanians forbade. Same story with the people searching our bags: they inspected every little thing, scrutinizing our clothes for Hebrew labels. They chastised us for buying "enemy products", as if we committed treason. I vividly recall the large pyres nearby, raging in flames from confiscated clothes. My mother argued with them: "'Do not buy Israeli products,' are you kidding? There's nothing there but Israeli products. The air we breathe is Israeli. Are you going to confiscate that, too?"

I understood little at the time. Looking back, I see the comically sad irony of the episode. In the name of helping the Palestinian cause, those people were imposing a heavy tax on Palestinian individuals, taking away their very clothes from them. More absurdly, as it turned out, while this went on, Jordan's King was conducting secret talks and understandings with the Israelis. In the end, mother was successful in keeping our clothes. She convinced them to cut out the offending labels, thus preventing the Hebrew letters from contaminating their Arabic virginity. Some pants had the Hebrew letters on the waistband, and so could not be kept intact while undergoing this surgical castration. Now that I understand better, I feel sorry for her and all the Palestinian mothers who endured this, and contempt for the emasculated Arabs who allowed it to happen. Perhaps by reprimanding us for dealing with "the Enemy", they thought they could mask their own impotence in confronting it.

Ironies abound. In 2003, a news story surfaced about Jordan's newly-formed joint free-trade industrial zones. The trilateral agreement allows Jordan to sell its products duty-free in American markets, provided a minimum of 7% of each item's value is made in Israel. According to the article, to satisfy the quota, the Jordanian clothing companies use *Israeli labels and zippers*! So much for the bonfires on the Bridge! (Egypt signed a similar agreement in 2004, committing to 11%.) Perhaps that is Israel's solution to the "Arab demographic threat" – control the Arabs' *zippers*?!

But I digress. Sometime in the mid-afternoon, the insanity came to an end, and we could finally leave. Once out of the Bridge, it felt like freedom. It was another hour in yet another taxi to Aunt May's farm on the remote outskirts of Amman, where we would arrive completely worn out. Mom's oldest sister, Aunt May, had moved to the "East Bank" with her husband before 1967. The War left them unable to come back. I remember two occasions when they could obtain the Israeli permits for brief visits, once in the 1970s, and again for Sandra's wedding in the early 1980s.

The Bridge, Reversed

Sooner or later, we had to put up with the dreaded reverse trip. The Jordanian side was usually uneventful, barring the flies. The process was hectic and lines eternals as we waited for document checks and boarding. Again, we worried about catching the last bus.

Across the Bridge, I was convinced the air-conditioned Israeli building was a torture chamber in disguise. Holders of foreign passports went to a different terminal, so the Palestinian experience on the "Arab Bridge" was cloaked from the eyes of the world. If we were lucky, we were out of there in four hours. More often, we spent the entire day in that building, inching through the three stages in assembly-line fashion: document check, body search, and baggage search.

As soon as we dismounted from the bus, we were separated from our bags and directed to Stage One. I remember little about the document control, my dad handling everything. We complied, despite the unfairness of the Bridge procedures, as if we understood such behavior permissible for an occupying power. From experience, protest only brought more delays, and the simple truth was that they carried rifles while we were unarmed. They frequently made examples of people. If someone complained about the long line, the soldiers ordered him to the back of the line. Soldiers at the Bridge rarely talked to us politely. They barked their orders: "You! Come here!" "Stand there!" "Open the bag!"

Stage Two was perhaps the most dreaded, for the humiliation if nothing else. First we entered an elongated, stuffy room with no windows, and three doors at the other end. A long wooden bench extended in front of each door, all the way towards us. Before sitting at the near end of one of the crowded benches, we dropped our shoes into a crate for separate screening. The men were separated from the women, but up to a certain age, I stayed with my mother, as I was registered on her passport. We slowly edged sideways as people from the other end got called. When the time came, the door opened and they beckoned us. Barefoot, we stepped into a dim hallway with a series of small stalls on either side, hidden by drab opaque shower curtains. Our inspector (a female soldier for the women and children) pointed us to an empty stall. Loosely drawing the curtain, she first asked us to empty our pockets, then to take off different pieces of clothing, methodically searching each piece with a metal detector. Holding our passports above the pile of clothes on the table, while we stood in our underwear, she interrogated us. "Where have you been?" "What did you do outside?" "Whom did you meet?"

Looking back now, this form of body search was completely

unnecessary from a security standpoint. (In Tel Aviv airport, we simply walked through a metal detector, at most taking off a belt.) The detectors alone were sufficient for finding hidden weapons. Perhaps the guards at the Bridge looked for banned books or PLO publications, but then why did we have to answer their questions while half-naked? It seemed their sole purpose was to psychologically dominate us. The little child that was me did not understand what was going on. I could sense something sensuous about having a uniformed young woman order me to take off my shorts and search me so intimately. At the same time, I could feel a deep shame, especially *no one* talked about it. I was allowed into the women's room until I was eight, by which time I had experienced that kind of search over ten or fifteen times.

After the body search, we continued to the other end of the hallway to retrieve our shoes from a conveyor belt. We then turned left, for the third and final stage, into a corrugated metal annex with fans dangling from the high ceiling. On the other end, we could see the taxicabs waiting outside the large open door, with the rosy sandstone hills behind. The sight of the landscape only stimulated my desire to be outdoors and go home, but we had luggage to be searched. A long counter, segmented into stalls, divided the room in half. To the right, behind the counter, was a sea of unopened suitcases waiting to be examined. To the left, rows of crowded seats. Israeli border guards stood behind the counter, each searching someone's suitcase.

We waited what felt like hours for our turn. Name called, a soldier escorted us to identify our bags and drag them to his or her stall. One by one, each was opened, emptied on the counter, then sent to a separate room for inspection. The suitcases sometimes came back with ripped linings. Meanwhile, the soldier went through the pile of contents, item by item, with a metal detector. Nothing was spared, not even the underwear. They threw away (or rather confiscated) perfumes, ink pens, and medicines. By that stage, we were too exhausted to argue. Once that was over, we knew, we would be free to head home.

At the end of this madness, we were left with empty suitcases and large piles of clothes to re-pack. I never understood why my mother cared to pack things neatly while anticipating this fate. No point in worrying wrinkly clothes or broken items. Just shove them in the suitcase and get out, before they change their minds. The taxi ride back always seemed longer. Perhaps it was the steep uphill grade, or the scalding afternoon heat. The only comfort came at the end of the climb, when the silhouette of Jerusalem loomed ahead, signaling home.

We were told at the Bridge that these searches were for security. From their questions, we could guess they wanted to ensure no one smuggled bombs, weapons, or banned literature, and that no one communicated with the PLO. Yet, by harassing the entire population like this, Israel only crowded the PLO recruitment offices. As policy, Israel had maintained that "there were no such thing as Palestinians. ... They did not exist," in the words of former Prime Minister Golda Meir. The Israeli government and army kept referring to us as "Arabs". Looking at the waiting rooms on the Bridge, I saw people from all walks of life, patiently waiting for the same dole of abuse: the olive farmer next to the university professor; the construction worker next to the grocer. Rich or poor, we were all subjected to exactly the same treatment, had to go through exactly the same steps, the same searches. There was an overwhelming sense of brotherhood in those rooms. Even if Golda Meir was right, if there was never a Palestinian people, *the Israeli Occupation created one*.

The system clearly operated for the benefit of one group of people. All others were expected to sacrifice their time and dignity in order to ensure the favored group's security. This assumption of superiority is an ingrained and persistent feature of Israeli thought. During the Oslo "Peace Process", the humiliation, segregation, and control intensified. Checkpoints multiplied while separate roads were erected, for Israelis only, who could travel freely while Palestinians endured great hurdles to go to the next village. Today, Israel's ideology of Jewish-supremacy is embodied in the Wall. In a different place and age, Rosa Parks refused to give up her seat, under the "colored" sign, to a white person. In Occupied Palestine, we do not even share the same buses, roads, border crossings, or cities. Segregation is complete.

The Airport

As an alternative to enduring the double-trouble of traveling abroad through Jordan, my family started flying through Lydd Airport (renamed to Tel Aviv or Ben Gurion Airport). For that, we traded our ID cards for temporary travel documents, and applied for a one-time "Exit visa". Upon our return, we were expected to trade it back for the ID card, so the process needed to be repeated for the next trip. Sometimes it seemed the whole point of these procedures was to discourage travel, or, for those already abroad, returning home. For a two-week vacation, a typical annual allotment in American companies, a trip to the West Bank was hardly worth it.

Incidentally, we subsidized the Occupation through the fees for official documents like ID cards, travel documents, or bridge permits. The two-year expiration for travel documents ensured frequent renewal and a constant stream of income.

Since most flights took off in the morning, we typically left Ramallah by 2 AM to leave enough time for the searches. At the airport, we endured an average of *four hours* of search and interrogation. First, we stopped at a checkpoint at the entrance, unloading all the bags for a quick inspection. (Until 1990, we could drive our own cars to the airport). My last time there, in 1999, I was late for my flight and the entrance open to us was crowded, as every car was thoroughly searched. The driver of my taxicab, from Jerusalem, offered to take me through another entrance, open only to yellow license-plate holders. The guard there stopped us, and after a couple of questions identified me as Palestinian. Never mind I had Canadian citizenship at the time. Since we were the only car being searched, the soldier took his time. He was young, and going by the rulebook. He kept asking me if I was "nervous" – apparently their manual instructed them to look for signs of nervousness as evidence we were hiding something. Of course I was worried, slow as he was, that I'd miss my flight!

Passing that outdoor stage, we pulled into the terminal. Before getting to the check-in counter, we joined a long line of people for the second security check. Here, everyone got searched and interrogated. It was amusing to stand behind an Orthodox Jewish family in the same line, knowing their bags were to be opened too. The similarity ended there. Searches of our bags were far more thorough, the questions more invasive. Eventually, the Israelis built a separate room for us so as not to delay the remaining passengers. We waited in line with everyone else, then upon our turn, were escorted to the "Arab room" like suspects on watch lists. I was hoping my American friend Will, when he visited in 1999, could avoid this fate if he said nothing about staying in Ramallah. Finding souvenirs in his luggage (that he could have gotten in Jerusalem), they asked where he purchased them. Unused to their grilling, he admitted Jericho, and was escorted.

Inside, the normal routine transpired, bags emptied and sent to a special machine, while the security guard ran a metal detector over every item. They checked our bodies with a metal detector in a screened room, but unlike at the Bridge, where they were perhaps emboldened by the absence of foreigners, we were not stripped. In the airport terminal, the Israelis kept a semblance of respectability.

The guards' suspicion and paranoia was absurd. One time we were sending off Basman to college in America. My mom had packed him home-made cookies in a metal chocolate box. As soon as they found the box, the guards immediately raised a security alert, forcing a total evacuation of the terminal. A bomb unit took the box to probe it, only to find out it held cookies.

Another time, after settling in the USA, I took Paddington, my old teddy bear, to America. The bear, old as myself, was worn out and repaired in many places. The day before I left, my mother had patched holes in the hands and feet. In the Arab room, the guard noticed Paddington's stitches. She wanted to cut it open to check inside. "Look, it's just an old bear," I pleaded, asking if she could use the X-ray machine instead. Fortunately for Paddington, she was sympathetic and the bear got a free X-ray exam.

By the time we checked in, it was already past departure time. Planes out of Tel Aviv were delayed until all the passengers had been examined, which usually meant missing our connecting flight in Europe. (For some reason, travel agents never accounted for the inevitable by prolonging the Europe layover.) Airport security guards were more polite than the Bridge soldiers. After a four-hour search and a delayed flight, the same guard who X-rayed Paddington actually apologized for my inconvenience, and presented me a "Ben Gurion Airport Authority" pen as a consolation gift.

Arrival at Tel Aviv airport felt easier, lacking the stress of a flight to catch, but took hours all the same. Entering the terminal, we lined up with other passengers for passport control. Once identified, Palestinians, even those carrying Israeli citizenship, were escorted to the Arrivals' "Arab room", while Jewish Israelis and foreigners whizzed through. There, we all waited an hour or two before a guard was available to interrogate us, search our bags, and bodies.

A foreign passport is no help. After becoming a Canadian citizen, I once showed my Canadian passport at Tel Aviv Airport, hoping it would simplify travel to Jerusalem through the multiplying checkpoints. The guard at the counter examined it, then asked me "I see your place of birth is Jerusalem, how is your Hebrew?" Seemingly innocuous small talk, yet a devious method for winnowing us. After admitting my ignorance of the language, she asked if I had an Israeli ID. I could not lie. Immediately, I was segregated to the Arab room, but not before she stamped my Israeli ID number on my Canadian passport. In other words, I was no Canadian citizen to them, but a second-class resident of the West Bank. An Israeli friend told me that, had I spoken Hebrew to her, the next question would be "When is the next Jewish Holiday?"

In Europe, connecting flights to Tel Aviv had an added security check at the gate. Transiting through Amsterdam's Schipol airport once, I readied my Canadian passport at the Tel Aviv flight's gate. The Dutch officers were friendly and courteous, and the questions were ordinary. But there was one that annoyed me: "Mr. Zaitoun, *with your Canadian Last Name*, what are you going to do in Israel?" I was shocked into silence. I badly wanted to give the speech about Canada being a country where it was unlawful to discriminate by national origin, and that questions like that were prejudiced and inappropriate. Yet he was doing only what he was instructed to do. After spending eight hours flying over the Atlantic, I only wanted to move on. The giveaway, of course, was the "place of birth". Its inclusion on passports facilitates discrimination based on ethnic origin in every country that has no respect for equality and civil rights.

State of Statelessness

Palestine is real to me. That's the country of my birth. Occupied, perhaps, yet real enough to be touched along with the stones of the *sanasel*, inhaled with the April wildflowers, and tasted in the *za'atar*, Palestine's blend of thyme and spices. This Palestine had no place within the international system, which seemed intent on spotlighting the vacuum.

The first time I heard the word "stateless" was when my parents and I went to America for Basman's college graduation ceremony. At the immigration desk in JFK Airport, we presented the entry forms we received on the plane, in which my parents had entered "Palestine" for citizenship. The officer looked through his books for a minute, then asked us to fill out new ones and write "STATELESS" instead. "Stateless?" My dad asked him. The American officer kindly shrugged his shoulders, with a sympathetic look on his face, "I'm sorry, but that's the law!" We complied, knowing that this good gentleman had no choice but to do his job.

Even in more amiable settings, the innocent question *"Where are you from?"* had far from simple answers. On that first visit to America, I offered to take a photo of a nice couple at a restaurant in San Francisco. We made small talk, and the question was popped. Not knowing how to answer, I tried "Israel", so they asked me how to say "'Good morning!' in Yiddish." Bad choice!

Two years later, when I came back for school, I tried a different answer.

"Palestine".

"Where is that?"

"In the Middle East, you know, occupied by Israel? In the news every day?"

"Oh, yeah."

Soon, a friend of theirs walks by, and my new acquaintance is eager to introduce us:

"Hey Brad, let me introduce you to Sameer from Pakistan!"

Or,

"So what do you think about relations with India?"

The "West Bank" rang no bells either. Only after year 2000 did Ramallah sound familiar. So, if I cared to answer correctly, I had to give people a short lesson in history and geography, invoking "the Middle East", "Yasir Arafat", "Jesus", and sometimes "Bethlehem". At some point, I stopped caring.

"Where are you from?"

"Pakistan!"

But seriously, growing up without a country left us psychological scars, for countries pervade all aspects of life. It is not simply about a passport, travel, or the occasional question or two. Every day, we turned on the TV to watch 'Jordan', 'Israel', 'Syria', 'Lebanon'. Every country had its own TV and radio stations, except us. I watched other children singing songs for their respective countries. I saw military parades and national celebrations. I saw kings and presidents and prime ministers. Not that I cared for any of that hullabaloo, but the eternal question in my child mind was *"why were we different?"* Children's programming on Jordan TV showed the queen visiting children's centers on holidays. I wondered, "where is our queen, our children's center, our national holidays?" Sometimes I wished to appear on a children's show like the ones broadcast on Jordan TV, but of course those were for Jordanian kids.

I loved to travel, especially flying. For most of my childhood, I dreamed about becoming an airline pilot. I read books about flying, joined junior flying clubs, studied how airplanes worked, even came up with a design to convert my bicycle into an airplane by adding wings and a propeller. Thinking to use Ol' Granny's Fig Tree Lot for an airstrip, I poured over maps, charting courses for possible trips. I wanted to fly to Cairo, estimating I could reach the pyramids in a matter of hours. I visualized myself on the trip, minute by minute, passing all the landmarks on the map, imagining how they looked from above. Before flight simulators, we had daydreams. In a world where Palestine does not exist, however, most daydreams are out of bounds, to remain unfulfilled.

We gave our mailing address as "Ramallah, West Bank, *via* Israel" to receive mail correctly. The '*via*' we inserted to keep our sanity. "Israel" was the internationally recognized postal authority, but that was not my country, or rather, "it" did not accept me as belonging to it. "Palestine" was the country everyone around me said was ours, except that nobody else in the world recognized it. Years afterwards, after the Palestinian authority took over parts of the West Bank, flew its flag, and issued stamps, I still had to deal with this ambiguity. I took a letter addressed to 'Palestine' to a US Post Office in the late 1990s. The clerk looked it up in a thick book, then told me "Sorry, you have to enter Israel."

Internet web forms are similarly skewed. Out of the pull-down lists of hundreds of countries and small territories and islands, I rarely find Palestine, the West Bank, or Gaza, as if we simply don't exist. I thought it nice to display "Palestine" next to my username on an online chess community, where I engaged opponents from all over the world. Not finding it in the list, I wrote to the site organizers. They responded with a "Palestine is not recognized as a country" line. Yet their list had places like "Western Sahara", an occupied territory with roughly the same international status as Palestine. Besides, this was not a United Nations agency, but a silly gaming site! How easy would it be to add a line to their form, instead of feigning adherence to "international standards" as the excuse to negate my identity?

Maps in the Western world omit us. Hallways of flags and lists of countries always meet me with a resounding silence. I am now nearing fifty years of age, born under an occupation that is still ongoing, and belonging to a country whose existence other people continue to deny. I feel invisible – as if I do not exist, or do not matter.

The arenas of international sporting events resonated with our absence. I learned that when I followed the 1984 L.A. and the 1988 Seoul Olympic Games. Everyone was represented in the opening ceremonies, except for us. There were no Palestinian athletes to cheer. Every other child in the world can dream about someday competing in the Olympics, and is given the opportunity to participate. Some will go on to realize their dreams, but, until recently, Palestinian children have been denied the chance to even try.

When I grew older, I learned of the 1972 Olympics in Munich, before my birth, when eleven Israeli athletes were kidnapped by Palestinian Black September guerillas and later killed during the rescue. Sad! The aftermath, enacted in Spielberg's *Munich,* in which Israel avenged the athletes, was also sad. I wondered about the prequel. Did the Munich kidnappers suffer the Olympics-exclusion scar? They grew up in the refugee camps of an unrecognized nation, ineligible to participate, while the Israelis who usurped Palestine by force, enjoyed the privilege of competing.

In the USA, the story of the Munich massacre continued to haunt viewers of every Olympics. Each time, NBC mentioned Munich in the opening ceremony at the Israeli team's entrance, and again at the Palestinian's (after its belated admission in 1996), and yet again at individual events featuring Israeli athletes. Is there no statute of limitations? The Palestinian athletes marching in Athens or Sydney were not yet born when the 1972 event took place. Yet here they were, introduced to American audiences with this allusion to the Black September kidnappers, as if they somehow shared the responsibility. We thus lived the double stigma of being excluded from the Olympic Games for most of the 20th century, then when we finally did participate, were tarnished with an added asterisk.

(After the Peace Process, without fanfare, Palestine was finally admitted to the Olympics, starting from the 1996 Olympics in Atlanta. This victory did not come easily, but only after a mass uprising that lasted several years, and the peace talks it birthed. Finally, at Sydney in 2000, and in the midst of a second uprising, Husam Azzam won Palestine's first Olympic medal – the Bronze in the Paralympics for, appropriately enough, the shot put event. I find it amusing that, handicapped by an Israeli bullet during the first Intifada, Azzam won Palestine's first Olympic medal for an activity that had come to symbolize our national struggle – throwing projectiles. He went on to win the Silver in Athens in 2004.)

6

School Years

GRANDMA OLENA DIED WHEN I WAS EIGHT. It took me a while to get used to her empty bed, inevitably finding it vacant every time I rushed to show her something. The following year, aunt Andrea moved to Jordan and the middle floor was vacated. We moved into her apartment, and for the first time, I had my own room, which I shared with Basman. A year later, Sandra got married and moved out. Meanwhile, Basman finished high school and turned 18, the minimum age for a driver's license, not that its absence stopped him from underage driving. I spent the summer with him in the old station wagon, riding shotgun. He would pop in a tape of Michael Jackson, ABBA, or the Police, blast it, and speed around Ramallah with the windows open, targeting certain neighborhoods with girls to impress. I dug the music and the rush, sometimes pretending we were on a mission, like the A-Team. Loads of fun!

Good things don't last forever, though. When that summer ended, Basman started at Birzeit University and had less time to cruise; a year later, he went to USA for college after Hakeem's wedding. My parents had finished the walk-out basement – the "Shelter" – into an apartment for Hakeem and his wife. Dad arranged for slaughtering a lamb on the doorstep. Someone dipped a palm in the spreading pool of blood, and pressed it over the lintel, echoing the Biblical Passover of the Hebrews. The newlyweds stepped over the pooled blood into their new life together. Being a vegetarian myself, out of empathy with the animal beings, I avoided the barbaric scene, and for months refused to visit them through that door.

Basman returned almost every summer. He worked at the store during the day, and afterwards we played a daily game of chess. We sat on the balcony, watching the street, drinking Cokes. At night, we cruised, or walked along busy downtown streets. With the intense afternoon heat dissipating quickly after sunset, people ventured outside, and stores opened into the night. Hole-in-the-wall food stalls specialized in *kebab*, *shawarma* (the traditional shredded roast lamb), *hummus*, or *falafel* (fried chickpea and bean patties). We ate those with thick, pocketed, pita bread we call *ikmaj*, or the thick-crusted, sesame-covered, donut-shaped *ka'ek* (round in Ramallah unlike its elongated Jerusalemite cousin). Vendors drove carts selling snacks: peanuts, pistachios, roasted watermelon seeds, roasted green chickpea pods, or boiled corn-on-the-cob. Parks were crowded, as were garden restaurants like *Na'oum*, or *al-Bardouny*. Both had seating in a terraced garden, played music, and served *mezza* dishes to accompany *arak* drinks and *arghileh* smoking. Na'oum was famous for filling an entire table with small plates, perhaps fifty of them, each serving a different dish. We sometimes watched movies at one of Ramallah's three cinemas: al-Waleed, al-Jameel, and Dunia. Most popular were Indian movies and Bruce Lee kung fu movies, although we also got the major Hollywood hits like Rocky, a few years delayed from their release date in America.

While Basman was away, my second brother Adnan returned from England with a doctorate, and got a teaching position at Birzeit University. In England, he had become involved in born-again religious groups. (I later learned he had protested Monty Python's *"Life of Brian"* on release night outside a theater.) Back home, he frequented the Baptist church and sometimes dragged me to their youth group meetings and Bible studies. He also got me a number of books and brochures, in Arabic, about the Bible. Though I enjoyed the set of comic books illustrating the Biblical stories, I was not as single-mindedly focused on religion. What drove me away from religion altogether was an incident one Sunday at the Catholic church. Sister Felicia, walking the aisles, stopped to ask why didn't I attend every Sunday. I innocently confessed sometimes going to the Baptist church. Woe fell down upon me! Better I stayed home, *or blasphemed,* rather than go to the Baptists. Thinking they were both Christian denominations that believed in the same scripture, I could not see the harm done, so was taken aback at her vitriol.

My thoughts propelled down the road of disillusion with organized religions. "God is everywhere," they claim, yet only "they" possess the exclusive access, while everyone else is to perish. I was sure that among the zillions of stars, ours wasn't unique in having planets that hosted life. Did Jesus get incarnated on every planet in the Universe? If he didn't, how were the aliens going to be saved? Forget aliens. Of Earth's numerous cultures, the Bible and Jesus descended to only one. Are the majority of Earth's inhabitants to perish? The church used the idea "saving them from doom" to "proselytize" other cultures, an operation that history proved was a cover for genocide and plunder. So did other missionary religions. How could Jesus be the "Prince of Peace", when his legacy was millennia of religious warfare?

The upshot of Adnan's faith were the pilgrimages his friends from England made, in groups and individually. He invited some to stay at our house, which broke the monotony for me. They toured during the day, and came back at night to play music and sing. Adnan toured individual visitors by himself, and I tagged along. When the reverend of Adnan's church visited with his mother, the trips were memorable, especially since the reverend's thorough Biblical knowledge led us to places unknown even to Adnan.

One excursion was to Mar Saba (St. Sabas) Greek Orthodox monastery. We drove through Jerusalem to Bethlehem, past the Shepherds' Field in neighboring Beit Sahur, and down a dirt road into the wilderness. The monastery was located at the edge of a cliff overhanging the canyon of Qadroun (Kidron), about halfway to the Dead Sea. There were no good maps or road signage, so we stopped repeatedly for directions. After that effort, I was disappointed that the monastic rules forbade entry to women, so the reverend's mother had to wait in the car. They banned men wearing shorts, too, so I waited with her. It was hot, and it seemed our party was inside for a long time. At least I got to brush up on my English keeping the old lady's company.

Backtracking to Jerusalem, we headed west on the Yafa road, stopping a little while later at the Arab village of Abu Ghosh. Our friend led us to a Benedictine monastery marking another site presumed to be the Biblical Emmaus. Among ruins from Byzantine and Crusader churches, an ancient well fascinated me. Looking through the safety grating covering the opening, I found it darker and deeper than I had imagined possible. The monks welcomed us with fresh-squeezed lemonade, which we sipped in the arched patio, a life-saver after the hours in the hot car.

We continued west towards Yafa. Jerusalem's road to Yafa is nestled in a valley covered with pine forests, keeping it shady and cool. The descent is less steep than the road from Ramallah, as the hills are cut in places to accommodate it. Along the sides of the road were several destroyed tanks left over from the 1948 war.

We exited at Latrun, then stopped at the adjacent site of Emmaus just inside the West Bank. A thriving village had existed on the site until 1967, when the Israelis expelled its inhabitants at gunpoint and completely destroyed it, along with two adjacent villages. The area was converted into a park called "Canada Park", where fast-growing pine trees, purportedly a Canadian gift to Israel, were planted to quickly cover up the ruins. Driving inside, we stopped in a few places to admire the natural spring, waterfalls, and lush vegetation. The hilliness of the site made for dynamic perspectives, but we weren't so fortunate to encounter the gazelles that roamed the park.

Among other new places we visited with Adnan's reverend was *el-Muhraqa*, the highest peak of Mt. Carmel in the North. It is the reputed site of the pyre Prophet Elijah erected in his challenge to the pagan priests, to see whose gods could light a fire (1 Kings 18). Our friend visited a building at the site belonging to the Catholic Carmelite order. I preferred to stay outside savoring the panorama from the overlook, and the vegetation and wildflowers in the area.

There was always something new to see on those road trips, a landscape in constant change. In the early 1980s, we noticed construction activity on the road to Tel Aviv near the twin villages of Beit 'Ur: nice upscale homes with red-tiled roofs and large gardens. It was a new Israeli "settlement" called Beth Horon (adopting the Biblical name of the nearby villages). Shortly thereafter, the Israelis opened a new road connecting Lower Beit 'Ur with the Jerusalem-Tel Aviv freeway, just before the airport at Lydd. This direct route was considerably shorter than the old one through Latrun. We hardly visited Latrun after the opening of the new road, and liking the shortcut, we did not question its motives. In retrospect, it's not hard to see the link between the new settlement and the road. The new houses in Beth Horon are more attractive with their faster connection to the large population centers of Lydd, Ramleh, and Tel Aviv. That association between road improvements and settlement projects became obvious a decade later, when the road-building hit high gear.

The new road cut through a forested area. Picnic tables were set up alongside, amid scattered debris of destroyed airplanes – a propeller here, a wing there – left as a memorial to one of Israel's wars. I was ignorant of the place name, as the only English signs simply said "picnic area". Today on the map it is marked as the "Ben Shemen forest" after the nearby Israeli settlement, but the original Arabic name remains a mystery. Likely it was named after Jimzo, one of the larger villages in the area, destroyed in 1948. We were always on our way elsewhere when passing it, so we never stopped to explore, thinking the forest would always be open to us. Later I saw beautiful photos of its trees and wildflowers online, and regretted not stopping by when we could.

The road to Jericho also changed. By the mid-1980s, it got wider and shorter. Corners were cut, and hills leveled. It made the trip faster and easier, but obliterated the mystique of the wilderness, and eroded the beautiful pink rocks. Just east of Jerusalem, a new Israeli "settlement" was taking shape. Perched on a hilltop overlooking the Jericho road, Ma'ale Adumim (Reddish Heights) expanded from nothing, until it became the largest Israeli settlement in the West Bank.

One time, Basman took me on a different road to Jericho, a shortcut through Taybeh northeast of Ramallah. Past that village, we understood why people preferred the longer Jerusalem road. The Taybeh road wound its way down a ledge skirting the cliffs, with no guardrail. Barely wide enough for one car and a narrow rough shoulder, the road hadn't been paved since Jordanian times. I was distracted from enjoying the sight of mountain goats hopping on the cliff above by the imagined fate of cars that slipped into the gorge below. The thought did not deter Basman from his usual racing speeds. I vowed never to ride that road again. (The vow didn't survive into the twenty-first century, when for years at a time, the slightly improved Taybeh road was the only one open to us.)

Basman's first summer back from USA, I went along with him and a friend of his to the North. We took Dad's new car, since the station wagon was too beaten up to leave Ramallah anymore. We had several choices of northbound roads to take. The easternmost runs through the Jordan River valley. Another follows the West Bank's central ridge, through Nablus and Jenin, to Nazareth. The remaining three roads run in parallel along the coastal plain.

We opted for a circuit tour, getting to Haifa by mid-morning on the westernmost road, a freeway following the coastline from Tel Aviv. As the coast narrowed further north, we could see the Mediterranean on our left, and the two other coastal roads on our right. (The middle one a shortcut through Hadera and Fureidis, the furthest hugging the foothills of the West Bank.)

Haifa is a beautiful city. Built on a promontory, the city extends for several hundred meters up the slopes of Mt. Carmel. We ascended along narrow zigzagging streets lined with sidewalk cafés. The upper parts of the city provide stunning panoramas of Haifa's white buildings against the deep blue Mediterranean. On a good day, one can see far up the coast, all the way to Lebanon.

From Haifa, we headed east to Nazareth, at the center of the Galilee, and Israel's largest "Arab" city. Like Haifa, it is built on slopes, some steep. Its old city is reminiscent of Jerusalem's, with covered streets and narrow thoroughfares. The Basilica of the Annunciation is the main landmark. At the highest point in the city, with a better view, is the Salesian Church of Jesus the Adolescent, where I had once attended a church retreat.

We continued east to Tiberias, a city founded by the Romans on the shores of the "Sea of Galilee" (actually a lake in the Jordan River). From the lakefront, we could clearly see the Golan Heights on the other side. One time with the family, I took a ferry to the ruins of Capernaum on the north shore. This time, we simply had lunch on the lakeside. I had fun dropping breadcrumbs into the water, attracting hundreds of small fish to the point of impact. Intriguing to think that those fishes' ancestors escaped the nets of Jesus' disciples.

From Tiberias, we drove down the Jordan Valley road, through Bisan southward to Jericho. Closer to the lake, vegetation was lush. The road crossed the river in several places, where we spotted people canoeing. Further south, the landscape turned to a desiccated yellow. Since the river here formed the border with Jordan, its banks were fenced off with electrified barbed wire, minefields, and sandbanks that were combed daily to detect infiltration. Vegetation reappeared as we got closer to Jericho, with banana and mango groves covering wide areas. Arriving in Jericho about mid-afternoon, we could stand the oven-hot air only long enough to buy a bunch of dates before jumping back into the air-conditioned car.

Starting third grade, I moved from the Catholic School to the Friends Boys School. Founded and run by American Quakers, it was considered the leading school in Ramallah. There, I spent about nine years, through junior high. I liked the Friends School, though I found it twice the work since we learned all subjects in both Arabic and English. The school had a separate "English-speaking" track for students who grew up in the USA, usually children of emigrants. They shared the same English-language classes with us, but took separate Arabic-language instruction. Apart from that split, each class stayed together in one classroom. The five minute breaks during which teachers switched classrooms degenerated into anarchy – a well-deserved breathing space for talking and playing. Determined to make the most of the two recesses (15 min in the morning and 30 min for lunch), we stampeded outside at the first sound of the bell.

The school was small: about 400 children altogether, divided into classes of 30 to 40 students each. However, the school grounds were sizeable. The main building, a large stone building in the old Ramallah style, with a red-tiled roof, dates back to 1913. It was used as a hospital during World War I. When I was a student, it housed the administration, teachers' rooms, high school classrooms, laboratories, library, and gym. Next to it, a newer building housed upper primary and middle school classrooms, plus the auditorium, art classes, and a small store. On the other side of the main building was the principal's house, attached to which were the 3rd- and 4th-grade classrooms. The buildings were surrounded by healthy swaths of open space: a paved yard around the central building, a couple of playgrounds, several paths through gardens, fields and wooded areas, and a small amphitheater. In addition, an athletic area contained two basketball courts that could be converted to a handball court, and a volleyball court. Near the entrance was a tennis court. Across a side street from the school, the school owned a soccer field, the only full-size one in Ramallah.

When we were young, we concentrated in the playgrounds at recess. The 30 minutes quickly disappeared, half of it spent standing in line at the small hole-in-the-wall school store for a falafel sandwich or a candy bar. The line was disorganized, older kids cut in front of younger ones, and the storeowner and his children could barely keep up with the number of students. In middle school, my friends and I began leaving the school at lunch break to go to the corner store, where we got the same candy bars for less money, and in less time.

We wandered more about the school grounds as we got older, preferring to hang out in remotest corners, far from the teachers. A favorite game we invented was "Baloh", our middle school version of tag. Dividing into two teams, we took over the amphitheater, the semicircular stage for one team's home, the stepped seating area for the other's. One person jumps the demarcation line, intoning "Balo-o-o-o-o-..." in one continuous breath, attempting to touch anyone from the opposite team, whose members scamper away, restricted to their own area. If he is successful, the person caught is "it", and play passes to the other team. If not, he has to return to homebase before running out of breath, or he's out of the game and his team has to send someone else. The last team standing wins.

(I regularly visited the Friends school after graduating. Throughout the 1990s, little changed, but by the mid-2000s, the school grounds looked markedly different. Two new buildings had popped up in the wooded areas where we strolled. A new upper level sat on top of the classroom building adjacent to the auditorium, connecting it by a bridge to the main building. The main building was expanded by reclaiming the attic area into classrooms. The labs and gym in the basement were moved to the new buildings, while the basement was converted to a spacious cafeteria with rails sharply delineating a queue. The old store was gone, its owner having emigrated to the USA, and the new cafeteria was operated by my classmate Najm. The changes are mostly for the better. I can see how this more intensive use of space has helped the school deliver a good education to more students. Simultaneously, I regret the loss of open space. The school grounds look so overcrowded, I wonder how kids today spend their recess.)

Some guys played sports all the time. I thought the daily physical education class was more than enough. The teacher – I am reluctant to call him coach – was amiable but not helpful. He was typically seen in a training suit, with a soccer ball under his arm, and a referee whistle round his neck. All he did for P.E. was walk us to the soccer field, hand us the ball, and referee while we ran around for the 45 min. Those who were good at soccer enjoyed it. Those who were not, got no attention, no coaching, and no advice on how to improve. Moreover, we had no other sports, except on rainy days when we hid inside the gym practicing gymnastics. A year younger than my classmates, I was shorter and less athletic. Needless to say, I was among the last to get picked out for teams, usually ending up playing defense on teams with a good offense. With the ball lingering on the other side of the field, I formed good friendships with the other defense players, Abdul-Lateef and Wasel, who weren't into sports, either. We spent games in an extended recess, chatting, sometimes about what a silly, pointless, waste of time was it to chase a ball.

My first few years there, the principal strutted with a look that sparked terror into our cores. We could sense the teachers feared him. Perhaps it was an exaggerated image he cultivated to get the job done, but ultimately he was harsh and tolerated teachers who beat "misbehaving" children. One teacher liked to put two wooden rulers together and hit us on our palms. Another had a glass ruler half-an-inch thick that he frequently exercised on us. He sought excuses to go on a rampage, sometimes walking around the classroom to inspect our fingernails, singling out those with untrimmed or dirty nails (often the country kids who had to help in the fields). One student in the grade above us, an instant hero, positioned his hand over the desk for the beating, then pulled it away at the last second, and the hated ruler was smashed to smithereens. We were happy to finish primary school and get away from their micro-dictatorships.

At the time I moved to middle school, word got to the American Quakers about the beatings and the tough principal. Being pacifists, they did not tolerate violence, and the old principal was relieved of duty and replaced with Dr. Musa, a former Professor at Birzeit University. Being school principal is not that glamorous. Dr. Musa was quiet and unassuming. He did not throw his weight around like his predecessor. We took that for weakness and often made him the butt of our jokes. Nevertheless, I liked his tenure. His first act was to put a ban on beatings. He also hired younger, more dynamic teachers who better connected with us. (An older alumnus later haughtily boasted that the school's golden age was in the 1970s, when the old principal was at his height, after which it "went downhill". Sorry, but I don't think so!)

Among the good teachers, I remember *Ustaz* (Mr.) Wajeeh, who taught us Arabic with a loud, vibrant, almost theatrical voice. I admired his teaching style and dedication. It was the first time anyone taught us how to appreciate poems rather than mindlessly memorize them. He supplemented the official textbook with copies he made of modern literary works more relevant to our lives. Thanks to him, my performance in Arabic-language class jumped from the bottom to near the top. Not everyone liked him. Some students considered every teacher fair game for poking fun. Well, Mr. Wajeeh had his idiosyncrasies, like the phrase he predictably blurted, at the top of his voice, at students passing notes in class: "You're a coward, *ustaz!*"

Another outstanding teacher was Mr. Salman, who taught us math and science. He also ran the science labs and gave us engaging demonstrations. His geometry exams consisted of one question – a problem so involved and incorporating everything we learned, that we'd be stuck by the period's end. Luckily, his class was the last, so he graciously extended his tests another 45 minutes. Our English-language math teacher was

Ms. Haniyeh, who had taught us art in primary school. Surreal to be making tie-dye T-shirts with her one year, and learning about imaginary numbers the next. I found American college-level math and science classes easy after that foundation.

Some English-language classes were taught by American teachers, usually young adults who stayed for a couple of years to build international experience. The exception was Mr. McKenzie, who lived in Ramallah with his family for years, and spoke impeccable Arabic. He taught us history, and later sports. I thought him an outstanding teacher.

We nicknamed our Arabic-language history teacher "Franco", after the former Spanish dictator. I don't know whether it's because his bald, rounded head resembled Franco's, or because of his habit of throwing pieces of chalk at inattentive students.

The Arabic-language part of our curriculum was a remnant of the Jordanian system. The textbooks were issued by the Jordanian ministry of education, printed in monotone on rough paper, with flimsy cardboard covers that bore the stamp of the Israeli Military Governor. The stamp certified the copy free from the word "Palestine". Entire sections were deleted, compared to their Jordanian counterparts: the recent history of Palestine, or works of modern Palestinian writers and poets, like Ghassan Kanafani and Mahmoud Darwish. The books I was using in the late 1980s had not been updated since 1971. The literature selections offered little from modern times, with most texts older than a thousand years, unintelligible, and completely irrelevant to our lives. The book teaching us "our" history was called "History of the Arabs and Muslims", inducing us to identify with the Arabs, and feel as if our history started with the birth of Islam. Meanwhile, the history of the more ancient cultures that inhabited Palestine – our actual ancestors – was presented like that of a foreign country. This policy continued similar policies from the British. One of the few material objects my mother had rescued from Yafa was a geography textbook. It opened with a map of the British Empire, covering the globe in patches of red. (I can see the influence of my parents' British education all the way down to my own writing and sometimes funny choice of words).

We were bound to that curriculum because the Jordanians imposed a nationwide test, the *Tawjihi*, at the end of high school. *Tawjihi* grades were a requirement for university admissions and job applications. The Friends School relied on the English-language track to augment the public school syllabus. We used standard American textbooks for world history, geography, math, science, and English. Some teachers educated us informally about Palestine. *Ustaz* Shami toured our classrooms every once in a while and lectured about politics. Back then, I cared little and found the politics difficult to understand. Yet somehow the lessons stuck, and decades later, I understood how right he was. A favorite subject of his was how the Arab countries had squandered their oil wealth and invested proceeds in foreign banks instead of their own countries.

A serious flaw was the split in the last two years of high school between a "science" track and a "literary" track, the latter encompassing humanities, social science, and literature. Such a split does not exist in America, where even college students are encouraged to study broadly. The track system rendered school no more than a vocational training center. Students did not acquire the broad background needed to be leaders and innovators. Instead, we studied to be engineers, accountants, or lawyers. Worse still was the favoritism among the tracks. People with the highest grades were automatically entered into the "science" track (but could change if they wanted). The bottom of the class ended up in the "literary" track. The system thus gave an undeserved prestige to a science education, as if science could solve all the problems facing our society (the bulk of which were social problems).

This attitude, widespread in the Arab world, betrays the wrong deduction from the experience of colonialism – namely, that the British and other Western countries dominated us solely because of their advanced technology. A less superficial reading recognizes that Britain's advanced technology and industrial power followed from its organizational advances – regulating markets, managing large numbers of workers, or creating a stable political system. Because of this misreading, we are stuck in a situation where the needed know-how that can pull the Arab world out of backwardness is scorned, while the cadres of scientists and engineers the Arab world produces cannot find adequate work at home, so flock abroad.

The Friends Boys School was literally a boys' school. Girls attended the Friends Girls' School, on a separate campus across town. For the last two years of high school, the girls moved to the Boys' School and we took classes together. It was a crude system that paid homage to a repressive culture of segregating the sexes, one that we students resented. The public schools, run by the Jordanians, as well as the Catholic schools, also ensured gender separation. Other private schools, however, had coeducational systems. Although the Friends' School was a more liberal private school, it depended on enrollment from expatriates in the USA. These parents sent their children back home to study *because* they were concerned about what they saw as licentious American culture. More liberal Palestinian Americans were content to let their children study in America.

Najm, Tigran, Shareef, and a few English-speaking kids would rush to the Girls' School at closing time and hang out by the gate, in hope of talking to the girls. The rest of us acquired a conditioned shyness that lingered for decades. After eight years apart, I had no idea how to even talk to a girl. A few years after my class had graduated, the Boys' and Girls' Schools merged for all grades, possibly driven by financial pressures and the inefficiency of having two sets of teachers. Somehow, I should find this development pleasing, but in the back of my mind gnaws the sore feeling of having been shortchanged.

Among several kids who moved with me from the Catholic school, Archie and Shadi lived nearby. At my new school, I was reunited with my childhood friend Kareem. The four of us ganged up to walk to school.

Shadi had undergone First Communion with me, then served the altar at the Catholic church since. We often made fun of Archie for his chubbiness, but he was a good sport and a good-natured guy. I could see his house from the balcony, so we sometimes communicated by arm signals. He had the best birthday parties, with dancing, his sisters inviting their girlfriends to keep it balanced.

At the top of the class was the unusually modest Waheed, whose name means "unique". A serious and dependable fellow, he rarely got involved in the horseplay that took place between class periods.

Abdul-Jabbar and I became close. We called him Abed for short (pronounced *uh-bed*). ("Abdul" literally means "servant of the," and is meant to be followed by one of the 99 Arabic names of the Lord.) Abed was the tallest guy in the class, and skinny as a reed. We sat near each other, exchanging paper messages. We rarely hung out outside of school hours because he lived in Jerusalem, where he returned after school. His father was a prominent Palestinian politician. In school, however, he kept low-key and stayed away from politics.

Abdul-Lateef, my buddy in soccer evasion (whom we also called 'Abed' when no other Abed was near), had a built-in magnet for trouble. Mr. Salman's chemistry demonstrations were an eye-opener for him. Perhaps it was the loud explosion when the chunk of pure sodium was dunked in a glass of water. For a while, he was on a hunt for elemental sodium. I wondered if he was behind the break-in discovered one morning in the school's lab. Fortunately Mr. Salman had the sodium locked inside a sturdy cabinet. Abdul-Lateef eventually got hold of a magnesium ribbon to burn, and devised a "bomb" made by filling matchstick heads into a metal bottle cap, covering it with a quarter and striking with a hammer. Saleem and he often escaped classes to go to a nearby billiard hall, where they played videogames and pool. Somehow, I resisted their attempts to drag me with them. Some combination of fear of my parents and respect for school kept me within the gates. Saleem was the youngest kid in the class. As daring as he was, he remained fearful of his aged father, and eventually got a harsh beating when his truancy came to the latter's attention.

Wasel and Najm lived in the same narrow alley in the old city, but they couldn't be more different. Wasel was serious and rather nerdy. Quiet and soft-spoken, he excelled in school. Najm, whose name means "morning star", was one of the older kids in the class and the resident trouble-maker, along with Tigran and Shareef. Tigran was older and tougher, so students kept out of his way. I should have known better, but I ticked him off one time, and ended up getting a beating after school. A year later, we became friends. I found out his dad was rough on him. I sensed him intelligent and capable, someone who might have cared more about school if he was given a reason to care.

Sajid was the kid sent to the principal most often. He rarely took himself seriously, preferring instead to be the class joker. We became close in 9th grade when he sat right behind me. Caught passing messages, that was the first time I got in trouble at school. The teacher kicked us out. Soon, Shareef and Najm misbehaved and were sent to join us. It was nice to have company. "What are we doing here in the hallway," someone suddenly blurted, "let's go to the playground!" We rushed out of the building and straight into Mr. Musa, the new principal. I forget how my friends convinced him that we were supposed to be out in the yard. They knew the ropes.

Rasheed transferred from a different school in 9th grade. His magnetic personality quickly made him popular. He was among the few who preferred playing basketball to soccer. Shareef was arguably the most popular kid in the class. He engaged Rasheed on the basketball court, knew how to talk to girls, and was sophisticated. His 14th birthday party was talked about for weeks after.

Faris (pronounced *fur-ess*) was a leader among the soccer majority. I don't recall ever seeing him off the soccer field during recess. He ate, drank, and breathed soccer. Like him, Hameedo lived on the field, and captained a soccer team in PE class. He came from a poor family and was academically weak. What kept him in school was his superb athletic abilities. He was kind to me, took me on his team despite knowing full well that I cared less for soccer. At times he encouraged me and did the coaching the teacher had abandoned.

The walk to school took fifteen minutes each way: five minutes towards the city center, five through the crowded *Manarah*, and another five through el-Bireh. On our way back, we stopped at a comic book store to buy weekly Egyptian children's magazines. *"Mickey"* and *"Pocket Mickey"* were Disney comic books translated to Arabic, probably under franchise. The same publishing house in Cairo also issued *"Sameer"*, my namesake, which featured articles and comic strips, some of those original Egyptian creations. My brothers Hakeem and Adnan had kept a pile of vintage *Sameer* magazines from the 1960s, and each issue had four pages of serialized *Tintin* comic strips which I dug like a treasure. (With the covers worn away, I used the Tintin stories to sort the magazines in the right order.) Eventually, I collected all the *Tintin* books in English and became an avid fan. Sometimes I made a detour down Main Street to al-Quds (Jerusalem) Bookstore, near the Catholic church, which had a wide selection of Egyptian detective stories for teens. I got hooked on "*The Five Adventurers*" series, teenage friends who romp around Cairo solving mysteries. By age 13, I also stopped at a record store to buy music tapes.

Back home, I finished homework quickly so I could watch TV. At the time, we only received a few government-run stations that broadcast only part of the day. Each country operated one or two channels, with the reception from our house clear enough only for the Jordanian and Israeli stations. Programming began in the afternoon, lasting till midnight, except on weekends and holidays, when they started in mid-morning. Jordan TV had good children's programming. For some time, my favorite cartoon was *Tom & Jerry*. As I got older, I got into *Scooby Doo*. I thought Shaggy and Scooby's "let's get out of here" approach most sensible. Later, I got hooked on dubbed Japanese anime, like *Star Blazers* and *Speed Racer*, and also *Grendizer*, a robot that can transform into a space ship. I watched the *Smurfs* and *Sesame Street* sometimes for amusement, but I was getting too old for those shows by the time they began airing in the Middle East.

After dinner, the whole family assembled in front of the TV awaiting the daily episode of whatever Egyptian drama series was running. Before that, we watched Israel's Arabic-language news (which lasted precisely half an hour), followed by Jordan's 8 PM news. The length of Jordan's news broadcast depended on the King's deeds for the day, as his news (followed by the prime minister's) preceded everything else. King Hussein traveled profusely, the news playing full footage from his official welcomes in every country, including the long lines of people shaking his hand. My love for travel made me envy the King. Since the position was hereditary, it was clearly my father's fault that I could never get the job, so I secretly resented him for a while. Late at night, we sometimes watched a movie. Jordan's Arabic channel played Egyptian movies, while its English channel and Israeli TV played American movies.

In the early 1980s, Egypt dominated the Arab world culturally. Most TV shows and movies were Egyptian, as was the popular music, theater, and literature. Everyone could understand the Egyptian dialect because of that. Egyptian stars were familiar household figures. I adored

Adel Imam, whose talent for comedy was unparalleled. Lebanese musicians were also popular, Beirut being the other cultural capital of the Arab world. Syria had a few famous actors, particularly Dureid Lahham and Nihad Qal'i. Later in that decade, we saw more of Jordanian TV series and movies. I particularly enjoyed *Haret Abu Awwad*, a sitcom centered on a small, tightly-knit neighborhood in Amman, especially since the Jordanian dialect and culture was close to ours and easier to understand. Under occupation, we had no Palestinian radio or TV, and the fame of our artists rarely extended beyond their hometowns.

School trips were for us daylong affairs held on a weekend. The buses left so early in the morning, we walked to school in the dark. Faris, who lived in a remote village, came by donkey as it was too early for public transportation. Two teachers chaperoned each bus. The most coveted seats were at the back, away from them. On these trips, Mr. Shami assumed the role of tour guide. He relished explaining the history of every landmark.

I was excited about my first trip in Middle School, to Ras an-Nakura, a promontory on the northern coast, at the border with Lebanon. It was farther than anywhere I had been in Palestine. The bus headed straight through the center of el-Bireh to the Nablus road, which hugged the western slope of the central ridge, following its winding contours. We passed the Israeli military camp at Bethel and a few villages. By the time we reached Silwad, almost halfway to Nablus, the sun peeked over the ridge. The golden sunlight glittered over the olive leaves, casting a spectrum of hues on the brownish soil. We passed several more villages before getting to the famous "snake" of Nablus, a road that crossed a steep valley by zigzagging its way.

We bypassed Nablus and headed straight north to Jenin, the northernmost city in the West Bank, where we stopped at a small park for breakfast. From there, we crossed the fertile Marj Ben 'Amer (Jezreel Valley), one of the first nuclei of Zionist presence in Palestine, and supposed site of the Biblical "Armageddon", continuing northwest to Haifa. With the coast narrowing northward, the wide sandy beaches at Tel Aviv and Netanya give way to rocky beaches at Haifa, and sheer cliffs at Ras an-Nakura, as the heights of Galilee kiss the sea.

Before reaching Haifa, we turned north towards Akka (Acre), then past Nahariyya, we got to a point where the road was blocked. Beyond was Lebanon, separated by military posts, radars, and observation towers. We rode a cable car down to the main attraction, caves the sea carved into the side of chalk cliffs. We followed a rocky and slippery path to the interior. The waves splashed breathtaking sounds and colors into the caves. With every lashing tongue of foam, salty droplets swirled in turbulent ecstasy, coating the rocks, the path, and our legs with the slippery seawater.

On the way back, we stopped at the al-Bahja Baha'i Temple near Akka, the headquarters of the Baha'i religion and shrine of its founder, Baha'u Allah. The Baha'i sect is famous for its cultivation of beautiful gardens surrounding its temples. I was wowed at the display. By late afternoon, we stopped at a park atop Mt. Carmel in Haifa to stretch our legs and enjoy the view of the bay. Cannons from the Ottoman period were poised towards the sea. On the way back, we headed home by way of Tulkarm and Nablus, where we stopped to pick up the famous local dessert, *kunafa*, a baked pastry made of pasta atop white cheese, drizzled in syrup.

The next year, we had a trip to Akka. We arrived too early for the safari park at Ramat Gan, our first stop, so we waited at an adjacent park. There we splashed among sprinklers, droplets brushed in gold by the rising sun. The zoo's lions didn't look as intimidating from the bus. Afterwards, we stopped in Haifa, where I hung out with Sajid and Wasel. A new cable car had just opened connecting the beach area with Mt. Carmel. We were impressed with its cars' design: spherical and transparent, providing an unobstructed view in every direction. As we ascended, a recorded message pointed out the main attractions.

We continued to Akka, an ancient Phoenician city mentioned in Egyptian records, just north along the coast. It was my first visit to this last bastion of the Crusaders in Palestine. The old city was a fortress, with thick walls bordering the sea, secret tunnels, and access to land from one side only. Napoleon's Eastern campaign stopped at Akka. In school, we learned that al-Jazzar Pasha, the Turkish governor of Akka was the one who stopped Napoleon's advance. In Western history books, the credit is awarded to Lord Nelson's fleet. I think the real credit ought to go to Akka's impregnable walls! It was impressive to walk atop them, looking far below at the waves crashing in vain at the foundations. Inside the city, we visited al-Jazzar Mosque, named after the famous governor. It was my first time inside a mosque, so I explored every corner admiring its architecture and intricate rugs and decorations. The octagonal structures and fountains in the courtyard complemented its expansive green dome.

On those trips in the 1980s, we often passed Israeli military transports – convoys of tanks and personnel all heading in one direction: north! Israel's War on Lebanon was raging. The unidirectional military traffic, continuing for years, underlined that war's drain on Israel. The leaders, like most other war-makers, blinded themselves to facts obvious to a child. Equally nonstop was the eastbound traffic of flat-bed trucks carrying pre-fabricated homes to plant in Israel's "settlements" in the West Bank.

In 1986, I made my first trip to Eilat, at the tip of the Gulf of Aqaba, which connects to the Red Sea. Eilat was a five-hour drive from Ramallah, as far as one could go without crossing borders. To make it back in one day, we were on the bus by 3 AM. Following the road from Jerusalem to Jericho, we branched south along the western shore of the Dead Sea. The only lights we saw came from the chemical factories harvesting the sea's salty brew. The air smelled of sulfur, while the chimneys spewed dark clouds. We still had a long way to go. Some tried to sleep on the bus.

We were already past the southern tip of the Dead Sea and into Wadi Araba when day broke, the sunlight shadowed by the gorge's eastern wall. As we neared Eilat, we were stopped at a checkpoint. A border area adjacent to several Arab countries, Eilat was a high-security zone requiring special permits that the school had obtained. We all exited the bus as the soldiers checked our papers, then searched us one-by-one upon re-entering. Finally, by mid-morning, we were on the beach.

Eilat is in a sub-tropical zone where the water is warm enough for coral reefs to thrive. Of more interest to repressed teenagers, Eilat's beach is topless. It did not help that our school was separated by gender. It was difficult to be polite and not stare. We made a brief stop on the beach before heading to the aquarium, the teachers struggling to corral us back into the bus for the excursion. It was my first time to one. The Eilat aquarium was a cylindrical structure under the sea, accessible by a footbridge from the shore. Circling its circumference, the windows opened to seascapes of exotic fish navigating a maze of corals. We took a tour on a glass-bottomed boat to see more of the underwater wonders. In the back of our mind, of course, were the overwater wonders, and we were happy to get back to the beach. Some of us swam, some rented paddleboats. Most, like Abdul-Lateef, Sajid and I, strolled back and forth wide-eyed on the beach. There was not much distance to stroll. You could see Jordan's Aqaba within walking distance, and Egypt not far off on the other side.

Summers were great! Three whole months without school, and without rain. Kareem and other friends joined the boy scouts for activities and summer camps. I never got into the boy scout thing, keeping myself busy with my own projects. A favorite was converting the dining table into a "city", where I installed all my toy cars, houses, animals, and train set. It took some negotiation with Mom as to how long I could occupy the table. Following Hakeem's example, I read extensively, about diverse topics, borrowing books from his library, as well as my parents'. Among my mother's books, I read a complete collection of Sherlock Holmes stories. Then I got into Agatha Christie mysteries, buying a number of her novels in translation. I also liked reading science, literature, and history. I delved into Hakeem's trove of yoga and exercise books, using his weight set and bench to train. The balcony facing the street became my favorite perch for reading. The blinding sun hit it only in the morning, and from there I could see Danny's house, so I could instantly change plans and go play with him. I devised my own secret way in and out of the house by climbing to the balcony from the yard below.

For two summers, my parents signed me up for a summer camp at the Ramallah Public Library – a couple of hours a day making crafts, and sometimes a short field trip across town. I explored the library's collection, but the holdings were dismal. Under "Science", the best I found was a 1950s Russian book (translated into Arabic) disputing the theory of plate tectonics, while offering dubious alternative explanations for why the contours of the continents matched across oceans. Our school library was no better. At a sale they held, the only worthwhile find was a travel memoir written by an Arab visitor to Europe in the 1800s. It gave a curious look at a historical era, but not much else useful to a teenager. All in all, Hakeem's library at home was more engaging and up-to-date.

Sometimes, I worked at the family store, mostly doing odd jobs. The store got busy at peak times, but otherwise we had little to do but chat or read the newspaper. I skipped straight to the comics' page, eagerly anticipating the daily strip by Naji al-Ali, the most prominent Palestinian cartoonist at the time. His cartoons provided scathing critiques of the politics of the day. The only side he took was the side of Handalah, his main character, a faceless child from the masses condemned to the refugee camps. Disheveled, in tattered clothes, and barefoot, Handalah was always shown from the back, observing the state of disarray in Palestine, the Arab world, and beyond. I was sad when Naji al-Ali was assassinated in the late 1980s. Some say the PLO killed him, but no one really knows. His honest and unwavering pen earned him too many enemies.

Basman used to bring me amusing gifts on his summer visits from America. The first summer back he got me a radio walkman. I listened to it everywhere, at home, while I read, on my bike. The stations were few. I was into Western pop music, but could only hear it on Jordan's English language station, and on the Voice of Peace, an Israeli station owned by peace activist Abie Nathan (who was constantly at odds with his government). The Voice of Peace broadcast from aboard a ship, which was the reason for their call "From somewhere in the Mediterranean, this is the Voice of Peace." I thought the concept was cool, and enjoyed their music selections. I taped my favorite songs from the radio so I could replay them. Both stations had an international orientation heavy on European artists.

I so wanted to make my own radio show. I used a dual-deck tape recorder to arrange my mix, and a mike to dub my voice-overs. Discovering shortwave radio, I dreamed of running my own ham station to broadcast my shows. The equipment was beyond my means, so I decided to make my own, tinkering with an electronics set made in Israel. It was crude and flimsy, with poor connections to the breadboard. The Radio Shack set Basman got me later was light years ahead. Eventually, I succeeded in building my first radio transmitter. You could barely pick up the signal in the next room, but it was a triumph.

I also inherited a chemistry set from Hakeem. Most of the chemicals were old and unreactive. Not finding all I wanted at Ramallah's one science supply store, I improvised substitutes. The store sold lenses, however, which I used to build my own telescope. Like my foiled dreams of becoming a pilot, opportunities were limited. By 6th grade, I was reading Basman's O-level science books, the British equivalent of a high-school diploma. I even grasped his college-level physics book, skipping over the calculus. By contrast, my own schoolwork was slow, prolonged, and boring, leaving me ample time to daydream in class.

The worst part of summer was the mosquitoes. Their loud buzzing and painful stings constantly awakened me at night. Sooner or later, I'd go on a rampage swatting them with my slippers, their bloated, distended bodies splattering a stain of the blood they had just imbibed. There was no avoiding them. Every house in Ramallah had a cistern underneath the yard, to collect rainwater in the winter for use in the dry summer months. Though we cleaned the cistern at the end of every summer, by next summer, the brackish water became a favorite breeding ground for those tiny villains. We mostly use the cistern to water the garden, conserving the city water, which drips slowly into storage tanks on the roof. Several summers I experienced water shortages, when the city water stopped completely. We drank bottled water then, but otherwise needed to switch the faucets to the cistern water for laundry, showering, and even cooking (thoroughly boiling it first). The shortages lasted from days to weeks. I preferred not to shower in the cistern water, but used to showering daily, I could only go so many days without one.

The high point of my childhood was in the summer of 1986, when I got my dream bicycle. I was thirteen and outgrew my first bike, a red one with two training wheels long removed. Daily on my way back from school, I stopped at a bicycle store in el-Bireh to eye this blue bike: large, three-speed, with springs and a large seat, looking more like a motorcycle.

Finally, my parents agreed that I was ready, sending Basman to help me buy it.

The same month, both Jawad and Danny got new bikes: Jawad's was similar to mine, but red, while Danny's was a lightweight BMX. The bikes brought Jawad, Danny, and I closer, simultaneously separating us from kids who didn't bike.

That summer was a blast. I dodged working at the store, signing up for a library course, or traveling anywhere, so I had the whole summer to bike with my buddies. I woke up early to make the most of the day, staying outside from 8 AM to 8 PM, coming back home only to drink water. Installing horns that made siren sounds, we pretended our bikes were police motorcycles, like the TV series CHIPS, and our cops-and-robbers games became faster-paced. Ramallah was not bike-friendly. There were no bike paths or large parks, so we rode on the streets. Our neighborhood was quiet, but every now and then a car or a truck could suddenly speed round a bend, as few streets were straight. Ramallah's hilliness constrained us to level roads along the ridges. We occasionally braved the downtown traffic, but never bothered going down the hill to the old city.

We wanted to go further, so one day we planned a trip to Rafat, a little village just south of Ramallah, in the direction of Jerusalem. It was connected to Ramallah by a narrow, little-traveled, but level road. It was perhaps only 30 minutes by bike to get there, but we took our time, stopping to explore a stone quarry, then taking a detour to a hill overlooking the Jerusalem airport. We waited a long time to see any planes take off or land, and they were small ones. There was nothing to do in Rafat itself.

For some reason I never understood, this rough kid from the next neighborhood, Murad, began bullying me whenever he could. He dared not approach when I was with my friends, especially Danny who was tough and could kick his ass. One time, he attacked me when I was alone, murderously clawing my windpipe till Nimer's mom luckily intervened. Something had to be done! I told my brother, Basman. Fortunately, I happened to call him at 5 PM, when he was about to drive the store employees home to their villages. I rode with them to point out Murad. Near his house, we ran into his younger brother. Basman opened the window and asked him about Murad's whereabouts. That was all it took.

Seeing a car full of grown men, he thought I'd assembled them to beat up his brother. For three days, neither kid even stepped onto our street.

One day, we were hanging out with a bunch of older kids when we spotted a squad of Israeli soldiers slowly climbing the hill towards us. Just a few years older, they wore uniform and full gear. Periodically stopping to check their map, it appeared they were on a training mission, yet obviously looking lost. One of the older kids among us worked in Israel and knew Hebrew. To mess with them, he pretended to be helpful when they got closer, asking them in Hebrew if they needed directions somewhere. Because his Hebrew was good, they were more trusting than they should have been, warmly thanking him and following his completely bogus directions. We could barely wait until they were at a safe distance before bursting out laughing.

Israelis treat you better if you speak their language. My mother learned Hebrew on her own, immediately after the Israelis invaded in 1967. This served us well when we were stopped at checkpoints, for instance, or when we needed to do some official paperwork. Mom therefore encouraged me to learn Hebrew, getting me a language book and several Hebrew children's books. "If you want to win, you need to learn the language of your occupiers," she repeatedly told us. She was right. Much of Israeli thought is expressed only in that language – obscured from the rest of the world. Meanwhile, a good fraction of Israelis knew Arabic well enough to understand us.

I forgot the Hebrew I learned, partly because I had few opportunities to practice, and partly because I had more pressing interests. I made it all the way to the end of the first language book, then stumbled. In a story about a Jewish American girl visiting Israel for the first time, I encountered some of Hebrew's more peculiar concepts. First was '*Aliyah*, a term denoting an immigrant's journey to Israel, symbolized as an act of "ascending" – as in climbing a mountain – to "*Eretz Yisrael*", the "Land of Israel". From '*Aliyah*, they derived the concept of "'*Oleh Hadash*" to describe a new immigrant, as distinct from a "*Sabra*", or a native-born Israeli. I found these concepts unpalatable, not only for their strangeness, but also because they excluded me from the world of the Hebrew language. Here was I, born in the land they called *"Eretz Yisrael"* – even the ID card they gave me says so – yet I was neither a *Sabra* nor a *'Oleh Hadash*. Indeed, Palestinians were not mentioned at all in that Hebrew language book, as if we did not exist.

Pondering the meaning of these words, I found the ideas repugnant since they whitewashed the horror involved in the depopulation, occupation, and control that my family and I had endured. The new immigrant who comes to *displace* us is, in their language, a devout being who rises up to the land promised to her or his forefathers. Later, I was to grasp the similarity to the American "Pilgrims" and "Pioneers" fulfilling their "Manifest Destiny" in claiming their "promised land" from "Indians". The very term *'Sabra'* was taken from our word *sahber*, for the cactus plant so prevalent in Palestine. They took our symbols along with our lands. The cactus plant in their language no longer denotes the hundreds of villages they ripped apart from the earth, but the seedlings they sowed in our place. Today when you fly into Tel Aviv airport, a large mural of cactus plants greets you as the plane taxis to the terminal. Even at thirteen years of age, I could not swallow this linguistic distortion, and a mental block formed against my learning Hebrew.

Other Palestinians had no problems with the Hebrew language. The young men who worked in Israel – in the farms, factories, and construction sites – absorbed whatever Hebrew they needed for their jobs, not from a book, but by use. Perhaps because of the way they learned it, they did not encounter the terms I found offensive. To me, however, Modern Hebrew felt unnatural and concocted, a language invented overnight to unite the diverse Zionists immigrants, rather than growing organically over centuries. In a sense, Modern Hebrew is as manufactured as the "settlements" with their planned layout and identical prefabricated houses.

I have so far used the accepted term "settlements" for those constructs, a usage I disdain. Creating a new terminology was the Zionist movement's first step towards dominating us, inventing words and place names that psychologically entrap those succumbing to their usage. "Settlement" is one such linguistic fraud, giving the impression of a planned community, which is one correct description, but one that entirely misrepresents the context. The word suggests a civilizing impetus amidst a wilderness, when in reality those communities are erected on stolen lands, taken by force backed by dubious means, in a legal system where the Palestinian owner has no voice. Furthermore, they are built as fortresses, oftentimes adjacent to Palestinian urban areas. There is no wilderness to tame. Only people to conquer. For the rest of this book, I will therefore use the more accurately descriptive term *"stolenment"*, instead.

Somewhere in the mid-80s I rediscovered Tanya, Jawad's sister. I had hardly seen her since her family moved to the end of the street. Her developing figure attracted my attention. Our interactions were innocent enough. She came to our hangout every once in a while looking for her younger brother. We exchanged small talk here and there. I liked her, and thought she liked me too.

There were no good role models for what to do about a crush. Guys and girls did not date and did not go out until they were engaged. Families were involved in matchmaking. Dating may be accepted in Egyptian movies, but we were told their culture wasn't exactly ours. So whenever I intended to tell her I liked her, I never gathered the courage to proceed. "There's always tomorrow," I thought, betraying a youthful illusion of ample time.

If I had wished for something, it was that I would get to spend the summer of 1987 exactly the same way I had spent the previous one. I was finishing 9th grade, the last one in middle school. The Jordanian education ministry decided, just our luck, to introduce an experimental 'Matriculation' exam, similar to the *Tawjihi* exam 12th graders suffered. The trial ran two years, affecting only the grade above us, and ours. Then it was scratched! The more interesting subjects the school offered suffered because we had to closely follow the Jordanian curriculum. Our summer lost the month of June to studying. Worse still, taking this government test didn't exempt us from taking finals at our school.

To further complicate things, my parents wanted to take me to attend Basman's commencement ceremony in Pittsburgh in early May, planning to stay a whole month. I made arrangements for missing the last month of school, and took my books with me with the intention of studying.

We were so busy in America, I opened my books exactly once. We toured the Midwest, California, New York City, often visiting relatives and friends of my parents, some they hadn't seen in decades. Basman rented cars everywhere we went and we hung out together. Madonna's "La Isla Bonita" was crowding the airwaves. It was just like old times – while my parents were meeting their friends, Basman and I were cruising down the Embarcadero, or looking for a parking spot in Manhattan. It was a bigger place to cruise, of course, way bigger.

To me, America was a dreamland. If I doubted the Hollywood movies, I had the testimonies of my cousins after their last visit, the mouse ears Maya and her sisters brought back from Disneyland, and the English-speaking kids in school who knew how to talk to girls. And if all that failed in convincing me of America's limitless opportunities, I had the ingenuity of the toys and gadgets Basman brought back on holidays. So I was excited about the trip. Finally! We did go to Disneyland, and I loved it, as I relished the spacious cars and limitless driving through expansive landscapes. Yet, I little expected to see a crumbling Detroit, or the homeless in L.A. and Chicago. Dazzled by the floodlights of skyscrapers in N.Y.C., the stench and fumes brought me back to the filthy ground-floor reality.

Back home, I had catching up to do. I spent June on the balcony studying. When the time came, I did not feel ready. We were shuffled into different testing sites so no one took the test with his classmates. I ended up taking mine in a public school nearby. The teachers overseeing the test, again total strangers, were lax, some even quietly volunteering answers. For the *Tawjihi* and this exam, it was rumored the Jordanians significantly reduced the scores of West Bank students, to favor East Bankers with opportunity. If true, we needed all the help we could get. At the end, I was sure I did well on most subjects, without the help. Yet my final score, when it appeared, was miserable – about 70%.

Soon after exams, my brother Adnan got married and we celebrated his wedding. He moved into the middle floor apartment, so I ended up taking over Hakeem's old room (minus the pyramid and bookcase dividers). It had a window facing the rolling hills to the west, which I liked. The rest of the summer, I went back to my bike with a vengeance, trying to make up for lost time. I hung out with Danny and Jawad. But I was also getting older and losing interest in children's games. I had my eye out for Tanya, biking to her end of the street one time too many. Sometimes she pushed her youngest brother in a stroller past our house. We exchanged our "hellos" when I was on the balcony, and that was that.

That fall, I started high school. We finally joined the "big guys", and could attend their activities. Our first event was a bonfire, held jointly with the Girls' School. For weeks prior, some guys spent recess practicing dance moves in the bathroom. The bonfire was fun. Though we all got to dance, most were hampered by shyness and a total lack of experience. The rest, especially the English-speaking students who had known American schools, fared better.

Our second and last event with the Girls' School was a field trip to Caesarea, the ruins of a Roman city by the sea, halfway between Yafa and Haifa. We got to school early hoping to each pick two empty seats on the bus, holding one "for a girl". The strategy had one flaw: we rushed to the back, as usual. The girls in our class were few, and they all chose to sit in the front. So, for the duration of the ride, we boys resorted to being rowdy and making noise to attract their attention. Tigran, who brought along a boom box, blasted pop music, while we stood singing loudly. We might have gotten a few glances, but the girls did not look impressed.

Caesarea had a thick city wall surrounded by a moat. Inside were ruins of Roman-style buildings and a large amphitheater. The abundant cactus plants whispered of another recently-destroyed village. We walked along columned streets and followed a long aqueduct. Roman ruins abounded. I had not imagined, until visiting Rome, that Palestine, and the Middle East in general, had more and better-preserved Roman ruins than Rome itself.

I had decent plans drawn up for my life. I wanted to get better at talking to girls, possibly become closer friends with Tanya. I looked forward to the following year, when our classes finally became coed. I was also focused on my studies. If I did well in high school, I could study in America, like Basman, though I wasn't sure exactly what I wanted to study. My number one choice of becoming a pilot was squelched by the absence of a nation, let alone an airline. In any case, I intended to come back home after I graduated, like Adnan, to work in Ramallah and eventually get married. As of then, it looked like I was headed on a reasonable trajectory.

In the West, people like to think they have control over the course of their lives. They can plan ahead. Their decisions are their own. No one tells them what to do. That is the meaning of freedom. A pandemic such as COVID-19 felt disruptive and hard precisely because few were used to such unpredictability. Life, however, is chaotic. Small and seemingly insignificant events can assume greater proportions in retrospect, after their impact on our lives is felt. Especially in the unstable environment of Palestine, external events can easily consume the best-made plans.

Living under occupation, a colonized people, we had grown to accept some loss of control over our lives. A curfew is imposed and we cannot leave our houses, or a book is banned and we cannot obtain it. An armed soldier stops us at the checkpoint, and we have no choice but to show ID and comply with his requests. Still, we struggled to move our lives forward, to have some semblance of order and control. Nothing, however, prepared me for the events that took place as 1987 was drawing to a close.

7

Intifada

IT WAS A TIME OF GREAT DANGER AND EQUAL PROMISE, a time of rapid change amid long, quiet days. A developing 14-year old engulfed by his society's rapid political awakening. At first, I paid no notice. Protests, strikes, and Israeli soldiers shooting at stone-throwing children were nothing new. The calendar was studded with commemoratives: May 15, the day of Nakba, when most of Palestine was lost; June 5, marking the 1967 war when the Occupation began; Nov. 2, the Balfour Declaration, Britain's blessing for Zionist designs on Palestine; Nov. 29, Partition Day, when Palestine's fate was voted by the UN, instead of its own people. Hardly a month went by without a special day or two, so the protests that began on Dec. 9, 1987 were nothing unusual. Just another day off from school.

This time, the protests continued. Israeli violence in dispersing them drew bigger crowds the next day, and more localities joined in protest. Casualties from Israeli gunfire mounted. Our school teetered along through mid-December, sending us home early one day, closing entirely another, until time came for finals. With Christmas near, I was eager to get over my exams. I did not follow the news or stay informed about the events outside.

As we sat for one exam, the leader of the student body approached us proposing the school postpone the finals until after winter break. He was concerned about our safety amidst the commotions, and also about the academic performance of students who participated in the daily protests.

I had prepared well for the exams, so I did not like the idea, for postponing them a month meant studying all over again. However, a majority of students were on board. Some lived in faraway villages and had difficulty getting to school because of the protests. Others simply saw an opportunity for more time to study. So in the end, the proposal went ahead.

In retrospect, the idea of postponing the finals suggested a naïve expectation that, by January, the situation would get calmer, if not back to normal. Not even that politically well-connected student leader knew what to expect. By the closing days of December, it seemed that the daily protests would never end. Events carried a momentum of their own. Israelis were also taken by surprise. Perhaps misled by our docility at the Bridge, or in their workplaces and stores, they did not expect us to rebel.

During that long winter break, I mostly stayed home, reading the Odyssey and a thick book on world history that caught my interest, and taking occasional peeks at the world outside through the TV news. From the vantage point of the family store on Main Street, my brothers brought back daily accounts of protests and shooting. Graffiti appeared, announcing general strikes. Day-long strikes were called with increasing frequency, until *the* strike became perpetual. By January, it became a test of strength to see how long we could keep it. Everyone stayed home, watching news, and worrying about running out of food. Occasionally, the strike was suspended for a few hours to let people resupply their households. By the new year, the Arab news agencies had begun calling the uprising *Intifada*, or a "shaking off".

About 40 days into it, the strike was changed to a daily half-day strike, starting a routine that was to last till the end of the Intifada several years later. Stores opened in the morning only, officially from 8 AM to noon. Often, the workday ended as early as 10 or 11 AM, as the protests and stone-throwing shut down the city. People rushed about their business first thing in the morning, then hurried home for safety. The afternoons were spent at home, when the whole town quieted. Few ventured to the streets, the only sounds heard were the *adhan* and the occasional siren from an Israeli police car.

Leaflets appeared about once a week, instructing us how to resist. The leaflets bore the signature of the United National Leadership of the

Intifada (with the acronym *QAWM,* meaning people or nation), which represented all the movements and factions under the PLO umbrella. The Intifada became a test of our national will against the Israeli Occupation. We had to show unity to send a clear message that we wanted freedom. The leaflets stressed nonviolence. Firearms were not to be used. In addition to the strikes, we were encouraged to boycott Israeli goods, stop working in Israel, help each other, and form "neighborhood committees".

Some instructions were rather easy to implement. We stopped buying Coca Cola, made in Israel, replacing it with RC Cola, made in Gaza. It tasted harsher, but made us proud to be supporting Palestinian products. Some people planted "victory gardens" in their backyards. Other steps were more costly. Workers who heeded the call and stopped working in Israel needed other means to support their families. Palestinian policemen turned over the guns and refused to work for the Israeli police, but then what? With people working only half a day, the economy was at a standstill. It took heroic sacrifices from everyone for the strike to endure for years.

In the beginning, Israel took the challenge posed by the strikes seriously. For several months, soldiers did an afternoon tour of downtown Ramallah, forcing people to open their stores. If the owner was not there, the soldiers broke the padlocks with a crowbar. Storeowners simply used new locks the next day. The community spirit was such that no one took advantage of the broken locks to loot.

One day in early 1988, my brother Adnan was closing the store round noon, when a patrol of Israeli soldiers caught him in the act. They wanted him to open. He tried to reason with them: it's his family's store and therefore it's his choice whether to open. The soldiers, surrounding him and heavily armed, instantly responded with their clubs from all sides. He blocked their blows with his arms, only to infuriate them more, till one of them hit him on the back of his head with a steel construction rod. As my brother lay on the ground, another soldier pointed his rifle at him. My dad, who had rushed to the scene, intervened to stop them. It was the start of the "Iron Fist" policy, where soldiers had direct orders to "break the bones" of uncooperative Palestinians. The policy was instituted by then-defense minister and future Nobel Laureate Yitzhak Rabin.

The daily test of strength continued, escalating and sometimes bordering the absurd. When Israel switched to summer time in March of 1988, the Intifada leadership decided we would do so a month later. For the entire month we prided ourselves at keeping our own time zone separate from Israel, regarding that a symbol of our budding independence. Stores opened and closed following Palestinian time zone. The daily confrontations were consistently beginning at noon on the Palestinian clocks. For the rest of the Intifada, we continued the time zone challenge twice a year.

A Day in the Intifada

Helping at the family store sometimes, I got to witness the daily "clashes", as the international news called them. I dislike the terminology used by the media to describe our protests: *clashes* implies equality in armament and strength; *violence* and *cycle of violence* implies it is equally perpetrated by both parties; while the least apt terms, *riots* and *disturbances*, imply a disorganized mob bent on random, wanton destruction. It was not like that at all.

About late morning, with Main Street quiet and business going on as usual, a number of masked *shabab* (literally young men, "guys", though the term came to include the young women who participated) sprang out of nowhere. The masks were essential since the Israeli army photographed demonstrators to later identify and arrest them. The mask of choice was the *kafiyyeh*, the black-and-white checkered scarf we commonly wore in winter, which could be wrapped around the head and face at a moment's notice. It came to symbolize the Palestinian movement, but its prevalent use served the practical need of anonymity. The *shabab* hurriedly dragged improvised barricades – dumpsters, discarded antenna towers, large rocks, construction junk – so Israeli army Jeeps could not reach them. Tires were burned. Almost as abruptly, the Israeli soldiers arrived and began shooting. Trapped in the store, we closed the outside metal doors and hid inside, monitoring the scene through the crack underneath, and cringing at the thunder of gunfire.

The *shabab* usually had it planned: a group of guys gathered stones, while those with a better range threw them at the soldiers. They knew the alleys and had pre-arranged escape routes. The confrontations ranged from a few minutes to over an hour, depending on how long the shabab held off the soldiers. Soon enough, the whole street was littered with debris: stones, bullets, broken glass. The occasional tear gas canister was picked up and thrown back at the soldiers (raw onions were used as an effective antidote to tear gas). Several months into the Intifada, the Israeli army occupied rooftops of tall buildings in the downtown area, giving them perches for sniping at the *shabab*. This did not deter the demonstrators.

It was almost like a game – a deadly game, for often it ended up in blood. Casualties were many, and fatalities not uncommon. After witnessing this spectacle every day, I learned to recognize the type of gun and projectile used by their sound. A live bullet made a whistling sound as it flew by. With the bad publicity live bullets generated, the Israeli army introduced "rubber bullets" which have a metal interior and can break bones, then "plastic bullets" which are round metallic shots coated with a thin plastic layer. Like other Palestinian teens, I had a shell and bullet collection I gathered in the aftermath. Some items bore a "Made in U.S.A." stamp, a small part of the multi-billion dollar "foreign aid" to Israel imposed on American taxpayers.

The "game" invariably ended with the *shabab* vanishing into the alleys, and the soldiers chasing them from neighborhood to neighborhood, street to street, yard to yard. Guys caught by the soldiers expected a severe beating, and possibly arrest, whether for throwing stones, distributing flyers, or writing on walls.

Somehow we made it home every day amidst the confusion, exchanging our individual accounts of the day's events. Often we could still see the clouds of dark smoke from burning tires and tear gas rising over Main Street. The soldiers sometimes chased children down our street as protests dissolved, beating those caught in plain view. One time, from the cracks in the dining room blinds, I saw them beat a reporter for photographing their violence, leaving him hunched on the sidewalk with a broken camera. We turned on the radio to hear the names of the casualties read, in case there was anyone we knew.

Once things quieted down, a dead silence reigned. The afternoon strike was respected. People took long naps, or tended their vegetable gardens. Few ventured outside. Whenever I went to see my friends, my parents gave strict instructions to stay close to home. Israeli army Jeeps patrolled the streets, speeding to surprise us round corners. We had to be on guard. You never knew when they were going to stop you. The soldiers had guns, and power, but they were still 18-year old conscripts. They could do whatever they wanted with us, for fun, and get away with it. So we kept away from the streets, and our ears became attuned to the sound of Jeeps.

Sometimes, we heard random gunshots echo over the hills. In the beginning, we listened intently, attempting to locate the source and infer what was going on. Did the sound come from the old city, where afternoon and evening protests were common? Or was it closer to us? Eventually, the sound of gunfire became so commonplace, nobody cared. You filter it out the way those living near airports ignore the roar of airplanes. Evenings were spent mostly in front of the TV. I got into the habit of staying up late at night to watch *The Benny Hill Show* with Hakeem on Israel TV. Outside, it was so quiet you could hear sounds from all over the city. Wedding parties became more subdued. No one wanted to appear to be enjoying themselves in these circumstances. Some took advantage of the lowered expenses of weddings to get married. A baby boom ensued from the Intifada, as people spent more time at home.

That the Intifada survived despite all Israeli attempts to crush it was a source of inspiration. That teenagers armed with no more than stones were able to hold off the might of the Israeli army was previously unthinkable. After decades of repression, any thought of liberating ourselves from the Occupation was regarded as a pipe dream. So with the Intifada, despite the bloodshed, the pain, and the fear, excitement filled the air. Freedom seemed imminent.

"School's Closed!"

Life became slower. The long afternoons gave us ample leisure time. Like the isolation of the COVID-19 pandemic, decades later, we had less running around, and more time to rest, and to think about the important things in life. People busied themselves with social visits or serving the emergent neighborhood committees, but time was aplenty. Some bemoaned the tedium. For nearly a year-and-a-half (Feb. 1988 to July 1989), with few brief interruptions, the schools were closed (with no online learning). Some classmates found jobs, with Kareem and Rasheed working at a pharmaceutical plant near Beitunia. I worked at the family store, but businesses were closed most of the time anyway, so I had ample free time. They say idleness is the Devil's playground. For me it was an opportunity to read books – all kinds of books. I read poetry and literature, but also became interested in something more immediate and purposeful, the Intifada adding a sense of urgency.

Naturally, I wanted to learn more about Palestine, its history and how the Occupation came into being, and how to get out of it. Israeli censorship was heavy. Few books about our history were accessible. The very word "Palestine" was forbidden, expunged from our schoolbooks. The only sources of knowledge were oral histories from our parents and grandparents, and banned books. I was therefore excited to find a pile of old books belonging to Dad stashed somewhere at the bottom of a cabinet. Rummaging through it, I found a few relevant titles: a book with a missing cover about the life of Yasser Arafat, apparently written in 1975; a couple about the 1967 war, one of which was written by King Hussein of Jordan himself; two more about the 1956 war, one by Sir Anthony Eden, the other by an Egyptian general; and several monographs about the 1948 conflict and earlier. Nothing much, heavily biased, and seriously out-of-date, but given the information black hole I was in, this was hot stuff.

There I was sitting for hours and days, reading contraband material, sorting through different accounts, thinking for myself. First was King Hussein rationalizing his loss in the 1967 war, a moving account, but far from believable. Numerous conspiracies surrounded his family, and the "brave resistance" of the Jordanian troops during the war conflicted with eyewitness accounts I had heard. The war books were too narrowly-focused to be useful. The most credible ones were the Palestinian accounts of our expulsion from Palestine in 1948, which broadly agreed with my parents' narratives. Most useless were the numerous agreements, pronouncements, and "white papers" produced by Britain during the Mandate, none of which was faithfully implemented.

Reading between the lines was a habit I learned to cultivate. Every day during the Intifada, I read *al-Quds* newspaper, discussing articles with those around me. Having no television or radio stations of our own, we had to listen to other countries broadcast: "This is the Voice of America, Jordan, Israel, BBC, Radio Monte Carlo, Syria, ..." Each station reported the same events, but as I noticed, accounts rarely agreed. Outsiders might be baffled by the contradictory news reports. With a front-row seat to the conflict, I had the opportunity to test the faithfulness of the news agencies.

Israel's Arabic-language news was the least reliable. They consistently deflated the number of Palestinian casualties, and acted as a mouthpiece for the Israeli military. Its funny language set it apart: "Palestinian *saboteurs* attacked the *defense forces* with stones in Nablus, and the army responded by firing rubber bullets and tear gas. Five *terrorists* were injured." Other news stations had their own idiosyncrasies. I personally liked Radio Monte Carlo, which I thought was the most fair and accurate, but I listened to the others to expose myself to all points of view. I idled the afternoon away tuning my short-wave radio back and forth between the newscasts. At one in the afternoon came Israeli news; 2 PM, Radio Monte Carlo; 3 PM, the BBC. Evenings were similar, with TV replacing radio as the centerpiece. Listening to Intifada news was a practical need. We needed to know what was going on, and where, what was open and what was closed, and which roads were safe.

In between the newscasts, I enjoyed listening to music, on the Voice of Peace and elsewhere. I became hooked on the BBC's Top 20 Countdown every week. They favored British and Australian music. What drew me to that particular show, however was the melodic voice of its female host (think Arabic with a British accent).

A Palestinian radio station emerged from the Intifada – al-Quds radio, broadcast from Syria on behalf of one renegade Palestinian faction. The Israelis were constantly jamming it, and it countered by changing frequencies often. Its daily broadcasts were devoted to news about the

Intifada, nationalist songs, and talk meant to boost our morale. New nationalist songs emerged. Contraband tapes were sold under counters and copied secretly to spread the banned revolutionary music. I bought my first revolutionary tape "Dawleh" or (Palestinian) State, celebrating the declaration of independence of 1988. It was recorded and produced in Ramallah by friends of my friends, with Rasheed from my class drawing its artwork.

In the summer of 1988, the Seoul Olympics were a welcome distraction, especially since I had exhausted the few DOS-based games on Adnan's new 8086. Not bothering about getting up in the morning, I was glued to the TV, catching events live, flicking the remote among the four stations we could receive. It was the first Olympics I really cared about, and the last I could fully enjoy, overwhelmed later in life by responsibility, and hampered by restrictions on Olympic coverage in the US. (For some reason, the government-owned stations in the Middle East competed to provide free, live, and uninterrupted coverage, allocating time for the "minor" sports as well.) The flawless performance and poise of the Soviet gymnastics team impressed me. I had a brief crush on their star gymnast, who was my age. All the daydreams of meeting her ran through my qualifying for the next Olympic Games. That required a team, a state, a citizenship.

Schools opened in January 1988 (when we took our postponed finals), but only briefly. Under the guise of ensuring the children's safety, the Israeli military governor ordered all the schools in the West Bank and Gaza closed, indefinitely. They effectively made our return to the classrooms contingent on "quiet" – our abandonment of resistance to the Occupation – with the added bonus of depriving us of an education. It mattered little to them if we missed a year or two of school. After all, the Israeli military had kept our universities closed throughout much of the early 1980s, substantially delaying Sandra's degree from Birzeit.

After a few months of school closures, it was clear that this was for the long haul, so we had to take action. I was in 10th grade at the time, expecting to finish high school in 1990. The Intifada leadership urged us to organize home education and secret classes. The Israelis threatened severe measures against "unauthorized education", such as demolishing any building used as a substitute classroom when schools were closed. East Jerusalem schools remained open, since Israel considered the city its own territory. We lost Tigran and Abdul-Lateef to East Jerusalem schools, but the hassles of commuting there on a daily basis kept the rest of us from doing so. The difficulties of the commute forced Abdul-Jabbar, living in Jerusalem but attending our school (when it was open), to stay weeknights at his uncle's place in a village closer to Ramallah.

When schools reopened in June 1988 (also briefly), ours was prepared. Like everything else, schools also observed the half-day strike, so the teachers gave us handouts to study at home in the afternoons. By that time, some teachers had already found jobs elsewhere, so the school had to replace them. Mr. Wajeeh, sporting his distinguished voice, left to become a radio show host. Decades later, I ran into him at Birzeit University, where he was teaching journalism. The ineffectual sports teacher also left, so Mr. McKenzie took over coaching. I liked him better. He introduced us to other sports such as basketball or bodybuilding, and for the little time we had, coached us individually. It meant so much to us that, while other American teachers left, Mr. McKenzie stayed, unafraid to share our fate.

A friend of Dad's suggested I study independently for the GCE – the British high school certification, which I could obtain by passing a number of subject tests. Seeing no better alternative, I got the study material from the British Council in Jerusalem, bought the textbooks, and began studying at home, on my own. I allocated a set number of hours for studying, and kept at it daily for several months. This valuable experience strengthened my ability to learn and work independently, and developed my self-discipline, qualities that were to serve me well later in life. I kept a strict routine, studying each subject for some 45 min, and systematically reviewing past lessons. Though I was making progress, the main drawback was the lack of social interaction with peers.

The next time schools reopened in December 1988, we were shuffled into 11th grade to make up for lost time. The big deal, of course, was that 11th grade was when the Girls' School joined us. At first, the shyness was petrifying. I was attracted to one girl, Veronica, and was thrilled when the chemistry teacher assigned us to be lab partners. It was nice to chat through the endless tasks of stirring solutions, but the school closure was reinstated only a few weeks later.

The Friends' School did not give up. In early 1989, they organized a secret study program, despite the strict Israeli orders. To keep a low profile, they admitted only two grade levels each day, with our turn on Saturdays. It was daring, given the school's location next to the main police station, where the Israeli army was permanently posted. We were instructed to arrive individually at different times, and leave individually, using the side gate of the school on the opposite side from the police station. Keeping our distance, we used the 3rd and 4th grade classrooms on the far side of the school. The desks were comically undersized. This program lasted a couple of months at most, then it was back to studying for the GCE.

Finally, a handful of my classmates called our class to a meeting, secret of course. I heard about it from Waheed. One-by-one, we trickled through a crack in the gate of the Friends Girls' School to a rendezvous point at the elementary kids' playground. There, we agreed to hire teachers and meet privately for lessons. For a place, we rented a classroom at the Languages Institute, which, as a vocational training center, remained open. We collected money to pay for everything, then met every morning for three hours, taking courses in math, physics, and chemistry. The Languages Institute was located across the street from the Israeli-run post office, another permanent post for soldiers. We entered individually, right under their noses. This program actually worked great, lasting several months till schools reopened in the summer of '89, during which time we covered a good stretch of the textbooks.

At the Languages Institute, we arranged the desks in a big circle, unlike the files at school. My seat ended up directly opposite Veronica's, and often our gazes met. A teacher's question, directed at me, invariably brought me back to life. Still, I didn't have enough courage to tell her of my crush. I was in perpetual waiting for the right moment. We talked as friends, but after the lessons we parted our separate ways. I would go back home thinking about her. "Tomorrow, I'll tell her," but 'tomorrow' the same thing happened.

Going to School

Physically getting to the Friends' School was an ordeal. My normal 15-minute walk went right through the Manarah and past the police station, where soldiers stationed there could stop us. Injury or arrest were added threats if protests were to erupt, as they commonly did there, especially about the time of our walk home.

I walked home together with Kareem, Archie, Shadi, and my neighbor Maya, who was now in our class. We plotted our route each day like a military operation. Usually, we opted for a parallel path bypassing the *Manarah* through the Qaddura refugee camp. We took a peek at every street corner to make sure the coast was clear. Sometimes we got trapped in a neighborhood, with stone-throwing on both ends of the street, leaving us no refuge but to duck into the nearest store.

One day on our way home, there were no protests. From the corner of our eyes, we noticed a sniper rifle trained straight at us from a rooftop, where soldiers were now stationed. They were possibly just messing with us, but there was no time to evaluate the options. Kareem split into a crowded side street and I disappeared behind him, full-speed ahead.

Eventually, we needed rides. On 'hot days', we got out of class to find cars lined up at the school entrance, and in the mornings, my brother Basman alternated with Maya's mom to drive us to school. The car followed circuitous routes around the town center. The shorter one cut through the Qaddura refugee camp to El-Bireh, making a wide swing around the school from the back. The other rounded the outskirts of Ramallah through the old city, and across the Bir Zeit road then up a hill. The details of the routes shifted daily as we evaluated our options at the intersections. What once was a 15-min walk became a 30-min drive.

Driving was perhaps safer than walking, but not entirely. In May 1988, Basman returned from America after completing his Master's degree, new to the Intifada lifestyle. Unaware that the Israeli army had closed the town center one day, he took the car to run some errands. Soldiers posted there signaled him to stop, but he didn't understand what they wanted and slipped a few more yards. Instantly, they ran after him and banged on the car. When he lowered the window to talk to them, a hail of fists landed on his head through the open window. He came back home, not half an hour after leaving for his errand, with his face puffed up, black and blue, and bleeding red.

The Friends' School itself was surrounded by a high wall and a barbed-wire fence. That hampered us from leaving to participate in protests, and somehow kept the soldiers outside. Nevertheless, the adjacent Israeli police station peeked right into our classrooms. Every once in a while, some kid threw a stone over the fence, and shooting followed, ringing right into our classrooms. At such times, we hurried out of the room, crowding the stairwell while we waited for the shooting spree to end. Eventually, all the glass windows on the police-side of our building had been shattered. We were lucky that the walls of the school buildings were built of thick stone in the old style. Years later, though I was horrified at every school shooting in America, it did not occur to me that I had repeatedly experienced school shootings. It was normal that they shot at us, school or no school.

A few of the older students, especially the high-school seniors, were already active in PLO-sponsored youth organizations. They left their classes every day to participate in protests, against the teachers' wills. One day in the summer of 1988, student activists from a higher grade asked my class to join in a protest. Given our location, we expected a rapid response. My class talked it over and we decided to go ahead. Most of us, including myself, had not participated in one before, but nobody wanted to act chicken, so peer pressure won a silent victory.

We assembled in the far corner of the school. The taller students helped us climb over the fence, instructing us to quickly cross the street and hop over the opposite fence onto the school's small arboretum. There, other activists asked us to collect rocks as heavy as we could carry and toss them onto the street to make a barricade. While we did that, the organized students were stationed behind trees on the sidewalks, throwing stones at the police station. I did not waste time observing, but kept to my task, hauling rocks as quickly as I could.

The soldiers were on the scene in no time. The arboretum was on a street corner. Hidden by the trees and a medium-height stone fence, we laid low. From the positions of the guys on the main street, I could tell they were surrounded from both sides. Suddenly, the signal was given to run. We followed the leaders deeper into the arboretum. I took one glance toward the side street and saw a disabled army Jeep. It was battered by stones, steam rising from an engine leaking fluids. No soldiers near it, and not the time to slow myself looking.

We hopped over low terraces towards neighboring houses. Outside one was a garden hose with the water flowing. The leaders reminded us to wash our hands in case we're caught, as soiled hands were taken as evidence of stone-throwing. We ran over the *sanasel*, from house to house, until we made it to the next major street. We quickly crossed it and ran down a long stairwell along the hillside. We were out in the open. Having finished next-to-last in sprinting races at school, I surprised myself overtaking more athletic classmates. We crossed another street, hopped through more private yards, until we reached the ledge of a high terrace wall, three or four meters high. I hesitated. The other guys said jump, and jumped themselves, so I figured why not? Afterwards, I was proud of my highest jump to date. There, we stayed in that yard, out of sight, keeping quiet. The owners of the apartments in the building were nice, letting us stay and even serving us drinks, though they could get into trouble for harboring stone-throwers.

Suddenly, a lady recognized me from one of the balconies – they were friends of my parents. Yikes! At that moment I worried more about my parents knowing than arrest. Thankfully, she was discreet. Arriving home, I finally noticed the soreness in my feet, which I had to soak in cold water. Not expecting this adventure, I wasn't wearing the right shoes.

In the long, lazy afternoons, or the long, quiet nights, I had plenty of time to reflect, and think, and daydream. Soldiers stop me to ask for ID and harass me. Instead of giving in, I surprise them and grab one of their weapons to defend myself and subdue them. A certain girl is naturally on the scene. Silly, perhaps, but there was little else to dream about.

The Dark Side

No Palestinian family was spared by the Intifada. Hundreds of thousands injured, beaten, or imprisoned. Some experienced the worst, their children murdered, or deported. Beneath the excitement, pain and grief lurked – a grim reality that must have weighed on my father's mind as he waited on the porch for my return from school each day.

A year after surviving that brutal beating, Basman was shot. He was walking back from work when a protest erupted nearby. He ducked into a side street, but not before a rubber bullet bounced off a wall, hitting his back. Lucky for him, the wall absorbed most of the impact.

Abdul-Jabbar's father was being held without trial, under Israel's "administrative detention" clause, even before the Intifada. As soon as the one-year limit expired, the Israelis released him then rearrested him, keeping him detained for years. Throughout the Intifada, when times were difficult and people needed close connections for support, Abed was deprived of his dad.

Some of my friends were arrested in the aftermath of protests. Even though they were minors, Israel held them without trial for months. Sajid was sent to the Ansar-3 detention camp, an improvised tent prison in the desert for the influx of Intifada prisoners. After three months in the heat, he was released for "lack of evidence". With Israeli prisons at capacity, they needed room for more. As a former prisoner, Sajid's orange ID card was replaced with a green one. In Israel's color-coded version of "democracy", a green ID forbade the bearer from leaving the West Bank, so Sajid could not go to Jerusalem or Gaza, let alone the outside world.

A similar fate in Ansar-3 befell Najm, who inherited added scrutiny because his late father was a journalist whom the Israelis had detained and tortured for two-and-a-half years without trial. In 1991, Najm wanted to go to college and the only opportunities were abroad. The Israelis offered him a bargain. In exchange for the special permit he needed to leave the borders, he had to sign a statement agreeing not to return for the next five years. Najm chose the college education, and thus was effectively exiled from his home.

Sajid was re-arrested, then released under difficult conditions. Since he also had French citizenship through his mother, he opted to give up his Israeli ID card for the freedom to leave the country for college – another deportation that went unrecorded. He lived in Jordan for years, unable to go back and separated from his family, until the late 1990s when deportees returned during the Peace Process.

In time, more friends were affected. Saleem, the truant pool-hall devotee, was sent to Ansar-3. Faris was shot with a "plastic" bullet. He pointed to us the dark blue area near his shin were the bullet was still lodged. He could walk, but he could no longer play soccer. Faris was then imprisoned, released, then imprisoned again, his family not informed where he was held.

The Intifada transformed society. Having touched most families, Israeli oppression was losing its power to intimidate us. Within, the absolute power of parents was shaken. No parent wanted their children to risk injury or arrest, but with the whole society enmeshed in a popular uprising, few parents had the power to stop their children. The young made their own decisions, wearing their scars like badges of honor.

Israeli brutality hit close to home. One afternoon in the summer of 1988, I was home alone. My neighborhood friends Danny and Jawad knocked to see if I wanted to play. Danny was now thirteen, and Jawad twelve years old. The Intifada hadn't stopped us from riding our bikes, though we did it less often and stayed within our neighborhood. Having just picked up my GCE books to study, I apologized and told them I'd catch up with them later.

About an hour later, I heard loud screams from the street. The sound was nonstop, and getting louder, like someone being tortured. Peeking behind the curtain, I saw Jawad, surrounded by five or six Israeli soldiers in full uniform. They were pushing him around, clubbing him, pulling his hair, torturing him. His clothes were disheveled, his body bruised, his face puffy and covered in a mixture of tears and blood.

I later learned that Danny and he were riding their bikes near the end of the street, where the walls were plastered with slogans. Suddenly, they heard an army Jeep approaching. They had done nothing wrong, but worrying the soldiers would draft them to erase the graffiti, Danny made a split-second decision to run away. It was a silly move, in retrospect, as they left their bikes behind to run down steps and up alleys. Seeing them flee, the soldiers immediately followed. Danny, who was lean and strong, made the escape, while the chubbier Jawad was caught. The soldiers tortured him until he led them all the way to Danny's house. Danny was not there, of course, but his family was interrogated, and his name added to the "WANTED" list.

Danny had not cared for the liberation movement before this incident. We had play-acted protests – "soldiers and *shabab*", we called our game – but thus far, he had not participated in actual ones. Now, all of a sudden, he became hunted. He could not go home, and dropped out of school. No one knew his whereabouts, not even his family. Occasionally, he made an unannounced visit, telling us stories of his hiding with the *shabab*, then disappearing as swiftly as he arrived. This one incident totally changed his life. One moment he was a child on a bicycle. The next, he had to make one of two irreversible choices: either turn himself in to be imprisoned for a crime that was never committed, or join the organized resistance and spend the rest of his life a fugitive. He told us about the shed they hid in, stacked half-full of stones for self-defense. How they played cards deep into the night to pass the time, until they emerged to the deserted streets to scatter rocky barricades and write on walls – a romantically adventurous life, where danger lurked at every corner.

That whole incident was a sobering revelation for me. Had I agreed to go with my friends that day, I would have met their fates, either beaten and tortured, or hiding and on the run. One small random decision, and the whole course of one's life was changed. I rarely went outside after that, spending more time in the safety and security of my own room, studying, reading, listening to music, and daydreaming. My response to danger was increased isolation. Jawad also withdrew. I hardly saw him on the street anymore, and his family moved out of our neighborhood soon after that incident.

As for Danny, a year later, I heard someone screaming painfully outside. It was him, carried to his house by a couple of guys. I ran over to see what's going on. Apparently, he was about to throw a Molotov cocktail (a gasoline bomb) at the soldiers during a protest. Unknowingly, he had spilled some gasoline on himself, so his clothes caught fire. His back and arms were covered with burns. We had to peel his shirt off and treat him at home. A visit to the hospital guaranteed his arrest, as the army had set up a post there to arrest injured *shabab*.

The "Settlers"

Israeli soldiers were not the only danger. Thriving on occupied lands, the "settler" movement functioned as the Occupation's unofficial arm, if only out of self-interest. Moreover, the movement is dominated by militant extremists clothed in religion, who treat the Bible both as an authoritative history and a real estate deed. They regard all of historic Palestine as theirs – a God-given right – though our ancestors have continuously inhabited it for millennia. Forcibly occupying our land, they regard *us* as the squatters, whom their god has permitted to displace. They are rarely seen without their guns.

Though the settlers' extremism gave the impression they were the fringe of Israeli society, the stolenment program was backed by the state and the army. Most stolenments were officially planned by state agencies. The land for them was expropriated from its Palestinian owners under orders from the Israeli military. Settlers were encouraged to move there by financial incentives from Israel's Housing Ministry, while the Ministry of Transport cut new roads for their benefit. And finally, when settlers had any conflict with neighboring Palestinians, the Israeli army invariably aided the settlers. By their sheer presence in occupied lands, contrary to the prohibitions of international law, the settlers bolster Israeli aspirations for complete dominance over the Land.

During the Intifada, the "settlers" frequently went on the offensive to terrorize and intimidate us. They drove through Palestinian cities in the middle of the night in long convoys, shooting, burning, and leaving a trail of destruction. Their foray into our neighborhood one night left the smoldering carcasses of torched cars. Among them was Adnan's car – the same one he used to tour his friends from England. The street in front of our house was no longer a safe parking spot. Homeowners with driveways and yards invited their neighbors to cram their cars. At harvest, the settlers drove through Palestinian villages to burn crops. At the same time, the settlers' homes were safe within fortified stolenments surrounded by high walls, barbed-wire fences, and armed guards.

The Martyr

One day, I arrived at school to find the students skipping class and meeting in the yard. An "English-speaking" kid two grades younger, who went missing a few days earlier, was found murdered, likely by the "settlers". His body showed signs of beating and torture. Knife slashes, caning bruises, and cigarette burns covered his skin. We decided to march to his family's house, a good several miles away in El-Bireh to offer condolences and show support. On the long trek, while constantly on the lookout for Israeli patrols that might disrupt us, I was contemplating what brutes would do all that to a child – barely a teen. Apparently, they threw his body off a cliff when they were done.

Fortunately, we made it to the house without incident. It was his grandparent's house. The kid's parents, who were living in New Jersey, had sent him here to learn Arabic. The mood was strange, a stunned silence saturated with disbelief. They passed another round of coffee: dark, black, thick. The main part of Arabic funerary rites is a three-day period of chain-consumption of bitter coffee. Family members were telling everyone that this was actually a happy occasion because he became a martyr destined for heaven, repeating it endlessly, as if they hoped the repetition will make them believe a word of what they were telling us.

Shaking hands with everyone on the way out, I paused to offer my condolences to the kid's grandpa. He was staring out into space, oblivious of me and of everyone else, in total shock. The lines round his eyes were too deep, as if he hadn't had a wink in days, probably since the boy went out to play on the nearby hills and never came back. I wondered what thoughts went through his head. Was he thinking how could he face his own son, who entrusted him with the child?

I thought. Why?

For what '-ism' must human life be so desecrated?

Fatalities made an impact, especially in a small town like Ramallah. An employee at our family store, Salah, was driving in the old city when he was caught in the aftermath of a protest. The soldiers were chasing the scattering protesters through the narrow streets and alleyways. One youth, in his twenties, was apparently identified as a wanted Intifada leader. A special unit went after him. He tried to confuse them in the labyrinth of streets, but was ultimately cornered. The unit leader pushed him to his knees, then discharged a handgun in the back of his head. Salah, who was on the scene, immediately took him to the hospital, but it was too late. I can't forget the anguish on Salah's face as he recounted how "his brains spilled out inside the car."

General Strikes

Funereal church bells and the Muslim *adhan* joined together on afternoons when someone was martyred in Ramallah. We called anyone murdered by the Israelis a "martyr", whether he or she was active in the resistance, or an innocent bystander, and regardless of his or her religion.

At times like that, when a martyr had fallen, the Intifada leadership called for a three-day "remembrance strike" in his hometown (later cut to one day as significant events multiplied). Nationwide strikes were called for special events, such as the usual days I had enumerated, to which the Intifada itself added. The 9th of every month became a "day of wrath" commemorating its survival for yet another month. Its second year ushered in the anniversaries: of a prominent leader's martyrdom, or of particularly bloody days. The calendar soon became crowded. Not knowing when a strike could begin, or how long it might last, we had to be constantly prepared.

On strike days, the Intifada leadership wanted no one on the roads, to assert control over our territory. Large stones – makeshift barriers – were piled up at night, blocking every street in town. Palestinians working in Israel were warned to skip work that day, the trucks pooling them to their workplaces especially targeted. Some worked on construction projects in the stolenments. Needing those jobs to feed their children, some defied strike days. The shabab set up posts to enforce the strike, a barrage of stones facing violating cars, and that included "settler" cars.

Until 1993, the stolenments were connected to the existing grid of roads running through Palestinian towns and villages. Before the Intifada, relations with the settlers were tense but peaceful, with some Palestinians working in the stolenments, and settlers shopping in Ramallah on Saturdays. The Intifada made it dangerous for them to travel through Palestinian towns.

The "settlers" did not take stone attacks silently. They traveled armed, and often got out of their cars to shoot at, and even pursue, the *shabab*. The disproportionate power meant it was often the Palestinians who ended up on the casualty list. Children, emboldened by the Intifada and imitating their older peers, might throw stones at settlers, only to end up shot or beaten. The settlers reinforced their cars, covering windows with shatter-proof plastic films. By 1990, the Israeli army mapped paths for them through the outskirts of Palestinian towns, so settlers didn't accidentally stray into the town center. The designated roads were freshly paved, marked with a yellow line, and heavily patrolled by the army.

One strike eve, I got to observe the *shabab's* preparations first hand. Basman and I were home when we heard a commotion outside. Keeping the lights dimmed, we peered from behind the curtains. A van was stopped in the middle of the street. Six or seven guys, some wearing kafiyyehs, were tossing rocks from the opposite hill to make a barricade. Two more guys were spray painting graffiti on the walls through a stencil. I recognized one guy from my school. Swiftly, they had the road strewn with rocks. Seeing car lights approaching round the bend, we warned them. They immediately hopped into the van and sped away.

Another evening, Basman and I were driving to al-Tireh, back then at the outskirts of Ramallah and on a settler-designated road. As we approached a corner, the road was blocked, and a kafiyyeh-masked guy signaled us to stop by waving a large rock in one hand. He asked what were we doing, and where were we going. When he ascertained we were OK, he said the road to al-Tireh was closed, and pointed us to a detour to get back to town. We followed the short alley down a steep hill to the parallel road. As soon as we were out of sight of the main road, we saw tens of *shabab*, all masked and ready with piles of stones. It was an ambush, the few guys on the main street luring army jeeps down the alley. We promptly went back home and waited, listening in the direction of the old city, with prayers for the *shabab*. Sure enough, less than half an hour later, the shooting commenced from that direction.

One night about 1 AM, we heard loud knocks on the door. Soldiers! We worried – What did they want? They drafted my 60-year old dad, along with Maya's dad, and other neighbors to clear the street from the rocky barricades. Others, like two aged sisters from across the street, were put to erasing slogans from the wall, pressed to find their own paint and brushes. Having no brushes, the sisters resorted to using their late father's shaving brush. The whole neighborhood was up until 2 AM performing this forced labor. Perhaps the Israelis hoped that by exacting a price they could make us resent the *shabab* and rebel against the Intifada. The next day we woke up to find the barricades back in place, and the walls full of fresh new slogans. This forced labor became commonplace for a while, until the Israelis gave up, figuring it was better to let the old slogans stay, than to create clean surfaces for the sloganeers.

As for the barricades, the Israelis had another solution. Up late on a night watch, I heard the grinding whir of heavy tracked vehicles. I rushed to the window imagining tanks. It was bulldozers. The army used them to open the roads. Later in the Intifada, they upgraded their jeeps to lightweight armored cars mounted with a sort of snow plow in the front. They could drive fast while clearing the road as they go. Some had rock-proof cages on top where the soldiers could sit protected, and later they added paint guns to mark protesters for easier identification. These technological innovations perhaps changed the tactics, but they did not slow down the Intifada.

I was riding with Basman to Jerusalem one evening, when the soldiers stopped us along the dark part of the road, near the *Arak* distillery. That was not the usual location for a checkpoint, and what transpired was also unusual. Instead of checking IDs, the soldiers asked us to get out of the car, then hand them the keys. They wrote us a note, saying we could pick up the car the next day at the military governor's. They would not reason with us. Outright confiscation of property, no questions asked.

Stranded in the most deserted part of the Jerusalem road, we waited some time before a taxi stopped. The next day we got the car back. The army had used it for a covert operation to enter a Palestinian village and arrest activists, probably dressed in plainclothes as Palestinians. Their army jeeps would have raised the alarm, but an ordinary Palestinian car with a blue West Bank license plate would enter incognito. In the following months, car confiscations became more frequent. The car quickly aged and its body became battered after getting drafted, against our will, for a few of those operations. The only defense was to keep it in the garage and avoid travel, especially at night.

One particularly dark and quiet night, we heard soldiers knocking on our door again. Worried, we opened the door to find Captain Ezekiel, one of my father's business contacts in Jerusalem. His father originally lived in Aleppo, Syria, and was a friend of my grandfather long before Israel's founding. My only time inside a stolenment was when we were invited to dinner at his house in Gilo. The house was a nice stone villa no different than ours in construction style. The family was friendly, but the language barrier kept his children and I from serious play.

Ezekiel was now serving in the reserves and his tour sent him to Ramallah. Having nothing better to do, he led his squad to say "hello" to my father. It was awkward at first. Ezekiel asked his soldiers to leave their weapons at the door before going in. A few, especially the younger ones, looked hesitant. After all, we looked no different than the people they IDed every day, or the ones who confronted them with stones. Neither could I believe that the same soldiers I saw on the streets shooting at us and brutally beating people were right here in our house, peacefully sipping coffee and having a friendly chat with us. They were unused to letting their humanity show underneath the uniforms. This surreal and somewhat comical interlude was not repeated, however. It was perhaps the last time any Israeli visited us at home.

Repression

At about the third month of the Intifada, the Israeli army sealed the larger refugee camps, including al-Amari and al-Jalazon in the Ramallah area. The ugly barriers – concrete-filled stacks of barrels, three layers high – remained forbidding vehicle traffic till the Intifada's end. Soldiers checked pedestrians' IDs at the narrow gap left by the barrier. Not content with the sheer poverty and misery of the camps, the Israeli army turned them into prisons – ghettos within a bigger ghetto. The refugee camps were not self-sufficient but depended on the outside for jobs, food, and medical supplies. With Israel at the gate, the camps' residents were thus taken hostage, their basic rights treated as privileges at the discretion and mercy of the gatekeepers.

Foreshadowing Israel's Wall and the Gaza Siege decades later, the sealing of the camps was the first of a wave of "collective punishments" Israel unleashed to stop the Intifada. I disdain the term "collective punishment" because it implies wrongdoing, whereas freedom is a right, not a wrong.

After significant protests, we came to expect the declaration of a "closed military zone" in the locality where the event took place, and sometimes a curfew. The zones allow the Israeli army to clean up, away from the eyes of the international reporters. Homes raided in the dark, teenagers and young men suddenly turned political prisoners, in a system that gave them no vote, and little defense.

We knew a home demolition was coming when someone from Ramallah was arrested for throwing a Molotov cocktail. With his confession extracted, the parents were notified. They lived on the top floor of a multi-story apartment building. The army decided to demolish only his room, a corner room like mine. I went outside to watch the spectacle from afar. Though our street was blocks away, onlookers lined the sidewalks. The building, constructed from stone like everything else in Ramallah, was evacuated. Explosives experts laid charges. It only took one second – BOOM – and a void was left in the corner where the room once was. The rest of the building looked intact from the outside. The Israeli army left the disfigured monument a permanent warning, like the public hangings the British favored to intimidate our grandfathers.

In the war of ideas between the Occupation and the Intifada, the latter emerged a clear winner to those in my generation. Before it, like other young teenagers, I cared little about the liberation movement. I took the current situation – Occupation – as a given, and plotted my life within its parameters. Few of my friends were active in the resistance movement, and those were divided among splintering factions. At the beginning of the Intifada, many of us were not in favor of the general strikes, and wanted to get on with our business, be it selling groceries or taking finals.

Israeli repression highlighted the ills of the Occupation and convinced us of the necessity of freeing ourselves. Somehow, the equality of suffering united us. We were conscious that at any moment, the Occupation's tentacles can touch our lives. The knock on the door at night was all too common. The rounds of fire aimed at our schools. The school closures freed our time to get organized, learn about Palestine, and participate in protests.

The Intifada re-ignited long-lost dreams. Dreams within our reach, if we worked together.

Over a decade later, during the Second Intifada, the Israeli propaganda machine spread the soundbite "Palestinians teach their children to hate" (Googling the phrase in 2010, I got some five million results). An absurd idea, judging from my own experience. My parents never taught me to hate anyone, and I can't imagine other parents doing so. Neither did my teachers, who were protective of us, incite me to violence, as some pro-Occupation "nonprofits" claimed our schools to be doing.

So I did a little mathematical calculation. The activists of the Second Intifada, youths in their late teens and twenties, must have been children aged five to fifteen during the First. Palestinian schools were closed most of that time, so what those children learned about life, they did so from the school of the Occupation. They opened their eyes to a world where Israeli soldiers, armored and carrying automatic rifles, were bossing everyone around at the threat of violence. They saw older brothers beaten, cousins arrested and dragged to political prisons, or heard of someone in their hometown shot to death. Finally when schools were re-opened, some had to go through the refugee camp barrier to get there, encountering Israeli patrols on every street. All were locked up at home for 40 days straight because of the Iraq War curfew in 1991.

Five million Google results are wrong. If anyone were taught to hate Israel, the lessons were handed down directly, by order of the Israeli military governor.

8

Resistance Through Existence

A FLAG TIED TO A STONE, slung over a power line.

I took a detour, in case an Israeli patrol surprised me. The soldiers pressed passers-by to retrieve the offending displays, a job I could do without. Descended from flags of the 1936 revolt against the British and the earlier Arab revolt against the Ottomans, the Palestinian flag represented our long-standing aspirations for independence. Israel had it banned, deeming it the "flag of the PLO", which they classified a "terrorist organization". By the end of 1988, the Palestinian flag had become the center of contention on West Bank streets. The *shabab* painted colorful flags alongside their slogans. The Israelis countered by arresting people even wearing its colors: red, white, black, and green.

That's exactly how I dressed on November 15, when I strolled in defiance of their curfew to celebrate the declaration of a Palestinian State. I was not the only one, as a handful of flag-colored kites were flying, and people disregarded the curfew. Fireworks lit Ramallah that night.

The Intifada began as a mass movement from within Occupied Palestine. The rest of the world was caught off-guard, including the Arab countries and the PLO, which hastened to put together a political program. By the middle of 1988, King Hussein of Jordan gave up his country's claims to the West Bank, in recognition of our independence. On November 15, 1988, in what became the high point of the Intifada, the PLO declared an independent Palestinian State in a special meeting in Algiers. We tuned to radio al-Quds on the morning of the 15th. By noon, Palestine time, the voice of the PLO's top leader Yasir Arafat resounded reading the historic declaration, penned by the poet Mahmoud Darwish.

I took the declaration seriously: the birth of a new country – *my* country. I listened to radio broadcasts intently, keeping a list of countries that recognized the new state. The tally neared 80 countries by the end of the year. Rather than acknowledge the popular uprising's demand for freedom, the US government clung to archaic policy from a decade earlier, reiterating Kissinger's pre-conditions for engaging in "dialogue" with the PLO. Recognition was out of question. The State Department even refused Arafat a visa to enter New York City and address the United Nations.

The conditions were one-sided: renounce terrorism, with "terrorism" defined to include acts of resistance while excluding Israeli state terror; and unilaterally recognize Israel, while Israel continued to deny our own existence. The US and Israel wasted two decades with this stalling strategy. By the time they reluctantly recognized the PLO in the 1990s, that organization no longer represented all Palestinians, as the newly-founded Hamas was on the ascendant. Today, Israel and the US are repeating the folly by refusing to talk to Hamas.

As for the State of 1988, it came to nothing, essentially annulled or put on hold by the Oslo Accords. Its main contribution remains the morale boost and direction it has given us as the Intifada approached its first anniversary.

The leaflets from the Intifada leadership, in their emphasis on nonviolent resistance, encouraged the formation of "neighborhood committees" to conduct our local affairs. By the time of the Declaration, we saw those committees as the internal implementation of the state. Following the initial instructions, our neighborhood called a meeting to organize one. Adnan represented our household in those meetings. Committees of the larger neighborhoods organized home schooling and had an activism wing that participated in protests. Ours lacked the critical mass. Our immediate concern was to address basic services, like trash collection, that stopped when Palestinian civil servants resigned from the Israeli administration. We burned trash in the dumpster. It did not smell pleasant, but was the only option available at the time.

The Palestinian policemen had also resigned and turned in their guns and badges. The predicted reign of chaos never really materialized. Years into the Intifada, it was surprising to see that society was still functioning. At the center of this success was people caring for one another. Our main sources of insecurity were the Israeli soldiers, and the settlers' night raids. Our neighborhood committee organized a neighborhood watch, distributing a phone list so anyone could alert other neighbors.

Staying up was a treat I got to do only on Easter or New Year's. Now, without school, I lost semblance of a regular sleep schedule, so I kept the night watch when I could. The quiet nights gave ample time to read, keeping my ears tuned to any unusual sounds. I fell in love with Ramallah's sunrises. With our house on a western slope, we saw light long before the sun peeked over the ridge to the east. Little fluffy clouds, tinged with pink, floated against a clear blue sky. Slowly I watched the shadow of the hilltop recede, as more and more houses reflected the bright sunlight. Other times, the city woke up enveloped in fog. Dispelled by the rising sun, the fog settled into the valleys in parallel strands. Layers of ridges floated above the clouds, islands piercing a placid white sea, a serene scene far removed from the turbulent time.

One of the most daring acts of the Intifada was organized by the neighborhood committees of Beit Sahur, a Christian Palestinian town near Bethlehem, at the site of the field where the angels appeared to the shepherds to herald the birth of Jesus. After the PLO's Declaration in 1988, Beit Sahur decided that independence was meaningless as long as we carried Israeli identity cards and continued to pay its taxes. The cards were symbols and instruments of Israeli domination. The taxes, forced on us without our consent, subsidized the Occupation.

Shedding their fear of consequences, the citizens of Beit Sahur opted for civil disobedience, stopping tax payments to the occupier, and holding a mass ceremony where everyone burned their Israeli ID cards. Their courageous move posed a tough challenge to the Israelis, who were used to preying on lone individuals: would they arrest everyone in town?

Perhaps our greatest mistake during the Intifada was not following the example of Beit Sahur. Instead of summoning the courage, our attitude was "let's wait and see what happens to Beit Sahur." Had the whole West Bank acted together, Israel would have needed far more resources to enforce their ID and tax policies. Instead, by awaiting Beit Sahur's fate, we encouraged Israel to make an example of it. Tax collectors raided the city under the blanket of curfew. They confiscated everything from people's homes as "taxes": furniture, appliances, TVs. It was outright theft, exposing the Occupation for what it was. The people of Beit Sahur were unrepentant, but the episode remained a relatively minor chapter of the Intifada instead of inaugurating a new direction.

The longer-term damage from our inaction was exposing the effectiveness of dividing us. Seeing how we in Ramallah were unconcerned about Beit Sahur, Israel worked hard to isolate us from each other, such that different Palestinian towns could no longer coordinate their actions. Hence, the 1990s witnessed longer and more frequent "closures", approaching permanence. Jerusalem was severed from the West Bank, splitting the latter into Northern and Southern halves. In addition to hampering our communication and coordination, the Closure policy strangled our economy. (The Wall is the ultimate extension of that policy. In 1988, the same leaflets were easily distributed over the West Bank and read aloud on al-Quds radio, and people traveled to other cities to protest, meet, organize, and coordinate. Today, few can leave their local region if the Gates are locked.)

More serious than the geographic fragmentation were the societal divisions. I grew up in a stratified society. People looked up to wealth. City people looked down on villagers. Refugee camp residents were marginalized. The Intifada aimed to do away with those divisions, equalizing society and giving all of us a shared national identity. It may have succeeded temporarily but the divisions lingered. The Intifada was no match for the unstated ban on inter-religious marriages. Perhaps as a way for self-preservation for minority groups, people who cross religious lines are effectively excommunicated. Such harsh intolerance is unhelpful for our cohesiveness as a nation.

Especially after the civil disobedience of Beit Sahur, Israel issued a number of military orders that criminalized whatever we did to resist, in real time. The military governor's orders had the force of law, without any input from us. Tax payments and fees were a stream of income Israel jealously guarded, and furthermore added to our economic hardships. To force compliance, Israel made full payment of taxes a prerequisite to getting any formal document issued. When people stopped renewing their car registrations, a new military order authorized confiscating unregistered cars.

By the time I wanted to travel to America a year later, applications for a travel document needed stamps of approval from a dozen agencies, each of which consumed hours standing in lines. To get my stamps, I had to prove that my family had paid its taxes, paid the electricity and water bills, and had no outstanding warrants, parking tickets, or driving violations. On we went, with Basman chauffeuring me, from the electric company, to the police, to the motor vehicle agency, to the city, collecting stamps. Foremost, I needed a clearance from the military governor's office, confirming I was not on any watch list from Israel's numerous intelligence services.

It was an ingenious device to exert control, and at the same time divide Palestinian society into those who complied with the unfair laws and those who did not. Families chose to resist and not pay taxes — until they were faced with a crisis and needed a permit. Perhaps a family member needed to study abroad, needed surgery at an Israeli hospital, or needed to attend the funeral of a relative in Jordan. Then they had to go through the steps and prove that they are "good Palestinians". With Israel's firm control of the borders, we could never be independent.

The added restrictions created opportunities for Palestinians working in Israel's "Civil Administration", that is, those who had not resigned. You want a travel document? For an appropriate gift, they can help you navigate the Israeli bureaucracy and get the twelve stamps in one day. The line at the civil administration office is too long? They can take you in their own car through the back entrance and introduce you to the head of that department. As the rules became more complex, those intermediaries became more valuable to those who could afford them, and more detested to the people standing in the lines. Some people called them *'umala* ("agents", inexactly translated in the West as "collaborators"), a term that was broadly applied to anyone helping the Occupation. Incidentally, with the subsequent advent of the Palestinian Authority, people could still be found in the civil service who would circumvent the rules for money. We just stopped calling those intermediaries *'umala*.

Is someone who merely used his connections to help Palestinians get permits a collaborator? I vividly recall a heated exchange over this question, days after the birth of Adnan's first child, between him and his young and hot-headed brother-in-law. With no agreed-upon definition, and no transparency in the process, I wondered how many unjustly suffered the "collaborator treatment". To be sure some *'umala* carried guns, infiltrated resistance groups, or helped the Israelis arrest or assassinate an activist. With the entire population held captive in the large open-air prisons called "West Bank" and "Gaza", Israel had many levers for recruitment. The economy was battered by the strikes and curfews, and people were hurting. Some, arrested after a protest, were held indefinitely and offered to be released only if they pledged to "cooperate", in a twisted form of plea bargain.

The lurking presence of collaborators among us further stifled our expression. Dumbness was a habit people had gotten into long before the Intifada, and not just in Palestine, but elsewhere in the Arab world, where the intelligence agencies rule the states. From a young age we heard: "Shhh! Don't say that loud. Someone could hear!" Or, "Don't say that on the phone!" With the Intifada, we were warned about "birds". Once warned, we saw "birds" everywhere. The paranoia engendered by the lack of freedoms is suffocating. People become experts in self-censorship.

Shadi, my friend since the nun school, went to study abroad after high school. In 1991, his roommate was accused and convicted in a plot to burn the Israeli Embassy. Shadi was not directly involved, but weapons were found in their apartment. He was detained for six months before being deported to Romania. The conditions in prison were bad enough the prisoners went on a hunger strike, to the point he fell ill and had to be hospitalized. In Romania, he trained to be a bartender and worked a while, but decided to come home in 1993. Upon arrival, he was held for 24 hours at the airport jail, before being moved to the Ramallah prison. He told me the hardest part was seeing Ramallah, for the first time in three years, from that army jeep, knowing he could not go home to his family. He spent over a month of solitary confinement in a small cell, and was sent to Hebron for three days of questioning, but was finally released, presumably because they knew he had done nothing, and were swamped with more important cases.

I happened to be visiting, the summer of 1993, when Shadi was suddenly released. Sandra's husband warned me not to be too friendly with him: "Why did they release *him* so early? Others are spending six months or more for stone throwing, and he was involved in far bigger things." The implication being that Shadi must have offered them something in exchange for his early release, information, perhaps, or a promise to work with them. I did not buy that logic, and besides, I did not belong to any organizations, so what did I have to worry about? But such was the thinking: "Better safe than sorry"; "Fear, even if you did nothing to fear for"; and "Say absolutely nothing."

My high school class was once closely-knit. We had spent eight years together, from 3rd grade onwards. By the end of the Intifada, we fragmented among foreign countries and Israeli prisons, divided between "heroes" and "birds". Less connected after my departure to USA for college, on summer visits I relied on the others' advice to tell who is whom. Before the Intifada, we were *one* class. With the Intifada, the map of who was to be trusted had to be constantly redrawn.

The Israelis issued fake leaflets to confuse us. It was easy to tell the fakes from their language and content. The Unified Intifada Leadership (*QAWM*) was disciplined and responsible in its call for strikes. The real confusion started when Hamas came on the scene. Founded at the beginning of the Intifada, the Islamic Resistance Movement (Hamas) became visible in the West Bank in mid-1989. Refusing to join forces with QAWM, Hamas issued their own leaflets and their own calls for strikes. A rivalry was developing between the two leaderships, and by 1990, it was possible to end up confined at home for a week or two due to strikes called by both factions, combined with emergency strikes for fallen martyrs.

By my 1993 visit, that divisive spirit had spread to other factions, each issuing their own strike days and instructions. The talk of the town in my first week there was the big fight that took place in Ramallah between self-declared "patriots" and the Scouts' club because the club opened on a strike day. Packs of youths from each side were throwing stones *at each other*, endangering innocent bystanders. It took a patrol of the Israeli border police to stop the fight! Ultimately, our divisive society accomplished what years of Israeli repression could not – weaken the Intifada.

Economically, people in Occupied Palestine were strained even before the Intifada. Businesses like my family's suffered from high import duties and export restrictions. My own family was additionally targeted for an Israeli tax raid in the mid-1980s. I recounted how they surprised us in the early morning, while my father was out of the country, confiscating crates of documents, among them my school notebooks. We needed to follow up the next morning at the army headquarters in Beth El, as they questioned my mother and adult brothers. Phone service was not available between Israeli-controlled areas and Arab countries, so we managed to notify my father through Basman, who was studying in the USA. Dad decided to come back regardless. On the Bridge, the Israelis awaited him.

They held him at the police station in Ramallah, which was fortunate. Although visits were prohibited, there were no Israeli supervisors on the night shift, leaving local Palestinian policemen in charge after 11 PM. As soon as the last Jewish officer left, a Palestinian policeman called to tell us we could visit. Mom carried food for Dad. The police let him out of the cell for a while. After we left, he played cards and chatted with them.

After 15 days of detention, we secured his release by paying a substantial bail, which we had to borrow, the sum considerably larger than the taxes due. We were forced to pursue a court case to recover the excess. The case lingered for months, adding lawyers' fees on top of the taxes due, fines, and interest. I don't recall how it all added up in the end, whether we recovered a single penny, or had to pay even more. Financially, we were devastated, left with a gargantuan debt, and under scrutiny to collect sales taxes that no customer wanted to pay.

With the advent of the Intifada, the half days, and the semi-permanent state of strikes, the already-weak economy was further strained. In times of hardship, people concentrated on essentials. So while food and clothing businesses survived, everything else suffered. Movie theaters and coffeeshops, as well as restaurants, shut down. There was no room for entertainment. Tourism, an important industry for Jerusalem and Bethlehem, dwindled as tourists avoided the region. Hotels and souvenir shops were deserted and had to close. Yet, somehow, people coped.

To stay in business, my father needed new markets. He shifted to selling wholesale to retailers in the bigger cities. My brothers regularly made delivery trips to Nazareth, and sometimes Nablus. Gaza needed a special permit, so the Gaza retailers visited us instead. Business deals were often conducted at home, especially since the Gaza merchants could never make it to Ramallah before noon. The Nablus contacts visited frequently, but the Nazareth ones were too concerned about their cars getting stoned, as they sported yellow license plates.

I often accompanied Basman or Adnan on the trips, for safety, and the excitement of getting out of Ramallah. Nazareth was far. The most direct road, straight north through Nablus and Jenin in the West Bank, was populated by checkpoints. We therefore began westward on the Yafa road, took one of the coastal roads north, then turned back east to Nazareth. The trip took three hours each way. Once, Adnan stopped near the "Ben Shemen" forest to snap a photo of a triangular field surrounded by forests. I was puzzled, until days later when I saw him working on an oil painting of the scene. Curiously, he replaced the car with a horse-drawn carriage.

We preferred returning before nightfall, so we rarely lingered. I liked the steep, winding climb to Nazareth. I also liked the old city, with its covered suqs and maze of alleys, but detested the open sewers in its streets. My last memory of Nazareth from that era was the one time we stayed late. I was surprised and excited to see stores still open after dark. Streets were crowded and brightly lit, and business was going on as usual – a far cry from the sleepy Ramallah of the Intifada.

With the growth of the stolenment of Giv'at Ze'ev, opposite the army camp near Beitunia, we lost the Hills with the Faces. By 1990, a new three-lane highway was being cut right through them. What remained of those familiar landmarks would soon be out of sight, off the main road.

Nablus was closer to Ramallah, situated in the center of the northern portion of the West Bank. Technically only an hour away, it took longer because of the checkpoints. The city is nestled in the valley between two mountains, rewarding us with evolving panoramas as we climb the heights. Unfortunately, it was a challenge to arrive there before noon, so we often missed the *kunafa* dessert.

In addition to these destinations, Basman and I often went to Jerusalem at night to visit a business contact in the Armenian Quarter of the Old City. We parked the car just inside Bab-el-Khalil (Jaffa Gate), walking briskly and silently through the Old City's network of paved streets. We were constantly wary, as access to the Armenian Quarter lay through the heavily-policed Jewish Quarter. We refrained from talking so our Arabic would not raise suspicion.

It is ironic that we have traveled farther and more frequently during the Intifada than during the peacetime following it. The roads were open and there were no restrictions, perhaps because Israel needed the underpaid labor of Palestinian workers. Sometimes it was tense to drive with a West Bank license plate, but no harm befell us. The car broke down once near Haifa, as my parents returned from Nazareth. Within a few minutes, a Palestinian with Israeli citizenship stopped to help them. He confessed feeling obligated to help, guessing their West Bank plates at worst made them targets for extremists, while at best deterred other Israelis from helping.

Despite all the efforts, business dwindled. At some point the Gaza merchants could no longer make it to Ramallah. Travel to Nablus became more difficult. I made the last business trip to Nazareth in 1990, when I was back from America on my first visit home. After that, the West Bank was put under a semi-permanent Closure, and we could not easily go anywhere. My parents decided to move the business, and the family to America.

My family was by no means the first to leave. There was a continuous stream of Palestinian families emigrating to countries all over the world, wherever they could get a visa. Most would have rather stayed, but could not bear the tightening of the economic screw. Several Israeli political parties openly advocated what they called the "Transfer" policy, namely the expulsion of Palestinians from the West Bank and Gaza in order to have a more "Jewish" Israel in control of all the land of historic Palestine. In reality, this policy was already being implemented, gradually over decades by economic means rather than forceful expulsion, as was done in 1948.

The exodus affected Christians in larger proportion than Muslims. It was suggested that more Palestinian Christians emigrated because it was somehow easier for them to get foreign visas. Closer to the truth was the lack of outside support. Whereas Jews and Muslims can count on the support of numerous international networks and organizations, Palestinian Christians have the misfortune of being considered more Arab than Christian by the West, more Christian than Arab by the Arabs, and non-Jewish by Israel. Palestinian Christians naturally felt abandoned and had to face economic hardships on their own.

On trips to Jerusalem, I often browsed Israeli newspapers. One time in 1989, I saw a disturbing one-page ad in the *Jerusalem Post*, an English-language paper. The ad urged the Israeli public to oppose relinquishing the West Bank in a peace deal, for one vital reason. Israel needed the water underneath, claimed the ad, essentially admitting that Israel siphoned over 90% of the West Bank's water for its own use, and for that of the stolenments. The ad was signed by none other than Israel's Ministry of Water Resources. No wonder the shortages every summer! In 1993, Bethlehem went for three weeks without water.

A founding myth of Israel gives it credit for "making the desert bloom". This "desert bloom" propaganda flourished in the early 20th century, a time when greed was equated with "progress", and "industriousness" was celebrated, while "sustainability" and "resource management" were terms unknown. The fertility of desert sand is not the issue. Water is! The climate is dry, with the aquifers replenished mostly from the limited seasonal rainfall. Currently, the environment is stressed, more water is used than rainfall and the rivers can supply. The water table in the aquifers is dwindling. Unless new water sources are found, we have to learn to live within our means.

Our ancestors learned, by the experience of generations, to make the best use of the limited water supply and be good stewards for the land. They dug the terraces to slow the drainage of rainwater and refill the aquifers. Crop choice was another management strategy. Palestinian farmers learned to love and respect drought-resistant plants like the fig, olive, cactus, artichoke, and palm. Desert shrubs are appreciated as symbols of beauty.

Israelis retained the idea of beauty from their water-rich native lands in Europe and America – lush green lawns and sparkling blue swimming pools. They chose intensive irrigation to produce a wider variety of crops. Irrigation had existed since the dawn of civilization, where water was abundant – in the great river valleys of Egypt, Iraq, India, or China. The Israeli innovation that made the "desert bloom" was *unsustainable* irrigation, taking water from areas where the total rainfall is low. As I have noticed on recent trips, the Jordan River has dwindled to a trickle, and the Dead Sea shrunken.

Israel's history can be viewed through the lens of expanding its water resources. In the 1950s, Israel embarked on a canal project to divert the waters of the Jordan, antagonizing Syria and Jordan who shared that river. Israel's official justification for starting the 1967 War – Egypt's closing the straits of Tiran, Israel's outlet to the Red Sea – little explains Israel's attack on Syria and Jordan. The war ultimately expanded Israel's borders to include the water-rich West Bank, plus the Golan Heights, giving them a foothold on the Jordan River's sources. The War on Lebanon in the early 1980s extended Israel's reach over the sources of the Jordan, and accessed the Litani River deep within Lebanon.

Looking at that newspaper ad, I despaired that Israelis cared for peace. Alongside the water theft, Israel escalated its ecological war to drive us out of those lands they coveted. Under the guise of "security", I read that Israel destroyed nearly 90,000 olive trees between 1988 and 1992, an ecological tragedy since an olive tree took up to twenty years to become productive, and eighty to reach stable yields. Furthermore, it was an economic disaster to the thousands of farmers who depended on those trees for their livelihoods.

The economic damage during the Intifada cannot be solely blamed on Israel. Much of it was self-inflicted. To this day, I cannot understand how have we hurt the Occupation by ending our workdays and schooldays at noon? Strikes work by shutting down an employer, thus putting pressure for a more favorable bargain. Here, the strike only stifled our own economy. Closing retail stores left no outlet for our farms and industries. Incomes shrank, adding to the insecurity and uncertainty. Construction ground to a halt. A high price for asserting our independence! A more sensible approach would have been to restrict the strike to those working in Israel, while everyone else worked double-time and contributed funds to support the striking workers.

What sustained the Intifada was our willingness to endure losses and economic hardships for our cause. We lost friends to bullets, jails, or deportation. Others were permanently disabled by Intifada injuries. Our economy suffered and we spent years living without security. Damage in this context can only be judged in relative terms. Despite Israel's repeated attempts to crush us during the Intifada, we have not relented. We refused to be defeated. We endured, at great odds, because we knew and accepted the fact that freedom came at a price. What was different about the Intifada, compared with prior protests, was the extent of coordination and collective action, through which everyone felt involved in the struggle. We fostered a community spirit, and learned how to act in unison. For those in my generation, the Intifada was a school of character, and a time of excitement. We grew as a result.

Reflecting on my personal experience, the days I spent out of school during the Intifada instilled the independence and self-reliance that became the foundation for my future success. The momentous events around me gave me a direction and sense of purpose that I found lacking in teens and young adults in America among my generation. Fast forward to the COVID-19 pandemic and social isolation. I found that my Intifada experience had prepped me well and helped me be a better parent through the crisis and my daughter's school shutdown. I knew, deep inside, that we possessed the power to pull through this – that I had it within me. There was no reason to panic. I remained calm and collected throughout, not rushing to hoard, trusting that we would be fine, and reassuring my daughter that everyone else was going through the same ordeal.

The Palestinian experience was therefore not all negative. Palestinian rights' activists in the West too often emphasize *victimhood*. They want people to pity us, but that is not a good approach. In 2002, during the Israeli reinvasion of the West Bank, a student group on campus constructed a mock-refugee camp display to inspire students to think differently about Palestine. We painted the wooden shacks in graffiti. Standing in the cold, I finger-painted an olive tree on one panel. Admiring my work, I added a positive motivational slogan in the spirit of the Intifada: "Rooted on our land, like Olive Trees." The next day, I passed by the refugee camp to find that one of the student members had changed that to "*Up*rooted *from* our land, like Olive Trees." It made me sad. It also made me reflect that these American students, well-meaning as they were in their enthusiastic support for Palestine, had not grasped the essence of "struggle". As we learned in the School of the Intifada, a person who stands up for their rights is no victim.

9

Transplant

BY EARLY 1989, no end for the Intifada was in sight. My parents worried. Basman and Adnan were each beaten by the soldiers, for no reason. I had reached the age when youths joined protests, and with school mostly closed, my education was in jeopardy. Though my uncles had left the country in the early 1980s, and despite the outflux of family friends, my parents had prided themselves in remaining steadfast in Ramallah. For the first time, I heard serious talk of emigration. They visited the US that summer to evaluate prospects. They decided to move the business to Michigan, where they had cousins, and a large Arab community. Seeing a shorter path to citizenship in Canada, they chose to concurrently apply for immigration there, intending to live across the border from Detroit.

As for me, my parents dictated I be the first to move, having found me a boarding school in Michigan. Yikes! That news surprised me, coming as it did in August, a month before the new school year began. I did not want to leave. In the summer, the schools had reopened and we were attending regularly. I wanted to finish high school with the same classmates I grew up with. All my friends were here, plus, there was Veronica. If schools were closed again, I knew I could get a degree by taking the GCE, hence saw no compelling reason to leave, only another big hassle.

I protested, but there was no convincing them. So I played along. Several hurdles remained before I could leave. First, I had to get admitted. During the one and a half years when schools were closed, I had nothing to show for my independent studies – no grades, no transcript.

For the American school, it was no problem; the admissions office sent me a placement test, and called for a telephone interview. Impressed with my strength and my English skills, they admitted me into the senior year of high school, awarding full credit for the junior year I had not completed.

Next, I needed a travel document quickly. No problem either; my parents found a connection to speed up the process.

The biggest hurdle, confronting not just myself but every prospective foreign student, was getting the US visa. I arrived at US Consulate in East Jerusalem, acceptance letter and a thick file of documents in hand, to find a long line of people camped outside. One by one we entered the courtyard, filled out the application, then waited for our numbers. After more lines inside, I made it to the window. A slight typo, an obviously mistaken date on the school's "I-20" immigration form, and the clerk refused to accept my application. Upset about the wasted day and the hassle, I secretly hoped that was the end of my USA study plan.

The school FedExed me a new form, and I tried my luck at the consulate again. This time my application was rejected for lack of evidence of "ties to my home country". Again, I was secretly pleased. Time was running out. School started after Labor Day and the travel agent had already postponed my flight once. Back to the consulate with copies of my parent's bank accounts and house deed, I encountered the third rejection, for reasons I forget. The flight had to be postponed again, to Sep. 11. On the morning of the 10th, I went to the consulate again, for one final try. My parents were ready to give up if this attempt failed, and I was confident I would stay in Ramallah.

The consulate was less crowded now that summer was over. At the window, I was met by the US Consul herself. She gave me a brief lecture about America being a country of laws, stressing that my father's approach for help (behind my back) through connections with embassy employees was counterproductive. I was getting ready to walk away when, shockingly, she granted me the visa! My documents were correct, I fulfilled the legal requirements, and my lack of knowledge of Dad's attempts was obvious. Since that moment, I was impressed with America's respect for rules and procedures.

Most people get ecstatic at this point. I was dumbfounded. The worst had happened. In less than 24 hours, I would be on the plane, whisked away to America. I did not have enough time to bid everyone goodbye. What hours remained had to be spent packing my bags, deciding what to take, and making last-minute preparations for my trip.

I called a few of my friends to let them know, but I really hoped to see *her*. Yet, what was the point, now that I was leaving? I went outside. Sometimes she visited Maya. I sat on the front steps, watching the street, and waiting. Archie, Kareem, and a couple others swung by to say goodbye. Evening fell and I was still outside. This was to be my last night in Ramallah. My head was swirling. I looked up at the stars. Would this be the last time I see them from here? My parents kept calling me in, wondering why I stayed outside so long. They wanted to talk, but I didn't care to see anyone, blaming them especially for my imminent exile. I went inside, mechanically ate dinner, then moved to the sunroom, to take a last look at Ramallah.

At 2 AM, we loaded the suitcases. Not a wink of sleep. Tel Aviv airport, the usual searches. Somehow, I was entrusted with an elderly lady heading to Chicago along my itinerary. She didn't know a word of English and I was volunteered to be her translator. Like most flights leaving Tel Aviv, our flight was badly delayed. By the time we got to Amsterdam, our connecting flight had departed. A sixteen-year-old traveling on his own for the first time, with an aged lady in his care. We lined up at the crowded customer service desk. Only one flight per day to Chicago, and we missed it. The airline offered us a hotel night. I was already late for school, so I asked if they had other options, considering my final destination was Detroit. They offered to route me through New York, on a flight leaving that same afternoon. I then convinced them to make similar arrangements for the old lady. In all of this, I had no time to ponder the unknown I was flying to!

In quiet moments on the flight I had fleeting memories of Dani, Jawad, and the friends I had left behind. I recalled a dream I had when I was little: gradually opening my eyes from a good night's sleep, I found myself in Ol' Granny's house. My entire life with the Zaitouns, including all my waking and sleeping hours, and all the dreams therein, had been one long dream. I awoke again to find myself back in my crib in the Zaitouns' living room. The Chinese philosopher Zhuangzi once dreamed he was a butterfly, but wasn't sure if perhaps he was a butterfly dreaming he's Zhuangzi. Likewise, I emerged confused as to my identity.

Sometimes I thought of Danny as my alter-ego. His life would have been mine had the stork dropped me one house away: his losing his mother when he was six, the worst day of his life, he told me; the toughness he had to cultivate to survive on the streets; and his hunted life, driven underground. The burns.

A split-second decision the day of the incident gone the other way, and my life would have jumped to a different timeline. A profound and sobering truth!

Late at night, we made it to JFK, only to find my suitcases were missing. Apparently, they were still in Amsterdam awaiting the next day's Chicago flight. All I had on me was a tiny briefcase with stationary and a book. I continued to Detroit, where I found Mr. Chandler from the school's admissions office waiting. It was well after midnight. He drove for a long time on dark country roads to get to the school. I had no idea where we were, and was surprised at Michigan's darkness. Exhausted, I plopped on the bed as soon as I got to my room. The next day, Mr. Chandler was kind enough to take me shopping for essentials till my suitcases arrived, promising to inquire at the airport every day. He personally brought them to my room a few days later.

Cranberry Hills

Within days, I found my way around the new school. People were friendly, and curious about this new student, coming up to talk to me. The teachers were sympathetic to my transition. I quickly got used to the new routine. I ate meals at the school cafeteria, went to classes, explored the campus. In the evening, we hung out at the dorm. A teacher sat on duty all night. The school imposed study hours, but I found myself studying outside of those because of the volume of homework. For English literature, we were expected to read a dozen books a year, whereas in Ramallah we only read excerpts. Late evenings, we watched TV or played Foosball in the large game room. The TV was tuned almost permanently to MTV, back in the time when MTV only played music videos.

Making friends was not easy, joining as I did during the senior year. Most students already had their circles, and had known their friends for years. Almost everyone in the dorm was into a sport, playing hockey or lacrosse outside all their free time. I was unacquainted with most American sports, so found it hard to connect. Ultimately, I hung out with other newcomers, internationals, and oddballs.

My next-door neighbor, Slava, who came from Poland when he was six years old, suggested I join him on the Chess Club, in lieu of a sport. We played chess nightly, in his room as he had a tape player. The only music he played was Led Zeppelin. I could not comprehend how someone could listen to only one thing when there's so much music out there. I got sick of it, thinking it monotonous when it was all I heard, but missed it once I moved out of Cranberry Hills. As for me, my only music maker was the radio alarm clock Mr. Chandler helped me buy on the first morning. I kept it tuned to Top 40 stations, but was disappointed with their repetitive selections and lack of breadth.

Down the hall was Zack, who only listened to Simon and Garfunkel. I knew him from my social studies class, where I sensed he cared deeply about issues of social justice. Zack organized a sit-in on Martin Luther King day to protest the school's non-observance of it. In this first exposure to activism in America, we skipped classes and sat in the quad for part of the day, taking turns reading from King's speeches. Unfamiliar with US history, the sit-in was my first exposure to King's struggle and legacy.

A clique of guys often snuck into the bathroom after hours to smoke cigarettes, and possibly other things. Reminding me of the "troublemakers" at my old school, they were likely the ones my parents had in mind when they warned me. I knew Greg from my physics class. His sport was soccer, so we kicked the ball around a few times. Barry, with long straight hair in the style of Tom Petty, was a permanent fixture in the game room, facing the TV. We often chatted about music videos, and occasionally played foosball. The late-night gang was friendly and repeatedly enticed me to join them. I must have appeared square, because I had no interest in their bathroom activities.

Not that I heeded my parents' warnings! Weighing on my mind was the exorbitant tuition I knew they were paying for my school, so I felt obligated to excel and study hard. The Intifada had matured me. Life had a meaning, and a goal. I felt on a mission. Those American kids could smoke and drink and do drugs, but I had no time for that. I was not against having fun, but did not feel I needed those crutches to have fun. In contrast, I thought the American kids were interested in those distractions because they had nothing serious to occupy their time, no goal in life to focus their attention.

Was it guilt?

I couldn't say I felt guilty for escaping Danny's fate or that of my classmates. Indeed, I was thankful. Perhaps I was guilty that I was thankful. Yes. That was it. I was safely in America while my friends in Palestine constantly faced danger. I had no scars to show, no embedded bullets in my bones, and no beatings to boast. I had never seen the inside of an Israeli jail, nor was I on the run. Moreover, I did not want any of those things. Leaving felt like abandoning the struggle for which my friends had endured their tribulations.

Then again, I wasn't the only one refusing to join the Cranberry Hills troublemakers. Those who had to work to afford the school found no time for such luxuries. Slava delivered newspapers in the dorms every morning. One holiday when he went home for a week, I did the rounds on his behalf, carrying the heavy stack of the Detroit Free Press up flights of stairs, down hallways, and around corners. The bra pages in the Sears ads fascinated me. Nothing as explicit is printed in Palestine. In addition to my lack of experience, my interaction with girls suffered from the same hurdles as making friends in general. Mostly, though, I was not in a stable place in my life. I thought my stay there was temporary. In less than a year, I was to go to college, returning to Palestine eventually. I couldn't see the point of starting anything.

Early on, I became disillusioned with my physics teacher, Mr. Wigner. My lab partner, the Iranian-American Yasmine, and I worked meticulously on the first lab experiment, carefully detailing our measurements. At the end of class, he looked at our result, and immediately accused us of making the numbers up.

"This is too good to be true, real data has random errors."

There was no discussion, no chance to be heard. "Zero!" Something had to be done!

Seething with the sense of injustice, Yasmine and I hatched our revenge plan. The next lab, we pretended to go through the experiment, but made up our own numbers, according to what we expected from the equations in the book, then added "random" errors. Checking our results, Mr. Wigner fingered his red beard while he examined the data over the top of his glasses. "Hmmm, this looks reasonable. I see errors. Good," giving us a full grade! Seeing how that worked, we continued that practice for the rest of the year. We did the experiments anyways for our own edification, but wanted the added laugh at his expense, wondering if he'd ever notice.

Notwithstanding the enormous reading load, I came to enjoy my English literature class, thanks to the creative teaching of Mr. Linden. He held outdoor classes in fine weather. Sometimes he took us to the amphitheater to re-enact plays, making literature come to life. I learned to better appreciate the texts I read, looking at them from multiple perspectives. I was not used to this style of immersive education, even the arrangement of desks in a discussion circle was a rarity in Ramallah. Knowing I came from Palestine, Mr. Linden once invited me to a panel discussion on the Middle East at a church he was involved in. The panel featured a Palestinian, an Israeli, and an American speaker. I felt compelled to challenge the Israeli speaker when he opened with "Israel took control of the Territories when the Arab countries attacked it in 1967." From everything I'd read, it was Israel that launched the first strike, decimating Egypt's air force with a massive bombing campaign. Moot point, perhaps, but I couldn't stand the injury to Truth. I pointed this out in the Q&A, starting a debate. A few months in America taught me to be more assertive, and not fear expressing my opinion. Truth demands champions.

I chatted often with Mr. Kourosh when he did night watch at our dorm. A Jewish Iranian-American, he was naturally interested in the

Middle East. He invited me to discuss my experiences in Palestine with his current affairs class. I was not sure what to expect. As the questions landed, it was clear that the students' knowledge about Palestine came from a different perspective. The Israeli point of view was prevalent. I briefly narrated what I went through, and that got the class thinking and talking. I appreciated the fact that students could express their opinions in a respectful environment, and was impressed with their open-mindedness and willingness to listen. The experience helped me understand what American kids thought.

Not everyone was so open-minded. At my first school convocation, I met Rob, who wore an Israeli Army T-shirt and was certain we were the "bad guys". From the moment he learned of my place of origin, he kept taunting me and loudly assuring me that Israel "was going to win". Little did he know about me, other than I was "the new Palestinian". All I wanted was to be left alone. I did not wish any arguments, and cared less for what he thought. In the end, I found the best strategy was to ignore him and not take the bait.

My history class took a field trip to downtown Detroit. After driving by the walled and guarded mansions of Grosse Pointe, our van exited the insulated freeway onto what looked like a war zone: entire blocks of boarded up and graffitied houses; giant holes punched into the sooty brick walls of abandoned warehouses. My suburban classmates, who grew up hearing whispers to "lock your car doors" in downtown and to avoid certain neighborhoods, had not seen such a place before. Though in Palestine my family was considered economically better off, we lived but two blocks from the refugee camp, which I sometimes took for a shortcut to school.

Most people conceive of Hell as a hot place. One winter in Michigan is sufficient to shake that conviction, particularly the winter of 1989-1990, which registered as the coldest in 20 years. My coat exhausted its usefulness by October, prompting me to buy a heavier one. By November, the October coat proved inadequate, and I had to upgrade once more. For two months (November to January), the temperature barely rose to

0°F, during the day. It was too cold to do anything outside, except walk from the door to the bus and back. It was even too cold to snow, apart from a clingy thin layer that fell in early November and refused to melt. In between classes, I nestled in the warmth of the school library, where I found a more diverse selection of books than anywhere in Ramallah.

The school had two campuses, the other one housing the girls' dormitories. Each campus had its own cafeteria, but on weekends the school ran only one cafeteria, and stopped running the buses. It was fine for the kids who had cars, but once the temperatures dropped, I stopped bothering to go to the other campus. The mile walk in the wind chill was not worth it, while hitching rides was the luck of the draw. Later, Slava showed me a shortcut by walking over a frozen lake. I had never imagined one could walk on a lake, and was hesitant at first.

As a vegetarian, I found little to eat in the cafeterias. Cheese pizza on pizza nights was the best treat, otherwise, it's over-boiled mushy vegetables with zero protein. The only other food option without a car was a canteen in the dorm selling candy bars and such, or pizza delivery, which involved waiting outside in the cold for longer than comfortable. Hence, I starved myself to sleep many a night rather than break my self-imposed prohibition on eating meat.

The school had assigned me a host family – the parents of a Palestinian-American kid in my class, Tom. They invited me to their place on occasions, where we enjoyed the Michigan games and played cards. Unfortunately, Tom wasn't in any of my classes, and since he lived home with his parents, we interacted little, until years later, when we lived in the same dorm in college. I also visited Aunt Amelia, my parents' cousin, who lived in the Detroit suburbs, staying at her place on vacations when the dormitory closed. She had several married children, whose kids were closer to my age. The family was welcoming and fun-loving, often getting together at someone's house for food, music, and dancing. My parents visited in December for the legwork to establish the business, then in March, my mother came back with Basman to officially launch the enterprise.

It was a busy year. I took my SATs, filled out applications for college, and, once I turned seventeen, began driving lessons. I could not believe the ease of getting a driver's license in America, compared to Occupied Palestine, where people needed over 30 hours of instruction with a teacher, and often failed the test. By the end of the year, I was driving, though I did not get my own car.

The year went by fast. Although Cranberry Hills was an enjoyable experience and a calm, serene, and peaceful time in my life, I longed to go back to Ramallah and reconnect with my old friends. I stayed a couple of weeks in Michigan afterwards, attending graduation parties and hanging out at my parents' store. Ultimately, boredom and homesickness drove me back.

Home Again

After spending a year in Michigan, my first impression upon seeing the coastline of Palestine was how *yellow* it looked. I had imagined Palestine as green as ever, but Michigan readjusted my color scale. Besides, it was July, and plants were getting dry after a month of no rain. The music of Umm Kalthoum wafted from the Hills with the Faces, her undulating voice hugging the rolling landscape. Maybe it was the car radio.

The Intifada was in full force. The half days of work, the strike days, the protests and shootings changed little. Adnan was making more trips to Nazareth, and I accompanied him on some. I tried driving in Ramallah. The narrow, crooked, roads were unlike the easy avenues of Michigan, and the car – a battered automatic – stalled up the steeper slopes. I was taken by surprise when someone beeped me for stopping at a stop sign. Having lived without police for three years, few cared for traffic laws. Especially after my experience in the USA, it felt like living in an anarchy – a real working anarchy.

My friends were still taking classes. Somehow the school sped them through and now they were in their senior year. Visiting the Friends School, I saw Veronica walking side-by-side with Shadi (this was before his stint in Europe). Abdul-Jabbar confirmed the two were seen together all the time. It was an interesting vignette into what life could've been like for me, had I stayed. It also rid me of any lingering interest in Veronica, which I had maintained largely as an excuse not to venture and meet girls.

By early August, my classmates finished school and had to take the dreaded *Tawjihi* exams. Upon their completion, we had a big celebration at Veronica's house that the whole class attended. That was to be our last time all together. About half the class ended up going abroad to study, mostly to America or Jordan. It took them months to get moving, as they still needed to take SATs, apply to colleges, and get visas. They could not take those steps earlier because of the uncertainty of their graduation date. Besides, they needed the *Tawjihi* exam scores, which turned out to be a fiasco. Because of purported arbitrary grade reductions, only 56% of students in Ramallah passed, my former classmates doing rather poorly.

Like myself, Rasheed and Archie had their US visas rejected the first time, but ended up going eventually. Maya and Wasel were luckier in getting theirs right away. Abdul-Jabbar and Waheed, on the other hand, attended Birzeit University, in the eponymous town 15 minutes from Ramallah. It had finally re-opened, secretly at first. Abdul-Lateef was the only one unconcerned with politics. He was still listening to Beastie Boys and dreaming of going to the States. While applying to American colleges, he signed up to study Hebrew at the Hebrew University in Jerusalem – "a different world", in his words. He was shocked at the abundance of beautiful girls from different nationalities, but could not communicate with them well, yet. Eventually, he did end up in America. I ran into Hameedo, my soccer captain, on a visit in 1993. He operated a food stall on the street, and was happy to see me back in town. Sadly, I was warned to avoid him because he had become a "bird", i.e. an Israeli agent.

It was the last time I saw Wasel, who stayed in America after his studies and never returned. I had also lost touch with Tigran since he moved to the school in Jerusalem. We finally met, 20 years later, in Southern California. Shareef, I was not so lucky to see again. In the early 1990s, he was out at sea in California, in a small boat with his cousins. He drowned rescuing everyone else when the boat capsized. I like to sometimes think he is hiding somewhere, like Elvis, the tragic story a mere cover.

Seeking the latest mysteries of *The Five Adventurers* before the summer was over, I was happily on my way down Main Street to *al-Quds* bookstore, when a vacant absence confronted me in its place. Demolished! Found only rubble in the corner on Main Street where it stood, the wall of the neighboring store shorn bare. Apparently, the bookstore's owner was accused of selling banned books. I paused, not knowing where else to go. A bookstore? What harm had the bookstore done for its death sentence? Among the debris, I sensed a rupture in the fabric that connected me to my past.

News of the peace negotiations was not encouraging. Amid a news stream riddled with talk of "Transfer", we heard of Israel's acceptance of elections to select our negotiators in the West Bank and Gaza, but with conditions. Israel insisted on excluding East Jerusalem, and reserved the power to bar any candidate it deemed affiliated with the PLO. In other words, the promised elections were to be anything but fair and free. We wanted the basic right to choose our own representatives without outside interference.

Meanwhile, with the fall of the Soviet Union, Israel was looking to attract Soviet Jews, presumably to bolster its "Jewish character". The government set a goal of one million new immigrants, obtrusive considering Israel's population of five million. While obstructing and delaying negotiations with us, the Israelis were busy preparing the ground for this influx. Israel negotiated a deal with the US government to restrict immigration of Soviet Jews to the USA, while loosening Israeli immigration laws for Soviet citizens to such a degree that non-Jews were immigrating. Unable to come to America directly, some used Israel as a stepping stone to get out of Russia, then eventually move to America. I met several individuals in the States who arrived that way in the 1990s. To this day, I also run into Russian "Jews" at the Orthodox Christian holy sites in Jerusalem, where they worship.

Michigan

In late August, I started at the University of Michigan, Ann Arbor. I became close friends with three freshmen who lived in my hallway in the dorm: Yesef, Moses, and Mikey. We often rode the bus together to our Engineering classes. Yesef's room was next door to mine. A Sephardic Jew from Venezuela, he had no problems befriending a Palestinian. We didn't talk much politics, but when we did, I found him open-minded and surprisingly critical of Israeli policies. Though I explained how we had no voice, no representation, no vote, and hence no peaceful means of effecting change, he somehow could not understand why we threw stones, seeing that as "violence." He played chess well, so we played regularly.

Moses, from New Mexico, lived right across from my room, and was such a practical joker, our freshman year wouldn't have been the same without him. He once moved Yesef's bed to the lobby. Another time he tied the doorknobs of Yesef's room and mine together, locking us inside. We had to call Mikey to help us out. Mikey was the more serious of the gang. An Italian-American music student, his violin was the most familiar sound on our side of the hallway. After he bought a computer, and games, his room became our favorite hangout. The four of us often stayed up late and screamed out the windows at 4 AM. In the second term, another student, Hyung, moved to the room next to Moses. As could be seen from his yearbook, he was the only non-white in his high school class in Colorado. We all appreciated Michigan's diversity.

That first year at U-M, my family's application for immigration to Canada was accepted. My parents moved to an apartment across the border in Windsor. I found the US-Canada border a breeze, completely unlike the Bridge to Jordan. One summer, I stayed in Canada and crossed the border daily to USA. All I had to do was show my documents and answer routine questions: "Where are you going? "Where will you be staying?" "How long have you been away?" The Canadians rarely looked at my passport, but were more interested in what I was carrying, as some Canadians chose to shop across the border to escape the higher Canadian sales tax. As long as I answered quickly and with confidence, I was fine. Deepening the contrast with the confounded "Bridge", I could show up any time of day or night, cross multiple times per day, if I wanted, and in my own car.

Re-entry to the US was painless too, except for one period in the aftermath of the 1991 Gulf War. Security was tightened at border crossings, and they scrutinized us more thoroughly. On my way back from a short visit, a US immigration officer denied me entry, explaining that my travel document needed to be valid for the next six months. Renewing my Israeli travel document required sending it to the embassy, and a month or two of background checks, after which I needed a new US visa from the consulate in Toronto. Trouble is, I had final exams to take in just a few days. Thankfully, the next day Tom's father – my host family at Cranberry Hills and an immigration lawyer – met me at the Detroit-Windsor tunnel. Within minutes, I was issued an I-94 card stamped "Entry for Humanitarian Reasons", so I could take my finals while renewing the documents. The six-month rule and these renewals shortened the useful life of my Israeli travel document to a little over a year.

The first semester at Michigan boded a good start – a new life. I was living on my own. I made new friends, and was looking to meet girls. I was doing well in my graduate courses. Ann Arbor being a fascinating place, I had much to look forward to.

I found a campus in turmoil. The administration was attempting to impose a new "Code for Student Conduct", and introduce an armed police force on campus. Protests and sit-ins erupted across campus, under the heading "No Guns! No Cops! No Code!" I walked one night through a tent city erected on the lawn of the President's house. It looked like a scene from the 1960s, complete with joints being passed around. There, I ran into a group of graduate students setting up a tent for Palestinian rights, under the banner Palestine Solidarity and Aid (PSA). Their flyers advertised an annual walkathon for Palestine in Ann Arbor. Blake was Scottish, studying literature and active in the student government. Fatima, Algerian, studied international law. Rachel, by her own definition "a total WASP", studied Near Eastern history. Later, they introduced me to Peter, now studying Engineering at U-M, whom I recognized from the Friends School in Ramallah. There, he was two years my senior, belonging to the same dabkeh traditional dancing group as my friends Sajid and Shadi.

The student movement succeeded in stopping the dreaded policy, for the time being. The University waited a few years until the students involved had graduated, then quietly introducing the cops, guns, and code.

By the end of my first semester, the focus of student activists had shifted to the impending Gulf War. Throughout the 1980s, the War between Iraq and Iran was a daily fixture in the news. While draining Iranian and Iraqi lives by the thousands, no one else in the world seemed to care. I didn't understand, therefore, what the fuss was about when Iraq invaded Kuwait in the summer of 1990. This was different, because the US intervened. The Cold War was over, and a new enemy was needed to keep the "defense" industries afloat. The Gulf War was to be a show of force baptizing a "new world order" in which America is boss. Over the months leading to the war, I listened with dropped jaw to the absurdities in GH Bush's speeches: inflating Iraq's power as the "4th largest army in the world," portraying Saddam as Hitler, and suggesting Saddam was going to invade the entire Middle East. Promulgating fear, those arguments took advantage of an American audience unfamiliar with the outside world. Drunk on the image of America's "greatness", few Americans bothered to keep abreast of world events, lending the majority to manipulation by unscrupulous leaders. Somehow, the war was portrayed as an attack on Saddam, when in reality, it was obvious that innocent Iraqis were to bear the brunt of the damages.

The activist network on campus quickly mobilized to protest the war. In addition to nascent e-mail activism, we had calling lists. I was on Peter's, who called to announce an event. I then relayed the message to people on my list. Yesef and I went to the night vigil on the eve of the war, which drew the biggest crowd I'd seen. As the war went on, activists peeled away. Their excuses disappointed me. The *Morally Weak* opted to "rally round the flag", as if the unjust war became just, now that hostilities commenced. The *Unprincipled* opposed the war only because they worried for the safety of American troops, but jumped on the bandwagon when the US was clearly winning. The *Timid,* largely those of Arab backgrounds who grew up under repressive regimes, kept their silence out of fear. The *Cynical* saw protest as a waste of time. The Michigan Winter took care of the rest, as if the war was *timed* for that. My last protest, a march to the Army recruitment office, near the war's end, had only a trickle of participants.

Propaganda against protesters branded us as enemies who preferred to see American troops die. Among the counter-protesters, waving yellow ribbons and American flags, were the ROTC recruits who populated the other side of my hallway in the dorm. Soon enough, hateful messages surfaced on my door, instructing me to "go home", and taunting me about Israel. My close friends stood by me. Mikey's immigrant parents were no strangers to the "go home!" sentiment, neither was Moses, who was proud of his indigenous Hispanic heritage. Yesef was himself outspoken against the war. Buoyed by my friends' support, I initially ignored the messages, kept wiping them off. At the same time, I was getting tired of it and applied to a few Canadian universities, if the US was going to be so unwelcoming.

Eventually, I felt I had to report the harassment to the University. The student in charge of our floor, after meeting with me and other students individually, organized a house meeting to discuss our feelings with regards the war. Some of the ROTC kids voiced their worries about people they knew fighting over there. That was an opportunity for myself and others to stress that we cared about the safety of their friends and relatives, and that we opposed the war because we didn't want anyone getting hurt for bogus reasons. The exchange was educational, and the hateful messages stopped. With the academic year over, I moved to a different dorm – on North Campus, closer to my classes.

Meanwhile in Palestine, during the buildup to the war, Israel distributed gas masks for fear of an Iraqi chemical attack, but only to its citizens. By January 1990, Palestinians in the West Bank and Gaza hadn't gotten any masks, feeling, as the war ticked nearer, that they were being used as human shields. My brothers Hakeem and Adnan packed up and, with their families, took one of the last flights to America, before Israel imposed a 40-day curfew on the West Bank.

Activism took the biggest hit from the war. The more protests one attended, the more despondent one felt, convinced at the futility of protest in stopping the oil-hungry American machine from waging war. The following year witnessed an utter lack of activism on campus. Even the *Michiganensian Yearbook* complained, declaring 1991-1992 a 'Year of Apathy'.

The apathy spread to me. Feeling that protests accomplished nothing more than self-therapy, chanting the slogans while shivering in the cold, I concentrated on my classes. I became interested in computers: how they work, how the chips are fabricated, how to program them, and how to use them to solve problems.

I made new friends on North Campus, most notably Will and Leroy. Will was of the sort too intelligent for his own good. He liked to debate complex philosophical ideas with me, but when it came to finishing his term papers, he spent hours pondering the deepest of dilemmas: whether or not to begin. Alcohol didn't help. I've seen him down a case of beer by himself in an evening. His Plan A was to inherit from his wealthy grandfather. Leroy was the more disciplined one. Older than us, he was paying his way intermittently through college, on his own, while working every other term to afford the tuition payments. His motto was "work hard, party hard," and in *that* order, he thankfully taught me.

SAMAR

At a meeting of the tiny remnant of Palestine activists, in a corner of the Tap Room at the Michigan Union, I was introduced to Gabriel, a faculty member originally from Lebanon, who had a serious proposal for us. If I recall, Peter, Blake, Fatima, and Rachel from PSA were all there, as well as a new guy introduced to me as Ayman (technically pronounced *aye-man*, but he went through childhood in Canada being called *eh-man*). Gabriel wanted to form a new student organization to promote Arab culture on campus. With the demise of political activism after the Gulf War, our best shot at bringing political awareness to our causes was to mingle with Americans on a personal level. Share our culture, food, and music. Gabriel had a name ready: "Society of American Arabs" (SAMAR), and volunteered himself to be faculty advisor.

The organization took shape over a few meetings. Bylaws were drafted. A charismatic new political science student, the second-generation Lebanese-American Chrissy, was nominated and elected Chair. Putting his expertise to use, Peter organized a *dabkeh* dancing troupe, which I ended up joining along with Ayman, Rachel, and Chrissy. It was fun. We met weekly to practice, after which we went out for drinks. Peter had an endless stream of jokes, and the company was evenly mixed between men and women. When we could, we staged performances on campus, typically in one of the dorms.

In the beginning, SAMAR held meetings at Gabriel's apartment. By the fall of 1992, we had grown. Leena, a Lebanese-American newcomer to the *dabkeh* troupe, ended up dating Peter for a while. Waseem, I knew from Engineering. Though in his 40s, he was still an undergraduate, as years of his life were trapped in a Palestinian refugee camp amid the Lebanese Civil War. I marvel how that experience never robbed him of his gentleness and sense of humor. Josie, an Egyptian-American, quickly became the worker bee of the group. She was meticulous and conscientious, and as a result was trusted more than anyone to get things done. Zaid meanwhile, whose family escaped the war in Lebanon when he was little, became SAMAR's resident joker. In my Middle East history class, he presented himself as an intelligent young man who asked the tough questions. With us, he was transformed. From pranks, to telling on people, to stirring endless arguments on the mailing list, he managed to get under everyone's skin.

One of the new recruits was Abdul-Azeem, a Syrian-American whose parents escaped that country's purges of Muslim fundamentalists in the 1970s. He considered himself, it seemed, more Muslim than Arab. We welcomed him to the group nevertheless. By that time, Gabriel had revealed to us, in a meeting, that he was "gay". It raised a few eyebrows at the time, because such things weren't admitted openly, especially in Arab circles. Most of us who knew Gabriel couldn't care less. He was a visionary in founding this organization and we were proud of him.

On US Elections night, 1992, Gabriel invited us to gather at his place to watch the results. We made predictions and chatted the night along while votes were tallied. The topic of the Gulf War came up, and Abdul-Azeem suddenly, out of the blue, said something like "What's worse for the Iraqis than getting bombed, is that they're getting bombed by gays." The room fell into an instant silence. We knew that Gabriel wasn't going to waste this chance to come out again. Peter and I hid our about-to-burst-laughing faces behind the large coffee-table books we were browsing. The rest waited breathlessly for Abdul-Azeem's shocked reaction. Abdul-Azeem didn't linger for long after stammering his way through an apology.

While active in SAMAR, I was also involved with Engineering organizations, and hanging out with American friends. Swept up gambling nights with Mikey and Hyung, Euchre nights with Leroy, and drinking nights with Will. That, and working hard on my classes, taking on more credits, so I could finish faster. I was still out of luck with women, though now I did have female friends and was able to overcome my shyness.

Living in a different culture separated me from myself. At times I felt like two individuals. I grappled with reconciling my new self with what I used to be. I am neither here, nor there. Neither fully American, nor fully Palestinian. I feel at home in either culture, but not completely. The rest of my years in America tell the story of that dance on the thin line of division, the story of my struggle to forge my unique identity.

Which cultural elements to retain, and which to replace? American culture prizes individual achievement and success. Independence is valued over getting along. Arabic culture, meanwhile, prizes the group, like the family or circle of friends, to which identity is attached. For years, I teetered between asserting my individuality and melding into the pack. At times I split, being part of the group with my Arabic friends, stressing my uniqueness with my American ones. This split only strained me with the restlessness of belonging nowhere.

I dreamed of assimilating into American culture while remaining inherently Arabic. My first decade in America, however, was not conducive to such innocent ideals. Events – the Gulf War, the "terrorism" label, sanctions on Iraq, movies demonizing Arabs, and the embassy bombings – rippled like earthquakes under the cultural bridge I was building. The rift was getting wider, my adaptability at capacity. By the end of the decade I questioned: "Do I have to detest my Arabic heritage to be fully American? Or should I instead withdraw from American society and cling to my 'Arabness', like most Arab immigrants do, my brothers included?"

Perhaps my Palestinian experience helped develop my spiritual fortitude. I lived in constant instability, as if I never were at home. Going to the USA, leaving home, living in a dorm. Always thinking about returning, but moving ever further away, entrenching myself into a life of transience and motion. From one dorm to another, to various relatives' places, sharing an apartment with my brother, moving to a different town in search of work.

I existed in a temporary state. Somehow, sometime, I would return. Eventually, I learned that the stability of "home" was the temporary illusion, movement being the underlying truth. Every time I returned to my parent's house in Ramallah, it was not the same. Ramallah itself has changed beyond recognition from the town of my childhood years. If I ever go back, it won't be a return to a place I've known; rather a migration to a new, unfamiliar, place. Had I never moved, I still would have experienced the changes, as if I was traveling.

People the world over preserve memories of their childhood, if only in photo albums, and care to see familiar places the way they used to be. This gives them a sense of security, predictability, and a meaning for life. In Palestine, an entire generation experienced complete dislocation within one year. My parents were thus transplanted elsewhere. The insecurity and dissonance this has created is beyond what many can fathom. But the process did not end with 1948. It has continued and continues to this day. My own generation was transplanted by yet another cataclysm, while back home, the place was changing to resemble a foreign country. Living far from home, with little hope of returning to what we left, the sense of dislocation grew more familiar, as if exile had become our home.

At some point I matured. Gradually, I abandoned the idea of going "back" anywhere. The pressures for movement have convinced me that my lack of a fixed abode is only an epitome for the exile of spirit we all experience. Life is fleeting, stability illusory – that is the thing all human beings have in common. People can believe they live in a place they call home. People can wish a particular state of affairs be permanent. People can attempt to grasp a particular moment and hold on to it forever. As the COVID pandemic has taught us, that will never happen. Things always change. People always move, in time if not in space. So, even if Ramallah never changed, I did.

In the spiritual journey, we are all travelers. All existence is temporary. "Where I lay my head is home," says the Metallica song. With this point of view, I learned to value the present. No longer do I dwell on memories, wishing to experience the taste again. Reminiscences are only that. The future generates no fear. It will be as it will be. In this long journey, the here and now is what matters. I can come and I can go, it is all the same. I must accept this transience. One day, in the end, I will go back to a permanent home.

10

Settlement

WHILE THE WORLD IN THE 1990s looked to a *settlement* of the conflict, Israel rapidly expanded its so-called *"settlements"* on what remained of Palestinian land. During my visit in the summer of 1993, I got to fully appreciate the magnitude of what are more accurately called "stolenments".

My life was at a critical juncture. I had completed my undergraduate studies in just three years and needed to decide what to do with my life. The rapid completion exhausted me. Though several graduate schools made offers, without US citizenship or a green card, I got few job interviews. I decided to attend graduate school in engineering, but was left with lingering doubts. Did I make the right choice? Would my US education be useful to me upon my return to Palestine?

My involvement with student organizations also occupied considerable time. I had been elected Chair of SAMAR. Already before the new academic year began, however, I was getting discouraged by the seething tensions and animosities plaguing the group. So far, I had tried to stay out of them, but as Chair, I could no longer dodge the issues. I had not been back to Palestine in years and it seemed like a good idea to visit.

June 1993 was also a critical time for Palestine. Odor of an impending peace deal had surfaced, under the name of "Gaza and Jericho First". The details were unknown at the time, leaving ample room for speculation. So, in addition to my personal reasons, I was on a mission: to get back in touch with Palestine and find out what was going on, with the eye of a reporter, taking extensive notes.

Return to the Unknown

The plane ride gave me time to reflect on the events and places I left behind, and to anticipate this second encounter with my country since my departure. So much changed in my own life in those three years, I wondered what enormous changes must have befallen Palestine and everyone else there.

After an eight-hour flight, an eight-hour layover in Amsterdam, and another five-hour flight, I finally touched down in Tel Aviv, late at night. The usual searches and interrogations amounted to little. In Amsterdam, they asked a few questions and quickly ruffled through the bags. In Tel Aviv, they did not even open any! The questions they asked were ordinary: "Who packed your bags?" "Did anybody give you anything?" Quickly and seemingly miraculously, I found myself outside the airport, heading on my way to Jerusalem, in the car of Hakeem's in-laws, the Bakers, who lived in Jerusalem and hence had the coveted yellow license plates.

The major change since my last visit was Israel's "Closure" policy. The checkpoints at the West Bank borders became permanent, requiring additional permits to cross. Since Israel considered East Jerusalem part of it, the city became out of reach. Knowing the scarcity of those permits, I decided to first spend a few days in Jerusalem. My strategy, exploiting a "loophole" in the Closure system for Palestinians flying to Tel Aviv, worked throughout the 1990s. Technically, I could be arrested if caught in Jerusalem without a permit. Still, I thought it was worth the risk, for I did not know when, or if, I could get one. Many Palestinians who worked in Jerusalem had to be smuggled into the city every day. Inevitably, they would get caught, as happened to my cousin Jameel. He had taught at the same school for years before the Closure was imposed. All of a sudden, through no fault of his, he had to enter Jerusalem stealthily to earn his living. When they finally caught him, he spent three days in detention at the "Russian" jail near the New Gate.

Early next morning, I surveyed Jerusalem from my hotel room window. Little changed, apart from a new major road cutting through its center (at the dividing line between East and West). After lunch with the Bakers, one of their sons, also named Hakeem, took me on a walking tour of the Old City. Since it was a strike day, everything was closed except for the holy places and the gift shops. We wandered through the narrow alleys, finding our way to the Holy Sepulchre Church, then to the *al-Haram al-Sharif* area housing the Dome of the Rock and the Aqsa Mosque. Surprisingly, it was my first time to visit those architectural gems from Islam's first century, some 1300 years ago. The Muslims had police stationed at the door to enforce strict visitation rules, a result of the repeated attempts by Jewish extremists to destroy the historic mosques and build the "Third Temple" on their ruins. Tourists were allowed during limited hours, from a specific entrance. At first, I was mistaken for an American tourist, and had to talk to them in Arabic to clear myself. Luckily, they did not ask for ID. On the way back, in the middle of the Old City's Muslim quarter, we passed "Sharon's House", a house recently purchased by Ariel Sharon, an Israeli minister widely regarded a war criminal. He did not live there, but the large Israeli flag covering its side and the large number of soldiers stationed underneath pressed the point. Hakeem quickly led me into a side alley to avoid an encounter with them.

That evening, the Bakers held an impromptu party on their roof garden. Their family had grown quite a bit, but their house was unchanged since 1967. Though they desperately needed space, they were afraid to expand it. The adult children couldn't move out, either, because there were no units available in Jerusalem, not for Palestinians anyway. Israel placed severe restrictions on Arab construction in East Jerusalem. Building or expanding a house required an impossible-to-get permit from the Israeli city council. At the same time, "unauthorized" construction was subject to demolition, a penalty Israel had executed in hundreds of cases, sometimes on a 24-hour notice. The Bakers coped by turning their roof into a hospitable roof garden that functions as a living space without walls, so it would not be considered an addition and bring the whole house down. They grew vines to keep out the chill and provide privacy, and added a swing, chairs, tables, and a fountain. It was comfy, and we stayed well into the night, eating and drinking, playing music, smoking *Arghileh*, drinking coffee, and playing poker.

The next day, I strolled along Salah-al-Din Street, the major thoroughfare in East Jerusalem. The strike over, it was livelier than the previous day, but the city was deserted compared to the way I remembered it. Because of its size and central location, Jerusalem attracted West Bankers for shopping or employment. Losing this traffic with the Closure, the Palestinian part of the city was effectively cut off, economically strangled. With the building restrictions, East Jerusalem had completely stagnated.

That afternoon, I headed to Ramallah, where a strike was observed for the martyrdom of a resident the day before. I found the city outwardly the same as when I had left it three years earlier, except for new construction activity that surprised me. Several new high-rises modified the skyline. *Na'oum's Restaurant* – a landmark – was torn down to make way for a new office building. Plots of land were rumored to sell for then unheard-of sums. Compared to what I was to witness in future visits, the construction I noticed in 1993 was the tip of the iceberg. It felt significant after the freeze of the 1980s and the six years of Intifada. The Ramallah of my youth was never to return.

My friend Chrissy, from SAMAR, was spending the summer in Ramallah to study Arabic at Birzeit University. Though her father was born to Lebanese immigrants, she grew up in an Anglo environment, so liked to rediscover her Arabic heritage. The moment I arrived home, she called to ask for help finding a place to stay, as the Birzeit student housing (at the Alhambra Palace Hotel) had not yet opened for the summer. My parents invited her to stay at our place for a few days. In the evening, I went with my sister Sandra to pick her up from Birzeit, where she was attending a conference on Palestine. On a narrow Birzeit street lined with parked cars on both sides, I slowed down to squeeze the car through. Not easy with the driver of the car behind me beeping impatiently, then rolling down the window to verbally harass me.

Chrissy liked Ramallah. She yearned to climb on the terraced hills we passed on the way back from Birzeit. Seeing a flock of sheep crossing the street, she commented: "This is so Holy-Landish". Little did we know that this Biblical landscape, unchanged for millennia, would soon come under assault.

The following day was not a strike day. I walked to town, and on the street encountered Waheed, then Hameedo, then Rasheed (back on a summer visit from Ohio). I found the city alive and thriving again. Restaurants such as *al-Bardouny, Rukab*, and the *Muntazah* park, which were completely closed at the start of the Intifada, now opened till 10 PM. The Closure of Jerusalem made Ramallah busier, and there was talk of Ramallah becoming the capital of a future Palestinian state.

This one day of bliss was not to last. The next day was a strike day again. Three of my first four days were general strikes! I took the opportunity to relax, welcome visitors, and see friends. I saw Danny who somehow was no longer on the "WANTED" list. He quietly painted houses for a living. The following days, I saw all of my classmates. We gathered in small groups periodically at peoples' houses, usually at Rasheed's, or Waheed's. Sometimes we hung out at the Scouts Club, which had opened a garden café. It was a good way to run into other guys from Ramallah. Two weeks into my visit, Archie arrived back from California.

Friends who stayed were attending Birzeit University. With all the closures, the average classmate was two years behind me. I rode with Abdul-Jabbar, who was studying economics there, for a visit. I found the campus tiny by American standards (only 2400 students), and self-contained. Separate buildings surrounding a central courtyard housed each of the colleges. It looked well-planned relative to the haphazard architectural styles everywhere else in the West Bank. Students knew each other and hung out in the courtyard between classes.

All the employees, from cafeteria personnel to professors, were on strike because they were months behind in receiving their salaries, due to Birzeit's shaky financial situation. Incidentally, when I visited again in 2004, it was the exact same story, employee strikes for unpaid salaries. Chrissy had spent three hours registering for classes even though the line was short. The system was disorganized and everyone took their time. Then, she had difficulties getting into the student housing, though she had pre-registered. While walking in Birzeit's courtyard, I met Tanya, who was studying business. We chatted for a bit. She had gotten 1st place in the *Tawjihi* exam. I thought she was looking good.

Demise of the Intifada?

Despite the prevalence of strike days, I did not witness the usual confrontations between the soldiers and the *shabab*. By my sixth day in Ramallah, nothing had happened yet: no protests, stone-throwing, shooting, or anything of the sort. Regular business hours were now extended to 3 PM. Even on strike days, people left their homes and travelled about, and roads were no longer barricaded. Graffiti multiplied as few bothered to erase it. Few soldiers were stationed in Ramallah, although many could be seen in Jerusalem, where daily confrontations were commonplace. Without the soldiers, Ramallah had the feel of an Arab city in, say, Jordan or Egypt. Despite the soldiers' occasional re-appearance, and despite the travel restrictions, regulations, and taxes, Israel's presence in our everyday lives seemed minimal. At the time, I felt it was the closest experience to a free Palestinian State.

In retrospect, the Israeli policy of withdrawing the army from the city centers was a more efficient way of controlling us. Whether it was a goodwill gesture for the peace negotiations, or simply motivated by tactical reasons, the redeployment put a damper on protests. The first protest in Ramallah took place on my seventh day in town. Chrissy came back flushed and out of breath from a trip to the post office.

"I almost got shot!"

She heard shooting, so hid in a store until things subsided. I immediately recalled Zaid predicting this reaction from her. Her American experience had not prepared her for the streets of Ramallah.

The next evening, we heard sirens and some activity on a nearby street. It turned out a car failed to stop at the soldiers' order. The soldiers shot at the car, killing one and wounding another. Instant execution for failure to respond to a police order. Naturally, the following day was a strike day. Friday, I witnessed large protests, as in the old days, with the smell of burnt tires and the sound of gunfire. Saturday was another strike, this one called by Hamas, to commemorate the deportation of 400+ Palestinians last December.

With all the strike days, I quickly slipped into my pattern of irregular sleep. I stayed up late at night, reading or writing, sometimes until dawn, then woke up as late as mid-afternoon. Other times I awoke with the morning *adhan*.

About halfway during my stay, I went to town on a particularly tense day. The soldiers were stopping young men and lining them up facing the wall across from *Rukab's Ice Cream*. Apparently, a protest had just ended. I kept to the other side of the street, and they left me alone. When I reached the *Sound of Music* record store, a group of kids nearby, 10-12 years old, were gathering stones. They were surrounded on all sides and had nowhere to run, but what did I know? The rules of the game had changed. Three years earlier, I would have turned back, but that day, despite the imminent confrontation, no one turned back and stores remained open. Suddenly, I understood the words of Gabriel, a survivor himself of the Lebanese Civil War, who recommended I visit Ramallah "so you won't lose your ability to survive!"

I hurriedly bought two tapes from the *Sound of Music*. (They only sold tapes as the CD player was yet unknown here.) The kids backed out of their plans and dispersed. I walked back past *Rukab's*, on the other side of the street. The soldiers were still there, having stopped more "guys" than before. They left me alone, perhaps taking me for an American. People were coming and going as if nothing was happening! In fact, it was the busiest day I had seen.

A few nights later, we heard continuous shooting for minutes. Dad said sometimes soldiers did that when they were patrolling a dangerous area. They shot in the air to scare off attacks.

Occupation by Roads

One day, I went to visit Abdul-Jabbar in his home village of Ein Sinia, north of Ramallah. We wandered among the fruit trees in the terraces of his uncle's village house. The village air was pure, the night quiet and beautiful. The stars were glorious. His family was welcoming.

On the way back, I passed by the stolenment of Beth El. It had grown bigger than Ramallah, and was alive, with plentiful water and electricity. The stolenments were hungry for lands to expand and multiply. With its quest to absorb one million Soviet Jews, Israel needed a $10 billion loan, equivalent to one fourth of its state budget. Citing the stolenments, the US refused to guarantee the loan, toppling Israel's intransigent Likud government. The new Labor government, led by Yitzhak Rabin, secured the loan guarantees by promising to halt stolenment construction. Rabin then diverted the funds to the largest-ever road construction project in the West Bank. The new "bypass" roads connected the stolenments directly while avoiding Palestinian towns and villages, making it safer and more attractive to prospective settlers.

The old roads traced the natural contours of the landscape, winding through towns and villages on the way. Many evolved from historic roads and trails, dating back to Roman times, or earlier. They left the bulk of the landscape untouched, free to be plowed and planted, filled with olive groves, or admired in its natural beauty. The Israeli administration left the old roads to rot. Potholed and partially caved in, I thought the Birzeit-Ramallah road unfit for driving. I took Chrissy on a short drive to Rafat, the village I reached with my bike. Barely fitting one car, with no shoulder, the two-way road was riddled with bumps and ditches. I had to drive half my car off the road to let opposing cars through. In contrast, the Tirah and Batn-el-Hawa roads at the outskirts of Ramallah, both of which were shared by the settlers, were well-paved, well-marked, and wide. The Jerusalem-Tel Aviv road, on which I came from the airport, was better than any roads I had seen in the States. Preposterous to drive on potholed roads in Michigan, then see taxes I paid to the US government subsidizing these luxury roads for Israelis.

Like the Ben Shemen road to Tel Aviv that bypassed Latrun, initially we thought these new roads shortened distances and simplified travel. At first, there were no restrictions on who could drive on them. Gradually over the 1990s, however, the Closure system ensured that these new highways were off-limits to cars with West Bank license plates, and to Palestinian passengers without permits. The roads became segregated, in place to serve the Israeli settler population.

The new roads cut through hills, took away agricultural land, and segmented the West Bank into tiny Palestinian islands. Riding along them in 1993, I imagined myself a tourist on his first visit, knowing little about this place. I searched hard to find any traces of Palestinian presence from the perspective of a "bypass" road. All I saw were Israeli stolenments, signs in Hebrew, and wide-open tracts of undeveloped hills and wilderness. The millions of Palestinians, the vast majority inhabiting the West Bank, disappeared.

The newest road to Tel Aviv was shorter, wider, straighter and better paved. The segment running through Upper and Lower Beit 'Ur was relocated to brush the stolenment of Beth Horon, leaving the Palestinian villages obscured by hills. How can a tourist driving through know that there is, and has always been, an Arab village called Beit 'Ur? Not knowing Beit 'Ur, how can they doubt that the new Beth Horon is the same Beth Horon mentioned in the Bible? Beit 'Ur's cactus-bordered fields are no longer visible, and the smell of the *tabun* oven has disappeared. Beth Horon, a vacant field a decade earlier, now appears a thriving city extant for decades, with nice stone villas, verdant parks and flowing water. The American tourist returns to a dilapidated Detroit or Los Angeles, singing the praises of Israeli ingenuity, little knowing the cost of "development" to Palestinians, to the tourist as a US taxpayer, and to the Land.

Having depended on through traffic, the economies of the Beit 'Urs and other bypassed villages collapsed. Villagers migrated to Ramallah and other cities. With this trend widespread throughout the West Bank, its population rapidly became urbanized, to the detriment of the environment.

After seeing Beth El that day, I reflected on the peace negotiations. What was it that made our negotiators so optimistic about getting our Palestinian state within the 1967 borders? I did not see the Israelis ready to dismantle the stolenments. Having invested untold billions into the stolenment project, Israel was spending another $10 billion on roads to connect them. Without their dismantlement, the best we could hope for was to have our government on small, disjoined islands, no different than Native American reservations. East Jerusalem appeared more remote. We were being denied access to it even as the negotiations were ongoing. It seemed Israel was working hard to predetermine the outcome of any peace talks with a *fait accompli*.

Intermezzo

When I was a child, my parents used the same word "settlement" to describe both the stolenments inside the West Bank and the Jewish cities in other parts of Palestine, like Petah Tiqwa, Hadera, or Netanya. It was not illogical. For my parents, the two kinds of projects served one and the same purpose.

The "settlement movement" predated the British Mandate, let alone Israel's founding. It aimed to establish a dominant Jewish presence in Palestine by constructing a network of *exclusive* urban and agricultural nuclei to absorb the growing numbers of Jewish immigrants. The segregated sites inhibited the immigrants' possible integration with Palestine's existing population. The sites were strategically selected: in agriculturally rich areas; commanding a hilltop or a major road; or threatening a Palestinian city. My parents witnessed how these strategic locations were used to encircle our communities and eventually evict us in 1948. Israel then seized the emptied lands for new stolenments to absorb further waves of immigrants.

After 1967, Israel hastened to extend the stolenment policy to the newly-conquered lands, never mind that international law forbade such population movements. The earliest action was to expand Jerusalem's boundaries, constructing stolenments north and south of the city to isolate it from Ramallah and Bethlehem. The new stolenments served the same goals as earlier Zionist ones: absorbing immigrants, solidifying control, and changing the character of the Land (to make it look like it was, and had always been, a "Jewish state").

With an Egyptian peace deal beckoning, the late 1970s saw a spurt in stolenment construction. The five-year interim period specified in the Camp David Accords, after which the status of the West Bank and Gaza was to be decided, was Israel's opportunity to create "facts on the ground", thus obstructing the return of any land. This pattern of accelerated stolenment construction while engaged in peace negotiations was to continue. By 1993, at the start of the Oslo "Peace Process", the total number of "settlers" was close to 200,000. By 1999, just before the Peace Process broke down, the total number of settlers doubled to 400,000 (with half living in the expanded East Jerusalem).

In America, free from Israeli censorship, I was exposed to a universe of books and material about Palestine's history. I read voraciously to make up for the dearth of material in Occupied Palestine. What I learned was alarming.

Dubious legal machinations were invented to usurp land for the stolenments. A military order closes off a piece of land "for security reasons", preventing its Palestinian owners from using it. Considering it "abandoned property", the Israelis return a few years later to confiscate it under another "law", with no compensation. Or, false witnesses, appearing masked in court, dispute the ownership of a plot of land. Daily intimidation, threats, and pressure are applied to recalcitrant Palestinians who refuse to give in. According to the Israeli peace group B'Tselem, by 2010 the stolenments controlled 42% of the land area of the West Bank, not counting areas controlled by military bases, the Wall, and border zones. Like their predecessors along the Coast, Israeli stolenments in the West Bank are exclusive communities open only to members of a certain religion.

The eastbound traffic of prefabricated homes was a prominent feature of my road trips in the 1980s, when long-term planning for stolenment construction became the norm, under the aegis of then "Housing" Minister, Ariel Sharon. "Housing projects" is a favored euphemism that disguises the stolenments' exclusivity and illegality. Sharon instituted the "Seven-Star Plan", which involved strategically-located sites and government subsidies to attract Israelis to settle. Nowadays, stolenments are mistakenly imagined as ideologically-driven projects, populated by ultra-religious inhabitants at odds with the government. In reality, the largest (such as Ma'ale Adumim, Ariel, Gilo, or Modi'in Ilit) are secular, government-planned metropolises that are best described as strategic. Ma'ale Adumim and Gilo, along with West Jerusalem and Pisgat Ze'ev, encircle East Jerusalem to entrench Israeli control over the city. Ariel extends a "finger" into the northern West Bank, splintering it into pieces. Modi'in Ilit, on the water-rich western slopes, assures Israel a foothold over the coveted aquifers. These government-approved stolenment "blocs" are sold as "suburbs" of Jerusalem, Tel Aviv, or Netanya, connected by wide, direct roads and offering subsidized housing.

These "blocs" pre-empt any peace agreement that leads to a viable Palestinian state, by ensuring continued Israeli control over critical issues: Jerusalem, water, and roads. Moreover, the stolenments project planted a constituency in Israel that would vehemently oppose giving up their privileges, and champion continued Occupation. New immigrants are routinely placed into stolenments or border towns in the North. The "frontier" aspect, with its accompanying insecurities and fears, further develops their mistrust of Palestinians.

Considering how stolenment activity was used to displace us in 1948, like other Palestinians, I felt threatened by their growing presence. From the road, each appears a highly-fortified installation, complete with a fence, minefields, and soldiers at the gate. The layout is defensive, buildings often encircling a hilltop, like wagons around a campfire, with a tall observation tower in the middle. Sizes vary. Some pack a maximum number of people in high-rises designed to change the demographic balance. Others have nice villas to attract individual settlers to unlikely places. Some like Psagot, on a hilltop overlooking Ramallah, or Beth El, sealing Ramallah's northern border, function as military encampments extending Israel's control over us.

Changing the Map

In early August, I attended a class reunion at Abdul-Jabbar's place in Ein Sinia. It was a smaller gathering, half the class being away. I carpooled with Archie and Shadi. Sajid followed us with Waheed and Rasheed. The girls drove separately. The reunion came only days after Shadi's release from jail. Soon as we arrived, the guards at the gate (for Abed's father was a high-profile politician) asked to see our IDs. We automatically complied, not giving it a second-thought. Letting us in, they held Shadi for "questioning", trading gibberish over their walkie-talkies. While we wondered what was going on, Shadi looked paler by the minute. Then out came Abed, laughing at his set-up.

Upon the second car's arrival, they tried pulling the same prank on Sajid, who had also spent time in Israeli prisons. He would not take it, arguing heatedly with them. He was here to see his friend and they had no business stopping him. Horseplay aside, we had a fun afternoon in the fields, grilling kebab, and reconnecting.

Veronica couldn't attend because she had just delivered her first child. News of her marriage had reached me in the States. Still, while I was used to my older siblings having children, having a former classmate become a mother was sobering. My female friends in America had no plans for marriage or children within the next five years; the male friends – not in ten years (although Moses did ultimately start a family earlier).

On the way back, we passed Beth El again, its barbed-wire electrified fence underscoring their insecurity. Zionist settlers were a minority in Palestine before 1948, as they are in the West Bank today. Culturally, the land they invaded was not a vacuum but had its own traditions, names, and character, developed over millennia of continuous habitation. To succeed, the Zionist movement needed to assert its own connection to the land, imprinting its ideology on the landscape – a Biblical Israel that continues uninterrupted to this day, on a land otherwise empty. Thus, the Palestinian villages that were evacuated in 1948 were not left to stand, but destroyed, their sites overturned and often replanted with forests. Roads were diverted from our ancient villages so they would become forgotten.

The landscape modification began with the names on the map, as continuing to use native place names would acknowledge the indigenous rights they wanted to suppress. As early as I could read, I noticed the road signs to "Yafo" and "Lod", for what my parents called Yafa and Lydd. Likewise, every place name was consciously replaced, in a process that originated well before Zionism. In Western travel accounts from the 19th century and into the 1930s, I encountered maps of Palestine divided into regions corresponding to the "12 tribes of Israel". Their geographical references are hard to follow, as there are no place markers welcoming you to "Ephraim" or "Dan". Yet those writers persisted in describing Palestine in terms of this mythical landscape.

With Israeli dominance over the land, this imaginary map began to be imposed over the physical landscape. New cities were founded to replace the destroyed Palestinian places. New place names were invented, like Herzliyya (named after Theodore Herzl, the founder of Zionism). Commonly though, the new cities were named after the Palestinian places they replaced, with a Hebrew, Biblical-sounding twist. Yibna morphed to Yavne, Beit Dajan to Beth Dagon, and Jimzo to Gimzo. Street names were changed, natural features renamed. Ironically, the Biblical names they chose were of earlier, Canaanite origin, as the Book of Joshua admits in lists of "existing villages" at the time of his invasion.

In the West Bank, Palestinian villages remain extant, leading to the absurd situation of two adjacent urban areas with similar names. Ma'ale Michmash assumes the name of Mikhmas, Beth El of Beitin, Rimonim of Rammun, Geva Benyamin of Jaba'a, and Giv'on of al-Jib, to name a few in the Ramallah area. The ancient Palestinian villages have vanished – a virtual destruction – as roads are shifted to the new places. The stolenments are a cornerstone of this project of geographic identity theft, since they create a network of new references to the landscape.

The West Bank, included within Israel's borders on Israeli maps, is referred to as *"Yehuda ve Shomron"* (Judea and Samaria) in weather reports. Ultimately, the new map makes it look as if Israelis have always been there, supporting (in a circular argument) their claim to the land. The tourist or new immigrant can relish learning the new place names and feeling a connection with early Jewish history, never mind that the names themselves are modern inventions.

Stuck in Ramallah

After a month in Ramallah during the summer of 1993, I badly wanted to go to Jerusalem. Sandra applied for permits – hers was granted, mine rejected. While we were confined to the West Bank, settlers and Israelis, some recent immigrants, could cross that imaginary border freely.

Confined to Ramallah, I turned to borrowing from Hakeem's library. I kept busy practicing *dabkeh* with the Sharaf dance troupe, at the Islamic Club in the old city. Having had only basic dabkeh training in Michigan, I struggled to keep up, but the group was gracious. I recognized almost-familiar faces among the members – turned out they were the younger brothers of my classmates Faris, Shareef, and Rasheed.

Finally, the Bakers invited us to a party at their house in Jerusalem, permit or no permit. Their son came to pick me up. Just before the checkpoint, we exited, driving around it via several alleys and unpaved roads. The Closure was easy to circumvent, a statement that rang less true with each successive visit.

I managed one day to finally wake up early enough for getting my application for a travel document stamped. Outside the Israeli Military Governor's, the short line was dwarfed by a disorderly crowd piled at the gate. I stood in the line behind a bearded man (the mustache-less Islamic beard). Like me, he was unhappy about people jumping the line, and repeatedly called on them to line up with us. They did so, but only after an army patrol arrived, scolding the crowd through loudspeakers. The soldiers even hit a few of those who delayed in complying. Strangely, I was inwardly happy. I wondered about the cause and effect. Our disorganization makes it easier to control us, while giving them the added pleasure of "civilizing" us, feeding their stereotypes about us as uncouth Bedouins. We cannot expect Israelis to respect us if we, Palestinians, fail to respect each other.

After standing in line for some time, I was let through the gate, where soldiers searched me and took my travel document. I then stepped into a medium-sized courtyard. A diverse group of people filled the benches, waiting for admission through the second door. I found an open seat in the shade next to a villager with a white beard and furrowed face. He had been waiting for hours. The guards changed several times, then took a lunch break at 1 PM and stopped calling names altogether, frustrating us further.

After three hours in the yard, my name was called. The soldier at the door looked at my paperwork and sent me back, claiming I needed to exchange the travel document for the actual ID card, at another office, before they accepted my application.

This made no sense, since all I wanted was a stamp on the application, which was destined for that other office anyways. I had waited so long. Can't they take it? He wouldn't budge, and threatened to kick me out as I reasoned with him. I left the place swearing at them. Luckily, I did not get hurt.

Sandra decided to intervene. She knew Hebrew. Sure enough, she was back with my stamped application in about 30 minutes. She had bypassed the inside line and gone directly to the second door. That's how I wasted my whole day for a piece of paper.

Demise of the Intifada!

By the beginning of August, business hours were to be extended till 5 PM! "The Intifada is over", everyone was saying. Monday morning, flyers were distributed by the "ten factions" calling for a strike Tuesday in solidarity with Lebanon, even though the fighting in Lebanon had ended days earlier. Nevertheless, it seemed the strike was to be implemented, as the organizers were among the more militant factions, opposed to the peace negotiations.

Thursday was the first day stores actually opened till 5 PM. About 7 PM, I was at the Islamic Club with the dabkeh group practicing, when we heard army loudspeakers declaring a curfew over Ramallah, "until further notice". My father sent someone with the car to pick me up. There were few soldiers in the city, so people were slow in responding, in contrast with the stringent curfews of my past experience: a wedding took place with car horns and everything; people still walked the streets that evening; and cars still drove, though off the main roads.

That night Army helicopters with searchlights could be spotted.

Someone had abducted an Israeli soldier near the old city. The soldier's colleagues shot at the getaway car, but it escaped. They chased it, later finding the car in Beitunia, all burnt, with the soldier inside. We finally heard a few shots, saw army cars and searchlights near the old city, and noticed ambulances passing by.

After spending a month in Ramallah in 1993, I came to appreciate the importance of rules in a society. Throughout the early years of the Intifada, a community spirit prevented internal conflicts and degeneration into lawlessness. That spirit had deteriorated. People took unfair advantage of the situation. The strong enforced their own laws on the weak, sometimes in the name of "patriotism". Without police or a working court system, the stronger side was compensated in a dispute, regardless of fault.

A relative of mine, George, an elderly, respected science teacher, had an accident that left him injured and badly damaged his car. It was the fault of the taxicab that hit him, which emerged virtually unscathed. Yet the taxi driver and his gang jumped out, severely beat George and forced him to pay for the damage of the taxicab!

Signaling an impending deal, the underground PLO factions had now surfaced as political parties to run in elections. Once banned "terrorist organizations", I saw the offices and newspaper ads for the Democratic Front (DFLP) and the Communists. People I talked to disliked the plethora of parties and "factionalization". At the Intifada's start, all were united under QAWM. Now, each faction called its own strikes without coordination. Not to be cynical, but perhaps Israel was counting on our penchant to disorganize: freedom to organize meant more splinters, disagreements, and divisions among us.

Our terrible strike policy was a prime example. It became a competition between factions to see who could get more people to comply. The self-interest of the faction for gaining limited political power prevailed over the interests of the people. I bluffed my way through a defense of strikes to Chrissy, but actually had no idea why people were still practicing them. Do the Israelis even want our businesses open? Are we defying anyone other than ourselves? Have we truly *helped* the Lebanese by *striking* in solidarity? Everyone complained about the economy. They blamed everything for it: Israel, the weather, taxes, ..., *everything but strikes*. Their denial irked me. How could business be conducted when stores were closed over 10 business days a month and opened for only half a day the rest of the time?! Education, too, suffered, as evidenced by how quickly I completed my degree compared to my classmates. Sinking our own economy with the strikes, we were making it likely that we'd sign any bad deal to get out of the mess.

Permit Granted

The last two weeks of the summer, I finally got a Jerusalem permit. It was valid for only three days. I could not stay overnight. I could not take our car either – that needed a separate permit. The only way to go was with a tour bus or a taxi. The Closure benefited the taxi drivers from Jerusalem, who became indispensable for transportation in this fragmented land. I decided to make the best of it and spend those three days outside of Ramallah.

The first day, I shared a cab to Jerusalem. It dropped me off at *Bab el-Khalil* (Jaffa gate) in the Old City. The Old City looked similar to how I remembered it from childhood. It was one of the few places in this country that survived the waves of change, remaining the same for what seemed like eternity. Narrow paved streets and alleys, frequent steps, sometimes covered. Stores huddled on each side: souvenir shops; tiny restaurants; colorful displays of sweets; spice shops exuding the muffled fragrance of cardamom, cloves, cumin, oregano, and rosemary. Swarms of people of all nationalities and languages: foreign tourists, Muslims, Hasidic Jews, Armenians, Greeks, Russians, Ethiopians. A scene reminiscent of old Islamic *suqs*, Jerusalem remains a living history book, open for everyone to read.

Omar's Mosque still stood next to the Church of the Holy Sepulchre, reminding us of his guarantee of freedom of worship for Palestinian Christians. It is said that Caliph Omar was visiting the Church of the Holy Sepulchre when time came for the Muslim prayers. The bishop offered him to pray in the church. Respecting its value as a Christian holy site, the Caliph refused to do so, praying outside at the spot later to become Omar's Mosque. Omar also restored the site of the Jewish Temple to a place of worship, after centuries of neglect following the Temple's destruction by the Romans in 70 AD, and annulled the Roman ban on Jews living in Jerusalem. Such religious tolerance was unusual for its time.

Leaving the church, I headed for the Haram al-Sharif mosque area, finding my way instinctively through an Armenian jewelry suq to the Muslim quarter. I passed Sharon's house. With that huge Israeli flag, it looked out of place. At one of the Haram gates, an Israeli policeman checked my ID and permit. Quickly, I was on the vast grounds of the Haram. I admired the Dome of the Rock's spectacular mosaics and inscriptions. It was my first time to enter it, leaving my shoes and camera at the door. I entered the Aqsa mosque next. The inscriptions and lighting were superb, but what enchanted me was its quiet and serenity, amplified by the miles of Persian rugs covering the floor. The outside world disappeared as I stepped into the silent coolness. Scores of people lay on the floor in deep sleep or meditation. Were they mystics seeking inspiration, or simply homeless persons seeking shelter in God's house? Outside, the vast treed courtyard had a still, peaceful air that invited refuge from the turbulence just beyond the gates.

The next day, I woke up at 5 AM so I could get to Jerusalem in time for a bus tour to Masada, where I joined a group of elderly Italian tourists. Our guide was an Israeli Palestinian from Galilee. We went on the road to Jericho, down to the Dead Sea, then drove south along its shore to Masada, about halfway to Eilat. The roads were in excellent condition. I was struck by the number of stolenments alongside. Most prominent was Ma'ale Adumim, which only a few years ago was barely visible from the main road. Now it had expanded into an immense city overlooking a long stretch of the Jericho highway. All I saw along my trip were desert cliffs, Israeli stolenments, and Bedouin tents! This is what appears of Palestinians to tourists: Bedouins, a point that has not been missed by Israeli propagandists. Although Bedouins constitute less than 5% of our population, their nomadic lifestyle makes them convenient for supporting the fabricated Zionist claims that Palestinians have moved here from neighboring countries, and only recently.

In a primitive chatroom running on the University of Michigan's mainframe computer (still running in the early 1990s), I had met Hannah. Upon learning I was Palestinian, she announced herself as "Jewish", but excitedly added she had met a Palestinian in Beersheba, on her recent trip to Israel. He had offered 80 camels as a "price" to marry her. She ended with the loaded question of whether I thought the price was right! Where do I begin? Educate her that we don't buy and sell people? Or that the Bedouins of Beersheba are hardly typical Palestinians? That no one I knew even owned a camel?

Her trip was organized by a program called Birthright Israel. I've seen their tables at student events, sometimes offering camel rides, and promising a "Free Trip to Israel!" to Jewish American kids. Later I got inside information from activists who had formerly gone through the program. The kids get to take a thrill ride on a Merkava tank at a military

175

camp, while being indoctrinated on how the tiny Israel is surrounded by enemies, and how the survival of Jews worldwide is dependent on Israel's military power. The mandatory stop to meet "the Palestinians" in Beersheba is part of the stagecraft. The image is reinforced by masking the real Palestinians from the rest of the world, closing our cities, isolating us with checkpoints, so visitors to "Israel" don't see us.

Masada, built on a mesa in the southern desert, was the last stronghold of the Zealots during the Jewish revolt against the Romans, c. 70 AD. When in 73 AD the Romans crushed the revolt and were about to capture Masada using a ramp, the story – historically-disputed – is that the Zealots committed mass suicide rather than surrender to the Romans.

What struck me was the care with which the Israelis resurrected this piece of history. Sites associated with Jewish history are better-preserved and better-presented. Archaeological digs focus narrowly on the few hundred years of Jewish rule, to the detriment of other layers and sites that are comparatively neglected. Palestine's rich history is condensed to a single layer. We cannot expect Israel to champion our history. That's our job, and I ask myself, what have we done? Walking through Jerusalem's markets, I encountered rows of Palestinian shops shamelessly selling offensive pro-Israeli propaganda. Among the racks of T-shirts I found ones in many colors with the logo of Israel's Occupation Army, the "IDF". Another boasted, never mind the pun: "I was stoned in Ramallah, Bethlehem, Jericho, …" I wondered if the storeowners were simply illiterate, or didn't care?

On the way back from Masada, I thought of our present besieged situation, the Israeli Romans surrounding us. How did we respond? Enter surrender negotiations? Settle for a tiny part, when all of Palestine was ours? Go for "Gaza and Jericho First", instead of "Jerusalem First"?!

Circle Tour

On the third and final day of my permit, I longed to go somewhere far, like the Galilee. My father rented a Jerusalem cab for the tour. In my diary from that day, I referred to that area as "Israel". Amazing how quickly I bought into their terminology, simply because I now needed a permit to visit parts of my own country. Perhaps the major purpose of the Closure was to limit our horizons and restrict our aspirations. We would not demand what we could not grasp.

Along the Beitunia road, I had my encounter with Beth Horon. We joined the freeway at Ben Shemen, then took the first exit, just before the airport. The road heads straight north to Hadera (which replaced al-Khdeirah). Alongside the road from Hadera to Nazareth (via Fureidis and Zichron Ya'acov), we passed new construction. We could see cactus plants everywhere, last remnants of the obliterated Palestinian presence.

Two hours after leaving Ramallah, we arrived in Nazareth, entering the city through its southern suburbs. Nazareth had grown substantially in the last three years. It is similar to Ramallah: an Arab Palestinian town, built on hilltops, with like climate and terrain. The larger Nazareth, however, was buzzing with activity. It took us a long time to reach the old city because of traffic jams. The sidewalks were likewise packed. With Nazareth both a tourist site and an administrative center, the city is said to be visited daily by a number of people comparable to its population!

I predicted Ramallah would look similar if the political situation was better. In Nazareth, stores opened all day, roads leading to the countryside were excellent, and a police force left no room for lawlessness. We walked inside the old city, visiting my father's old business contacts. Their businesses were running well, possibly better than our store in Michigan. The Church of the Annunciation was closed, so we headed towards Mary's Well to meet my Michigan friend Rachel, who was working in Nazareth that summer.

After a brief visit, we were on our way to Akka. We passed Shafa 'Amr, a large Arab town. The road signs all pointed instead to Shfar'am, the Hebraized name. As I surveyed the Coast, I thought of the paradox in claiming history as "justification" for the modern Israel. Whereas the Biblical Israel was rooted in the hills, in the West Bank and Galilee, early Zionist settlement favored the coastal plains, where modern Israel was ultimately founded.

Akka's population in 1948 was totally Arab, so the city was slated to be part of the Arab state in the UN partition plan. Nowadays, the city has a large Jewish majority, after Zionists from the surrounding "settlements" – like Nahariyya – had invaded it and expelled its Palestinian population to Lebanon.

As soon as we approached Akka, we smelled the sea's salty odor. With Michigan mid-country, this was the first time in years I had seen the sea. We headed for a store in the old city owned by an old business contact of my father, Yosi. His father immigrated from Bulgaria in the early 20th century. ("Penniless," my dad later elucidated – an addition evocative of lingering resentment over the home he had lost in Ramleh.) Later, Yosi came to own a store in old Akka, and another and a villa in Nahariyya. He was friendly with influential people on both sides, yet my impression was that he was an ardent Zionist. His son, like most Israelis of his generation, served during the war in Lebanon. During the Intifada, Yosi advised my dad to emigrate. Today, when we asked him whether <u>he</u> would leave the country, he answered jovially: "No way!" He was too happy here to leave for America.

Yosi invited us to lunch at an Arab-owned restaurant next door, in a renovated building in old Akka. The interior decoration was stunning! Inside, the place looked stylish and not at all what you'd expect from an old city. The wall-hangings and domes reminded us of the actual setting in old Akka. The food was great, "better than Na'oum". I wondered: had Akka remained Arab, would it have been preserved and presented so nicely?

After lunch, we headed to Haifa, passing through the old "settlements" built to surround Haifa and Akka. Shortly, we reached Haifa through the industrial zone and saw the oil refinery and the "check post" interchange. Haifa is a relatively new city, which developed rapidly after the British designated it Palestine's primary port. Its population was mixed, with about half Jewish in 1946. We passed through the old city: the train station, the harbor, and alongside old Palestinian houses. Most of those houses are now inhabited by Jewish Israelis, after their original residents were driven to Lebanon in 1948. We could tell those houses from the architectural style. Palestinians used stone construction whereas Jewish colonists from Europe preferred cinderblocks.

After looking at the "lost buildings", we ascended Mt. Carmel. On the lower slopes we passed through stores with Arabic inscriptions, the last remnants of Haifa's Palestinians. The view widened as we ascended further along the maze of narrow streets. Finally, we reached an observation deck near the peak, in an upscale area teeming with hotels, parks, and cafés. That day, the smog and haze limited our view of the coast. Up on Mt. Carmel, it was cooler and less humid than the rest of the city. A light breeze was blowing from the sea, and I wished I could stand there forever, savoring the view. Unfortunately, we had to go.

Enraptured by Haifa's beauty, I dreamed that, one day, I could live on Mt. Carmel. It was easier for me to reach the moon. Focused on a "Palestinian State", our peace negotiators appeared ready to surrender our right to return to our ancestral land on the Coast. We were at Israel's mercy for a permit to visit the city. Meanwhile, anyone from anywhere in the world, claiming Jewish faith, could choose to live in Haifa. Further, this endless stream of immigrants drove up the land prices. Yosi was telling us that a house on the upper slopes of Mt. Carmel was more expensive than a comparable one in San Francisco.

Descending, we headed along the coast for Tel Aviv and Yafa. We passed the 'Atlit high-security prison, built by the British, and surrounded by cactus to prevent escapes. The Israelis continued using it as a prison, Dad adding that Najm's father was here imprisoned. Caesarea followed, then Netanya and Herzliyya. We drove along the beach in Tel Aviv, stopping near the hotel area for a half-hour swim, my first saltwater one in years. We were the only Palestinians there.

Next, we navigated Yafa's familiar streets to the old city. Emptied of its people in 1948, this part of Yafa was renovated into a tourist attraction, with restaurants, stores, plazas, an amphitheater, and gardens. Now it is an "artist colony", a landmark, a scenic spot where couples take their wedding photographs. I asked Dad to take me to my mother's house (or the ruins of it), but he said it was too far to the south, and we had little time left before my permit expired.

So we headed back to Ramallah through Ramleh, where we searched for Dad's house. It was not easy, as the roads had changed. Finally, we found it still standing, in good condition. It was my first time there. I wondered how he must be feeling, unable to enter his childhood home, his memories locked inside. Dad then took me to see my grandfather's orange orchard. The wide stretch of land was divided among adjacent "moshavs" – the Israeli agricultural collectives farming our lands. Seeing all that was lost, Dad got depressed, recalling his own father's fateful visit in 1967.

Jerusalem, Again

Jerusalem is a drug. The next day after my permit expired, I was back at the Military Governor's to apply for a new one. I felt I did not get enough of the city. When it was freely open us, I did not care much about going there. Now that it was out of reach, there was little I desired more than seeing Jerusalem. I had to go through the waiting exercise all over again. In the inner courtyard, the soldiers held a stack of ID cards from which they called us in turn. For fun, or simply to irritate us, every once in a while they shuffled the stack like a deck of cards. After only two hours of waiting, I was called in to meet Captain Ilan. I was expecting a bearded, middle-aged soldier. Instead, I was greeted by a young, clean-shaven man, no more than twenty-five years old.

Captain Ilan asked in a perfect American accent:

"Why do you want to go to Jerusalem?"

The question, so natural from his point of view, took me completely by surprise. Why should I need a reason to visit my birthplace?

"I was born there and like to visit," I replied.

He examined my travel document for a few moments, asking me about the stamped "exit permit" for departure the following week. Where was I headed? What was I doing overseas? He seemed unconvinced. I waited outside for the decision, discouraged by his added scrutiny. Called to the door again, I was handed a permit, valid for three months, no less.

The next day, a Friday, I shared a taxi to Jerusalem with Chrissy. We were held at the checkpoint behind a long line of cars. With all the waiting to get permits, then waiting enroute, the tax on our time further hurt our productivity. Slowly we crawled, while private cars with yellow license plates whizzed by in their dedicated lane. The soldiers checked my ID and permit, but not Chrissy's American passport – she just waved it at them.

Jerusalem was heavily crowded because of the Friday prayers, so we followed side alleys through the Christian Quarter to get to the Church of the Holy Sepulchre, then shopped through the suqs on our way to the Haram. Chrissy was refused entry at the Haram gates, for only Muslims were allowed on Fridays. The owner of a store nearby offered to dress her in an Islamic *Hijab* scarf, then take us inside and tour us the mosque, for 100 shekels. Thinking to pull it off myself, I rejected his offer. We went to a different gate, with mostly Israeli policemen on guard, and found another store where she bought a scarf (for 20 shekels). The one Palestinian guard asked whether we were Muslims. "Yes," I replied in Arabic, claiming she was my cousin, but having grown up in the States knew no Arabic. That flew, and we were in. I had no qualms about breaking rules because *nothing* could be done in that place without breaking rules.

We exited the mosque near Bab-el-Asbat (Lion's Gate). Instead of returning by the normal route, we opted for adventure by walking atop the city walls. A designated path followed the contours of the wall, up and down, with frequent turns and corners. One side looked outward, through narrow, defensive slits, towards the Mount of Olives and East Jerusalem. The other side overlooked the domed rooftops of the old city, as picturesque as in 19th century drawings. Our trek was interrupted by defensive towers and gates, over which we climbed. Although the wall path was more wearying than the shortcut through city streets, I savored the adventure, and the glimpses it afforded us of Jerusalem's history.

At a hotel where we stopped for refreshments, we stumbled on a Muslim wedding party. It was gender-segregated. The women occupied the mezzanine level of the hotel, where no men were allowed except for the groom. The men stayed on the lobby level. The hotel hired female servers for the day to afford complete privacy for the women, and had an audio system installed to relay the music of the live band from downstairs. The cultural transformation amused me. I recalled another Muslim wedding I attended in the mid-1980s that had completely mixed company, and where women wore revealing fashions. Now, gender segregation became the norm. Suddenly, it seemed, everyone became a religious fundamentalist?! I suspected many wore religion outwardly out of fear of Hamas, or what others might say. The silent peer pressure again. No one wanting to appear different.

In Ramallah the next day, I tried going to the Friends' School. I walked as far as the *Manarah*, but a protest suddenly lit up, stones flying, tires burning, and soldiers shooting. The streets were crowded with pedestrians, so I could not see the soldiers' or the *shabab's* positions. I turned around and walked back normally through the roundabout way along el-Bireh's *Hisbeh* and the Qaddura refugee camp.

Sunday, I returned to Jerusalem, where Abdul-Jabbar took me to visit the Orient House, a historic building that served as the British Mandate headquarters in Palestine. In the 1980s, it was operated as the Arab Studies Society, and by the early 1990s, it served as the headquarters for the Palestinian negotiating team. There, I had friendly exchanges with Sa'eb 'Erekat and Hanan Ashrawi from the Palestinian delegation. Ashrawi asked about my brother Hakeem, whom she had taught at Birzeit.

A Vision to End the Conflict
The circle tour instilled in me the feeling that our ancestral land was along the Coast, destined to fall outside the narrow perimeters of the "State" our leaders were negotiating. Why should I forever be forbidden to rebuild on my grandfather's land? Meanwhile, the historic Jewish connection to Biblical sites centered on the West Bank. It seemed to me that a two-state solution, what all the leaders were pushing on us as the "only option", was one that nobody really wanted. It did not work in 1947, so what made us expect it to work any better in 1993? Did we struggle for a half a century, only to go back to the same antiquated ideas?

It was then, weary with those thoughts, that I dreamed of a more wholesome vision for the region. Two people sharing a single country, with equal rights. Every person free to live wherever they choose, and travel as they please, without restriction. In America, I experienced a functioning society where people of all nationalities live and work together, the diversity adding to the country's strength. If I can get along well with my Jewish friends and neighbors and coworkers in the US, then why not over here in Palestine? Is this such an impossibility as everyone pretends?

If all within this unified state are citizens, treated without regard to religion or ethnic origin, does it matter if it's called Israel or Palestine, or what flag it has? One can imagine a constitution protecting the equal rights of all citizens, regardless of who is in the majority; an army and police force open to everyone, perhaps using mixed units to build trust and collegiality; a new immigration policy permitting refugees to return to their homes and rebuild their destroyed villages.

We can expect entrenched interests to vehemently oppose this vision. Ideological Zionists committed to the "purity" of a "Jewish" state will reject it. So will those profiteering from the Occupation, not only the Israeli settlers, developers, and "defense" industries, but even Jerusalem taxi drivers leveraging their yellow license plates, tourist shops selling Israeli propaganda on T-shirts, and cameleers in Beersheba paid to offer young Birthright Israel "tourists" fake "marriage" proposals.

Excepting this thin layer of exploiters, the unified state will benefit individual citizens. Israelis will gain peace of mind, and the ability to live in the West Bank or even in Ramallah, if they so wished. Palestinians wishing so can return to their homes in Haifa and Yafa. A unified state will hopefully stem the population race that has wreaked havoc on the environment and drained land and resources. Everyone will gain a renewed economic prosperity, as billions of person-hours are diverted from conflict to more productive activities.

In hushed notes, my friends shared in this dream, hesitant to publicly utter such heresies. As I prepared to return to America after my longest summer stay in Palestine, Kareem and I recounted with envy the added rights Palestinians with Israeli citizenship had. Foremost was the right to travel, to wander, to go from place to place without interruption. My friend doubted Israel would ever grant us citizenship. I was more doubtful of a two-state solution we could spend a lifetime chasing. My friend and I both forgot that citizenship was not theirs to give, but ours to demand.

II

11

Hopes Of Peace

"WE MUST ADOPT POLITICAL STRATEGIES that show flexibility and practicality by acknowledging facts on the ground."

I turned the convoluted sentence in my head as I sat in the crowded auditorium of my old school in Ramallah. The speaker was a prominent member of the Palestinian delegation to the peace talks. After spending the summer of 1993 in Palestine, I was about to fly back to Michigan to begin graduate school. I cared to stay informed of the situation in Palestine because returning here was one of my options after graduation. How relevant is my US education here? Is there any hope for Peace?

Peace – the promised rain to a land seared by a sweltering sun.

Since becoming aware of the world, I heard talk of "*salam*" – "peace". I was four years old when Sadat visited Jerusalem. For days on end, I despaired for anyone's attention as the whole family huddled around the black-and-white TV set, transfixed at the live speeches. Later, when I overheard President Carter was to drive through Ramallah, I waited by the window all day in hope of catching a glimpse of the motorcade.

The forum at the Friends' School was announced a week earlier, after rumors of an impending peace deal proliferated.

I pondered the phrases again: Flexibility and Practicality, and Facts on the Ground. As if he was telling us, "Forget about returning to our Destroyed Villages along the Coast; the best we could hope for was a state in the West Bank and Gaza." His attitude bothered me. Perhaps he was right. Perhaps our aspirations for justice were unrealistic in a world where Justice wore a straitjacket instead of a blindfold. Still, starting negotiations with such a concession was a capitulation. After all, Israeli stolenments in the West Bank (the so-called "settlements") were also "facts on the ground" that make it "impractical" to recover those lands either. By the same token, we should acknowledge their domain over Jerusalem. Besides, if we accepted today's stolenments, then why not accept the ones to be built tomorrow, or next year, or next decade?

I badly wanted to say something, but the line for asking questions was too long. At least, the packed room boded a hopeful aura of a people wanting to participate in shaping their future.

The whole debate was moot. As we spoke, far away in Norway, the real deal was being conceived, giving birth to what became known as the "Oslo Accords" between Israel and the PLO, or simply "Oslo". While the world was spellbound at the "historic handshake" between Arafat and Rabin on the White House lawn, Palestinians everywhere were searching for copies of the agreement to find out what was in store for us.

The Accords

Past five years of Intifada, the Israelis were weary for a respite after exhausting all attempts at stopping our uprising. The PLO leadership, marginalized after Yasir Arafat's idiotic and immaterial support for Saddam in 1991, sold us the agreement as the first step in establishing a Palestinian state. Israel saw it as ridding themselves of Gaza and the Palestinian population centers, leaving the low-level policing activities to the PLO, so Israel could better concentrate on changing the map with stolenments and "bypass" roads.

This was not a reading revealed gradually after the fact, but one embedded in the text of the Accords. Back in Ann Arbor, I downloaded and read the 1993 Declaration of Principles, and later the 1994 Gaza-Jericho Agreement which focused on Oslo's initial implementation. By then I had become a regular at the Espresso Royale Café on State Street. Here, I often played chess with Blake. Rated a Master at the game, he was a formidable opponent. He was finishing his Ph.D. in English Literature, and had been dating Fatima for a few years. Other times, I played an

Arabic card game "*tarneeb*" (similar to spades), with Waseem, Ayman, and Flora, a new graduate student from Lebanon. In that milieu, Oslo made for heated discussions.

In broad strokes, Oslo defined a five-year transitional ("Interim") period during which Palestinians exercised limited self-rule over selected cities, while a "final status" agreement was to be negotiated. Craving peace as we were, the interim arrangements nevertheless alarmed us:

- Key issues (Jerusalem, borders, stolenments, and refugees) were not to be discussed until the third year.
- Stolenments were to remain under Israeli control. There was no ban or limit on stolenment construction. The agreement explicitly sanctioned building new roads to connect them.
- Israel was to retain full control of the border crossings and defense.
- Notably missing was any discussion of the status of Jerusalem. Nothing restrained the Closure policy Israel had already instituted.
- The Palestinian areas were bound to the same economic policies as Israel, despite substantial qualitative differences between the two economies.

My main concern was the stark imbalance – the benefits to Israel were immediate (stopping the Intifada and shedding Gaza), while the benefits to us were deferred, and pending further negotiation. Israel had little incentive to continue the process to the end. The Interim period, which began May of 1994 after signing the Gaza-Jericho Agreement, was a stalling tactic – a play for time. Without a ban on stolenments, it gave Israel a chance to continue building, laying more "facts" on the actual land, while simultaneously squeezing us out of Jerusalem. With our leaders' "pragmatism", by the end of the five years our bargaining position would have further eroded. Obviously, the PLO leadership did not appreciate the reality, or the magnitude, of the stolenments. From their exile in Tunisia, the numbers of settlers on paper looked reasonably small, a minor issue that could be resolved with a handshake. Our leaders-in-exile had no idea of the spiderweb of new roads rendering us invisible. They little appreciated the impact of Jerusalem's Closure on our lives. To them, Jerusalem was just one of many bullet points to be discussed in good faith when the final status talks commenced.

Resignations from the PLO followed the signing, including prominent personalities like Edward Said and Mahmoud Darwish, the poet who had penned the Declaration of Independence in 1988. Dr. Haidar Abd-el-Shafi, head of the official negotiating delegation, resigned his post after sounding the alarm in a quarter-page ad in *al-Quds* newspaper protesting "secret actions" by the PLO leadership. Oslo squandered the achievements of the Intifada, making it more cost-effective for Israel to maintain its occupation. What was sold as a "withdrawal" of Israeli forces from Palestinian areas was actually called "redeployment". A seemingly slight play on words, "redeployment" left the details of those movements to Israel's discretion. When the Israeli army vacated Ramallah's city center, it kept the military bases just to the south and north, controlling access, ready to re-invade, or enter and arrest people as sanctioned by the agreement.

Among Oslo's far-reaching consequences was the segmentation of the West Bank into areas A, B, and C, destroying the unity and integrity of the land, and legitimizing barriers and closures. Area A – city centers, basically – was under the Palestine Authority's control; Area C under Israeli control; and Area B under joint control. The areas were not contiguous but an intertwined complex maze of islands and disconnected pieces, its borders shifting with each successive interim agreement.

I never understood why have an Interim period at all. Oslo put the emphasis, not on the final peace, but on the Peace "Process", a term giving the illusion that we were getting somewhere. Immediately after Oslo was signed, Jordan and Israel negotiated and signed a final treaty in just two years. Hostilities ended and that was that! Why did we not go into the endgame, like Jordan, and sign the real thing? Why waste such energy negotiating a half-dozen agreements about a transitional period that supposedly had no impact on the final status? Prolonging negotiations with an "interim period" betrayed a lack of desire for peace.

Ultimately, with no shared vision and no guarantees for reaching one, the final status talks failed and the interim period took on a life of its own, leaving Israel in control. In other words, Oslo became the blueprint for making the Occupation permanent, with the West Bank further subdivided.

Meanwhile, the signing ceremony gave us, and the rest of the world, the illusion that the conflict was over. The US government dropped the word "occupied" from its lexicon. The illegal stolenments became merely "obstacles to peace", as Arafat's signature essentially legitimized their existence. Arabic countries and former allies of our cause like India and China reconciled with Israel. Even activists let their guards down, as if the Occupation had ended.

Michigan Again

Back in Michigan, I settled in a cooperative dormitory composed of small houses, some of which had a language/culture program. The University had agreed to SAMAR's proposal to designate one an "Arabic House". Will moved in as my roommate. Zaid moved to the room next-door, and Tom – my "host" from Cranberry Hills – down the hall. Into the kitchen's menu, I introduced several recipes for Arabic dishes, courtesy of my mother, which the other residents relished. The house gave us a venue for holding Arabic language hours and cultural events, such as *dabkeh* shows.

Across the street was the Nichols Arboretum (known as "the Arb"), a park large enough to get lost for an entire day. Will and I frequented it daily, sometimes skipping classes. Leroy, who stayed on North Campus, often joined us. In this laboratory of Nature, we savored Her transformations over the course of the clock and the seasons: the lush green of September shading the late summer heat; bright yellow leaves bathing in the morning sunlight; the quietness that winter's soft powdery blanket bestows. For the first time in my life, I knew Peace.

Already in graduate school and still under 21 years of age, I felt I had missed out on college life by finishing fast. Will, being older, bought alcohol for us. Our house, unfortunately, had been designated "substance-free". Will and I designated our room a "substance-free"-free zone, inviting other house residents. Zaid, next door, could hear the music. Being the clown he was, he couldn't resist teasing us about the partying, hinting he knew about our breaking the substance-free clause. He taunted me especially given my role in SAMAR, dangling his "damaging information". We usually ignored him, but in retrospect, inviting him to one of our parties might have been more effective. Ultimately, Zaid was harmless. He never followed up on his threats and insinuations. Where it counted, he was helpful and dependable.

Besides my classes and research, SAMAR kept me busy. A member drive in September was too successful, quadrupling our size to the point where the officers were spread thin. Suddenly, we had a larger volume of communication to deal with, bigger events, and more energy that somehow, I – as Chair – was supposed to channel. Had we stuck to the original idea of spreading our culture, the group might have stayed manageable. Our approach to activism allowed events overseas to impact our agenda. Our commitment to organize an event in response to every significant happening in Lebanon, Iraq or Palestine meant less time for our classes and personal lives. We added two officers from among the new members to assist with the load, but that ultimately brought trouble. The new officers had a different conception of the group's identity. In my experience with volunteer organizations, every member brings their own agenda, which complicates reaching a common goal.

When Will graduated in December, moving back to the western side of the state, I moved to Leroy's dorm on North Campus. I ended up sharing a bathroom with Finn, from Los Angeles. Let's say I saw Finn reading a book once, towards the end of the semester, when he woke up briefly from his partying stupor to realize he was failing all his classes. I usually joined him in the partying, but only following Leroy's advice: homework first! Consequently, I was acing grad school. Finn introduced me to Nine Inch Nails. Having lived most of my life in a place rife with injustice, I identified with the raw anger on the tracks. Among Finn's friends I became close friends with Roy, who at the time lived on central campus and often had to take the bus back after *Star Trek* ended at 2 AM. Some nights we went through the Arb to the tracks to await the long freight trains from Chicago, their sudden rush piercing the silent brilliance of the snow-covered ground.

By the end of the year, internal divisions broke SAMAR apart. Two factions were evident. The "Arab-American" faction was deeply concerned about US policy in the Middle East, and felt strongly about the group's activism. The "American-Arab" faction did not see the relevance of US foreign policy to their lives, joining primarily to connect to their roots and learn about their heritage. Newer arrivals, those with families and friends still in the home country, could not afford to ignore US foreign policy, so we flocked to the first camp. As did non-Arab Americans supportive of our causes.

This split resurfaces in Arab-American circles. I remember a conversation with a leader of a prominent Arab-American organization in 2003. On the eve of the Iraq War, I asked him privately why his organization wasn't opposing the war. He replied that their surveys show their members care most about anti-Arab discrimination, and less about foreign policy. A leader's job is to lead, not follow, but I spared him the lecture. As long as the US keeps waging wars against Arab countries like Iraq, US soldiers are trained to shoot at Arabs. Their training software spills into the videogame industry, and a whole generation of American kids is raised to shoot at Arabs. My personal safety as an ethnic-Arab in America therefore demands stripping US foreign policy of its anti-Arab, Anti-Muslim bias.

SAMAR continued under Leena's leadership. I withdrew from activism, focusing on my research and my own personal life. For the summer, I shared a house with Yesef (from my freshman year). The last time I hung out with Finn, before he moved back to L.A., was at a Nine Inch Nails concert at the State Theater in Detroit, where I got introduced to Marilyn Manson in the opening act – more raw anger.

Ultimately, the personal friendships forged were SAMAR's most important legacy. I continued hanging out with friends from that circle. Waseem, formerly infatuated with Chrissy, began dating Flora, whereas Leena and Peter broke up. By now, Ayman was dating Josie. Ayman and I, partnering once in *tarneeb* against Josie and Leena, came up with a message passing scheme that gave us a steady advantage in the game. The girls had no idea until we fessed up at the end, having to explain our bouts of laughter. Eventually, Josie and Ayman broke up, and so did Fatima and Blake. None of the romances within the group lasted.

By the end of my second year in graduate school, I became close friends with a new SAMAR member, Sarab. A Palestinian who grew up in Kuwait, she was living a happy and prosperous life, until Iraq suddenly invaded that country. Kuwaiti purges of Palestinians after the war forced her family to escape, where they landed in Canada. Our encounter was ill-timed – a month before her graduation. We stayed in touch briefly upon her return to Quebec, where I visited her twice, but it was clear we had different trajectories. Regardless, I was finally developing the social skills for interacting with the opposite sex that I should have learned a decade earlier, had I grown up in a less repressive place.

1995

By the summer of 1995, I had obtained enough results from my research to write a paper and make my first conference presentation. Computational science was rather new then, and I made an impact probing a decades-old problem with a simple computer model. With three weeks left to the summer, I decided to take a well-deserved vacation. Heading to Palestine, I saw for myself how the Oslo agreement was unfolding. By then, Israel had withdrawn from parts of Gaza and from Jericho, the latter a patch barely eight square miles. I was hoping to run into Sarab, who was visiting her grandparents in Bethlehem, but that did not happen.

En route, the plane detoured around the no-fly zone over Bosnia, where war was raging. My parents met me at Tel Aviv airport, having gotten a rare permit for the car, valid that summer only. At the West Bank's border, my dad had to stop in advance of the checkpoint, then walk there to deliver our papers. On the way to Ramallah, I noticed the high-rises of a large new stolenment under construction (Modi'in Ilit, as it turned out), and more new roads for Israelis. What surprised me was the construction in Ramallah. New buildings had seemingly popped out of nowhere. People here were optimistic about peace, especially with the sense that the city was destined to become the *de facto* capital of Palestine. I wondered how many actually read the text of the agreement.

Expatriates were returning and buying land. Landowners were building in hope of good returns. Foreign aid money flowed in. One of the hills adjacent to our house was completely carved out, as if to accommodate a massive new building, a hotel, we were told. Lost in the rubble were the fig and olive trees that peppered the ancient terraces, ruins of an old house, and a dried-up well. Lost, also, was the landscape of my childhood when that hill was my playground. Perversely, the owner ran out of funds before construction could begin, so a big, gaping hole was left an eyesore disfiguring the scenery.

The Israelis had withdrawn from Ramallah's town center, sealing the main roads into it with 3-ft cubes of concrete, so settlers would not stray into "Area A". As my dad circumvented them via side roads, I hoped those blocks would not become the borders of our state! The PLO were still negotiating a separate agreement before they could enter the city, but Palestinian flags could be seen.

The next day, I walked to town with Sandra, treading carefully as the sidewalks were crusted with construction waste – depleted heaps of sand, powdered stone, and gravel left by crews for the wind to blow into our homes. Traffic was as hectic as ever. On the street, tempers were short and manners in shorter supply. As Ramallah grew, I recognized fewer faces. Less than a tenth of the people on the streets were female. Women who dared to venture into town wore the *hijab*, understandable given how the men ogled a woman without one. The men's reaction was understandable, too, given they hardly saw any women in public. Repression is self-perpetuating.

People were happy to be rid of Israeli soldiers, and eager for the "Oslo police", as we called the PA security forces, to move into Ramallah. They hoped the PA would bring an end to the state of lawlessness I had witnessed on my last visit. Guns were introduced and used in weddings and celebrations, so the sound of gunfire at night now carried a different portent. In this environment, I wondered if the advanced science I was studying had any relevance. I had a strong feeling of estrangement, of having wasted my time.

The following day, I went to Jerusalem. Traffic was heavy, so the soldiers at the checkpoint did not stop us at all. It was great. Sandra was leaving to Jordan that afternoon. We drove her to the Bridge, then drove through

Jericho to see life under the Palestinian Authority (PA). Palestinian flags were flying, and life was quiet and peaceful. That was my first time seeing the Palestinian police, who wore uniforms and drove Ford trucks that looked like Israeli police ones painted in different colors. Some buildings had the Palestine Authority symbol, and a big sign at the outskirts read "The Palestine Authority Welcomes You". An unmanned checkpoint in the middle of the city had a large mural of Yasir Arafat. To enter Jericho, however, I had to pass several Israeli checkpoints. Quoting from my diary for that day: "It seems the changes are superficial."

We now had broadcasting and TV stations. The day before, the PA ordered the daily newspaper *al-Quds* closed for a few days, for publishing something unflattering of it. Ouch! In the early 1980s, Ramallah's popular elected mayor, Kareem Khalaf, lost his leg in a car bomb planted by Israeli terrorists. Rather than pursue his attackers, Israel deposed him, installing a puppet mayor, and put him under house arrest in Jericho, almost till the end of his life. After Oslo, his daughter, Daniela, hosted a popular show on Palestinian radio. 'Amr Diab's song "*Raj'een*" ("we're coming back") was her theme song, co-opting the metaphor of lovers re-uniting to the return of the exiles and refugees to their motherland. Months after my visit, I learned that she was imprisoned for three days and her show cancelled, for daring to criticize the PA. In 1998, Palestinian negotiator and spokeswoman Hanan Ashrawi resigned from the PA cabinet in protest for its corruption. She went on to found a human rights organization. Our freedom of speech, once severely restricted by Israel, became restricted by the PA. To the average man and woman on the street, in the refugee camp, little had changed. *Handalah's* ghost remained staring at a wall painted in slogans of freedom, dressed in the same tattered clothes with the slingshot in his back pocket.

The next day, a Monday, Ramallah was empty of its daily visitors from the countryside. I learned on the news that two buses had exploded in Jerusalem. The Israelis immediately retaliated by tightening the Closure, separating us from Jerusalem, and isolating towns in the West Bank. Even those with permits could not cross. The Closure became Israel's prime economic weapon. Borders were opened and permits issued only if we "behaved". People in Ramallah were frustrated. Why should we get blamed for anything and everything that happened?

Visiting my friends, I was surprised to run into Sajid again. He had returned from deportation on a temporary visa on his French passport, while his West Bank residency was being officially reinstated as part of Oslo. Rasheed was about to leave for Ohio. I missed saying goodbye to him Wednesday morning because I woke up late, but not to worry. He could not leave since the Bridge to Jordan was still closed because of Monday's incident. I then went to the Scouts Club to watch a basketball game. However, the game was cancelled because the team from Jericho couldn't make it with the road closures.

Since my stay was so short, I needed to move fast on renewing my travel document. With the help of a connection working at the ID office, and a brief chat in English with the Israeli soldier at the door, I entered easily and got my business done. A far cry from the daylong affairs of 1993, I still had time in the afternoon to go to town with Rasheed and Waheed. We ate ice cream at a new place called *Baladna's*. Rasheed, who was studying engineering at Ohio State University, was disdainful of a guy at a nearby table wearing an earring, an act supposedly antithetical to our conservative culture. Rasheed sarcastically wondered if that person would start a trend. Waheed, who was studying at Birzeit, disagreed, saying: "We have to allow him his freedom if freedom is what we want." I loved Waheed's solid logic, and his tolerance. The lesson of Abdul-Azeem making a fool of himself was not lost on me. The tendency of our culture was to oppress individual freedoms in the name of collective struggle. If we are to sacrifice and work hard for a Palestinian state, then live repressed in it like the other Arabs are repressed in their countries, then what is the point? What is more important: the State, or Freedom?

Ramallah finally had nightlife. At 11 that night, I went with my friend Dimitri to a new café called *al-Asil*, on the roof (7th floor) of a new building in downtown Ramallah. They served Arabic small plates and *arghileh* (hookah), and had a good view overlooking the entire town. One side had tables and chairs, the other, a traditional seating arrangement with pillows and mats on the floor. The crowd was quiet and someone played the *'ud* and sang, then everybody joined in. We stayed there until two in the morning! People were tired of fighting and were glad to see peace on the horizon. They wanted to party and forget about their worries and problems. *Al-Bardouny* was booming, so was the *Muntazah* public park. New restaurants opened. The pessimist in me wondered: how long was this going to last?

By 1995, the conflict felt only a marginal issue within Palestine. People spent too many years on the Intifada, and mostly wanted to get on with their lives. To people on the outside (activists, the media, and even expatriates), however, the conflict, and the Peace Process, dominated their image of Palestine.

That weekend I went to a dance party. Then on Sunday I went to a newly-opened swimming pool on the outskirts of Ramallah. The road to it was potholed from all the dump trucks hauling rubble from the construction sites. I had just learned to swim earlier that summer, and Dimitri offered to teach me diving, which he did. The cost was a bump on my head, thanks to the idiot of a lifeguard, who forced us to the shallow end.

Bored with Ramallah, I went with Dad to visit Mary's tomb in Jerusalem on her saint's day. We parked near the checkpoint and walked across. The soldiers, busy stopping cars, ignored us. We then hailed a cab for *Sittna Maryam* (Our Lady, St. Mary) church, at the bottom of the Kidron valley just outside the Old City. There, we went down a long stairwell to her tomb, lighting a candle for each step. On my last day, my parents took me to the sea at Bat Yam. We came back through Ramleh and Lydd. The construction boom in Ramallah paled when compared to the construction in Israel and the stolenments. Entire orange groves were torn to make way for massive developments near Lydd.

Extremism

The view from USA was different. CNN usually brought news of the peace process when an extremist, from one side or the other, made a dramatic attempt to stop it. Armed settlers gunned down Palestinians, suicide bombers blew up buses, and the media relished the bloodbath. I got tired from the condolences my friendly Jewish officemate and I exchanged every time something happened. Why should I feel responsible for every Hamas extremist, and why should he feel sorry for the actions of Jewish fanatics? I was not too keen on the Oslo agreement itself, but the "cycle of violence" was to no one's benefit, except perhaps the media's.

In February 1994, Baruch Goldstein, an Israeli extremist originally from Brooklyn and follower of the racist "settler" leader Meir Kahane, stormed the Abrahamic mosque in Hebron. Armed with an automatic rifle, he proceeded to gun down Muslim worshippers in the midst of prayer. Those inside had no escape. By the time he was overcome by the unarmed worshippers, he left 29 Palestinians dead, including children, and 150 injured. The Israeli soldiers posted nearby did nothing to stop him. He became a hero to Israeli extremists, his grave receiving ten thousand visitors in the 1990s.

In response to the massacre, SAMAR organized an emergency vigil on campus. We stayed up into the night making signs. Exhausted from all the preparations, plus classes and work, I came back from the two-hour vigil in the cold Michigan night to the sound of the phone ringing. It was Abdul-Azeem, furious. How come the Muslim student group was not informed of our plans for a vigil? They would have joined us. My friend suddenly forgot that he was, actually, on our mailing list, and was perfectly welcome to attend our meetings, and had indeed offered, as a common member, to act as a liaison. If he shunned us because we were more inclusive than he would have liked, that was his choice.

Hamas was the newcomer during the Intifada. In Ramallah, we regarded it with suspicion and obeyed its calls for strikes more out of fear than any love for their ideology. The group came to prominence when Israel deported 400 Palestinians to the border zone with Lebanon in December 1992. Purportedly they were Hamas members, but several of the exiles were Christians, and there were no trials of any sort. Lebanon refused to accept the deportees, so they remained on the border in a "no-man's-land" for well over a year. Daily news images of the men huddled around a fire in the cold of winter, trying to survive day to day, without capitulating or reneging their ideals, brought respect for Hamas. Unlike PLO leaders who were ready to make deals, the "Hamas men" appeared to have an unwavering spirit and commitment.

With PLO factions lining up behind Oslo, even the formerly radical Marxists, Hamas was the only Palestinian group left standing up for our Right of Return. The Closure, economically strangling us, ensured a vast field of disgruntled potential recruits.

Gaza in particular had the perfect explosive mixture to feed a militant organization like Hamas. Gaza's population was mostly refugees, living in dire conditions in crowded refugee camps, with population densities among the highest in the world. Half lived below the poverty line, and the ranks of the unemployed swelled as Israel closed Gaza's borders and replaced Palestinian workers with imported migrants.

Two months after Baruch Goldstein's shooting spree, Hamas detonated its first suicide bomb in a bus, killing eight Israelis. Though history was replete with suicide missions, from Samson to *kamikaze*, this was new to Palestine's modern history. I wondered what would cause someone to do this, and why? Resentment at the Occupation was no justification. Pointless retaliation for Goldstein's attack, perhaps? As Israel responded to attacks by stopping negotiations with the PLO, however, Hamas realized its own power to sabotage the peace process. Hamas hence stepped up its suicide attacks over the next two years, peaking in 1996.

To Palestinians, Hamas's operations exposed the weaknesses of Oslo, especially since Israel's retaliatory road closures affected the whole population. People had imagined that the "Peace" to be gained from the "Process" would be felt in a lifting of the travel restrictions. Hamas proved them wrong.

Like the "thoughts and prayers" after school shootings in America, both Palestinian and Israeli leaders condemned every single attack, yet did nothing to remove the root causes of violence. If anything, Israeli repression fed the languishing discontent. Ironically, both Hamas and Jewish extremist groups appeared to share the common goal of torpedoing Oslo, feeding off of each other's actions.

The peace process was not designed to withstand extremist attacks. In November 1995, Israeli Prime Minister Rabin was assassinated in Tel

Aviv by Yigal Amir, an admirer of Baruch Goldstein. Despite Rabin's previous role in the Iron Fist policy, and formerly the depopulation of Lydd and Ramleh, I was saddened at this turn of events. Judging by how history unfolded, none of the Israeli leaders who followed him possessed what it took to forge a stable peace.

Michigan Update

Typical of the transience of college campuses, my old friends, batch by batch, were moving away from Ann Arbor. Just before my Palestine trip, I attended the graduation of Chrissy, Josie, Sarab, and Leena. Chrissy moved more than anyone I knew, but surprisingly I saw her often as our paths continued to intersect. Josie went to Chicago for graduate school. Leena moved to NYC where I got to meet her husband a few years later. She had defied repressive Arab traditions and married outside her religion. Not for the faint of heart, for a Lebanese Christian like her, to marry a Lebanese Muslim – two groups that fought a bloody war for decades. The parents thankfully were supportive.

We had a goodbye dinner for Gabriel, who took a position in Montreal. Peter joined a big auto company and was traveling the world in short order. Ayman left for another big company, settling in Philadelphia where we ran the Philadelphia Marathon together. Zaid started medical school in Ann Arbor, but like all medical students, was rarely seen. Fatima moved to New York, working for the UN. The only ones left among my SAMAR friends were Blake, who was finding less time for chess as he finished his thesis, and Waseem and Flora, who had a serious romance that stumbled on the religious chasm again. He was Christian, she was Shi'a Muslim. Her family opposed. (She later ended up in an unhappy marriage to another Muslim, but managed to get a divorce and restart her life.)

Similarly, among my other circles, Yesef graduated and moved to New York City, eventually reaching a high position in the financial world. Hyung, I saw a couple of times in LA. I sadly lost contact with Mikey since the last time I saw him at Moses' wedding. By the time I graduated, Moses was raising a family in the Detroit area. I hung out with Roy and Leroy, Roy having moved to our dorm up north. The three of us made a new friend, Chris, from Arizona, who kept a chest in his room packed with music CDs, including an entire row of Nine Inch Nails rarities. Chris had the foresight to do a work-study where he spent the warmer fall semesters in Michigan, then headed to Arizona for winter. We worked out regularly at the university gym. He also introduced me to computer games and to the art of the shopping spree at record stores, where he knew no limit. After college, his floor-to-ceiling CD cases reminded me of Hakeem's old room.

Sometimes my American friends asked what was my childhood in Palestine like. Where to begin? How to express the lack of a country to those who experienced childhood in the most powerful country on Earth? The Americans I came across often took their many freedoms for granted. They commuted dozens of miles without issue, drove across state lines without stopping, traveled internationally with barely a question at the border, spoke their minds without fear, and read and listened to whatever they wanted.

Deciding to pursue my dreams regardless, I signed up for flying lessons at the flying club in the small Ann Arbor airport. I loved the view from the pilot's seat of a Cessna, surrounded by 270° of windows, with nothing separating us from the ground but the lift of the wings. The emptiness of the air felt liberating, especially compared to driving through Ann Arbor's narrow streets. I enjoyed the long solo flights, landing in Flint, Lansing, Grand Rapids, or across state lines in Ohio.

I concentrated on my research, publishing and presenting my work at conferences. I was fortunate to have an advisor like Prof. Liu. An immigrant himself from Hong Kong, he was sympathetic to the challenges faced by foreign students. He set his meetings with us graduate students at 4 PM, inviting us afterwards for a beer, then often returning to his office to work into the night. What I appreciated most was the space he gave me to develop my independent ideas. From him I learned that the most profound truths are the simplest.

Whereas my brother Basman had restricted his dating to women with an Arabic background, I was more open. By then I was as comfortable with English as Arabic, if not more. For a few months, I dated a young woman in my dorm from Grand Rapids. It was my first exposure to the power of cultural differences. Basman, meanwhile, identifying more with the culture back home, visited Palestine to meet women, and ended up getting engaged to someone from there. They set the wedding date for the spring of 1996, and asked me to be the best man.

1996

I flew to Palestine soon as classes ended. The wedding was scheduled for two days after my arrival, so I was plunged into the multiple receptions and home parties. I went out a few times with a young woman I met there. The nightlife in Ramallah had advanced; more new restaurants where we could meet, and a few dance clubs that ran late into the night. There was no privacy, though. Driving around town, we couldn't find a place to park away from prying eyes. I was told to beware the "propriety police."

The trip aligned with the extension of Palestine Authority rule to Ramallah. Elections in January had established Arafat as the first President of the PA. With the Labor Party in Israel still in power under Shimon Peres, that Spring witnessed the height of 'Osloptimism'.

The concrete cubes blocking Ramallah's entrances were removed, and the Israeli army had posted a checkpoint at the outskirts in Beitunia, separating areas A and B. They did not stop us. The police station and other Israeli posts in town were now turned over to the PA, which set up headquarters at the former Military Governor's, where I used to line up all day for documents. Traffic in Ramallah was heavy but less hectic, thanks to the Oslo police directing it. At night, they stopped cars in downtown to check for ID, "for your safety." The city was cleaner, and trash cans had been installed in public places. It was apparent that the PA was striving to be organized and lawful. The building boom had reached a new height, as everyone was optimistic about the economic opportunities peace was to deliver.

Alongside the Closure, Israel rid itself of Palestinian labor, replacing it with migrants from Asia. Soon after entering Ramallah, the PA stepped in with a wave of public works projects, most visibly, repeatedly paving the city streets. Unfortunately, the old cobblestone sidewalks fell victim as well.

In my youth, Ramallah's sidewalks were paved with large tiles of local stone, worn smooth by decades of pedestrian traffic. The tiles were uneven and slippery, and grass grew between the cracks, but they gave Ramallah its character, and a tinge of history. The PA replaced the tiles from most sidewalks with an uncomfortable 9" layer of concrete. Its sharp corners endangered children. The high step, designed to prevent cars from parking on the sidewalks, challenged the elderly. Aesthetically, the drab grey concrete was reminiscent of a slum.

Meanwhile, the stone tiles from the old sidewalks, I heard, were sold to scrap dealers, ultimately getting re-consecrated to pave nearby stolenments. My childhood friends and I played on those tiles. We walked over them every day: to school, to church, to the market. I knew their every crack and curve. Our children lost that connection. Instead, a settler's child may be playing over those same stones, absorbing the illusion that his city has existed for decades.

One day in 1999, after the PA had settled in Ramallah for three and a half years, I was driving Abdul-Jabbar to Ein Sinia. Near Beth El we smelled a horrid stench. It was coming from al-Jalazon Refugee Camp, which was well away from the road. The camp had open sewers, and on dry days, the smell traveled far. I wondered what was the PA doing. For battling unemployment, our pavements were sacrificed. Would it not have been better to install sewers in the refugee camps than to repave the roads and dig up the sidewalks? There is a certain aversion in Palestinian culture about doing *any* improvement to the refugee camps. The camps are *temporary*, their residents *will* one day return to their homes. So, for sixty years, they endured leaky roofs and sewage on the streets, because improving the camp was deemed synonymous with forfeiting their Right of Return. Such logic borders on conspiracy.

Going to Jerusalem was complicated by the tight Closure imposed for most of my stay. In April 1996, fighting between Israel and Hizbullah in South Lebanon had reignited in what Israel ominously named "Operation Grapes of Wrath," referencing American literature so as to stimulate US support. The week before my arrival, Israel bombed a UN shelter at Qana killing over 100 civilians. Israeli elections were also drawing near and Hamas stepped up its suicide bombing campaign, presumably in revenge for the Qana massacre. Palestinian police foiled several bombing attempts and arrested Hamas members. However, the PA controlled little territory, so Hamas was able to perpetrate several headline-grabbing attacks. Ultimately, Israelis voted in the anti-Oslo extremists led by Benjamin Netanyahu. It was as if the extremists on both sides were in league.

Life was completely unpredictable. One day brought quiet and open roads, the next, a bombing took place and the checkpoints closed for several days. To go to Jerusalem without a permit, Dad one day drove me through al-Ram, a neighborhood adjacent to the checkpoint. We parked on a side street, jumped a stone fence, walked back to the main street, and there we were on the Jerusalem side, where we hailed a cab. In my opinion, no closure, no matter how tight, was going to stop the determined bomber. What the Closure policy did was harm the ordinary citizen – the worker who had to commute to Jerusalem every day, the trucker hauling goods, the sick who needed to see a doctor.

This was the major flaw of the Oslo Process. Despite legitimate grievances about the agreement, and fears of giving up right or territory, vast majorities of Palestinians and Israelis wanted peace. Even among the few who rejected Oslo, only a fraction believed in pursuing violence to obstruct it. Yet Oslo's implementation granted that violent minority on both sides the power to call the shots.

Peres lost the elections because he appeared weak-willed, able neither to stop the attacks, nor to stand up for peace. To Palestinians, the attacks spotlighted the weakness of the Palestine Authority, for something as basic as travel to the next city was completely under Israeli control. Had Rabin survived, I'd like to think he'd be determined to bring the hope and optimism engendered by Oslo to fruition, but then perhaps not. The flaws were too deep in Oslo's DNA for it to succeed.

I applied for a "Palestinian Passport" (really a PA travel document), to replace the Israeli travel document. I got it the week before my departure, but it was invalid for travel until Israelis first "entered it into the computer", a two-week wait. The "passport" itself had the same Israeli

ID number printed on the front. It was becoming clear that the Palestine "Authority" had no real authority.

Before leaving, I stopped at the post office to buy stamps. These were the first stamps issued bearing the name "Palestine" since the British government in the 1940s. Excited to get this historic issue, I was disappointed at the choice Hisham's Palace in Jericho, a relatively marginal landmark. It was the postal version of the "Gaza and Jericho First" policy, the holy places in Jerusalem notably absent. We were still using Israeli Shekels, as the PA could not issue currency. A friend took me to see Arafat's helicopter, at a make-shift landing side in the backyard of his headquarters, now renamed the *Muqata'a,* the District. A gift from the Egyptians, the chopper still wore Egyptian colors and an Egyptian flag.

With a dysfunctional passport, I was forced to use my Jordanian travel document to travel via Amman. It was the first time I used the Bridge, or visited Jordan, since 1985. The Oslo Accords changed the procedure at the Bridge significantly. I crossed quickly and easily, for the first *and only* time in my life. It was also the only time I saw no Israelis as I left the country. My relatives drove me to Jericho. From there, I took a short bus ride to the Bridge, where the PA police inspected our bags and documents. The Israelis sat in a room behind a two-way mirror watching everything. The PA policeman took my ID and Bridge permit, put them in a drawer behind him, and sent them to the Israelis on the other side, who were running the show. With their blessing in the form of a stamp, I boarded the bus to Jordan and it was smooth sailing.

The arrangement let the PA save face. Though everybody knew the Israelis were in control, the absence of direct contact gave us the illusion of independence. We saw less of the ugliness of soldiers shooting at our children. Better able to live their lives unmolested, people trusted Arafat's promises of ultimate liberation.

As if I was destined to never enjoy a single peaceful Bridge crossing, this time the Jordanians were the ones to delay me. As the border guard searched my bags, he stumbled on a letter from Sarab revealing that we had met in America. After staring at it for a while (in total violation of my privacy), he escorted me to the Mukhabarat, the dreaded intelligence service. I had no idea what they were going to do. He sat me in a room for a long time while they ran checks on my passport information. I guessed they were suspicious about my blank record. Thus far, I had been flying through Tel Aviv, whereas other West Bankers studying abroad had a history of crossing the Bridge instead. Recalling the pyres used to burn clothes with Hebrew labels, I imagined the tortures they were going to put me through for flying through an "enemy airport". Finally, the guard brought me to his boss in another room, an elderly man wearing the traditional Jordanian *kafiyyeh*. The old man politely asked me a few questions, then apologized for the delay, adding "We just wanted to welcome you to Jordan!"

My sister Sandra took me to visit Aunt May's family, whom I had not seen for a decade. The children I played with were now adults. I visited Kareem and Sajid at their university. The mixed company on campus, with men and women in the same groups, was unlike Birzeit. Also unlike Birzeit, few women wore Hijab. After a night out, we stayed up till morning playing *tarneeb*. Flying back to Europe, my plane had a scheduled stop in Beirut. It made a wide detour (over Iraq and Syria) to avoid the Israel-Hizbullah fighting in South Lebanon. Beirut looked nice. I was awed by the stretch of beaches visible along the plane's landing path. There was almost no trace of the decades-long civil war, not from the air.

It dawned on me, aboard the long flight to Detroit, that the greatest failure of Oslo was the separation of people it engendered. My generation grew up knowing Israelis as human beings, working with them, trading with them, and having friendly relations. The Closure separated us. Few of us got Jerusalem permits, and while some went smuggled, most preferred not to risk it. By the end of the decade, many young adults in Bethlehem and Ramallah had not seen Jerusalem since their fifth birthday. That generation blossoming in the 1990s, when regarding Israelis, saw only soldiers or settlers. Similarly, as few Palestinians ventured onto the streets of Jerusalem, workplaces of Haifa, or the beaches of Tel Aviv, a generation of Israelis saw Palestinians only through their military service manning the checkpoints or facing stone-throwing protesters. The separation of people made it easier, during the troubled time of the 2000s, to disregard the humanity of "the other side," to engage in extreme acts of violence, and to become militant and uncompromising. The Closures practiced during Oslo led to a violent Second Intifada, its casualties an order of magnitude beyond the First's.

Oslo was not a real peace agreement, in the sense of establishing friendly relations between nations. It was closer to a ceasefire, and an uneven one at that. By failing to get people to talk to each other after raising their hopes of peace, the leaders failed to make the peace permanent.

12

Process Over Peace

WITH A DEGREE TO WRAP UP, I came back from Palestine to a busy summer. I lingered in Michigan for the month of June, playing Monopoly with my nieces, now pre-teens. I bought a car. July, I went to Washington, D.C., for a brief internship. That was where I met Ze'ev, the Israeli-American co-worker who doubted my Palestinian-ness. He was divorced and dating, so we talked about women and he gave me dating advice. We hung out a few times outside of work, watching a hockey game with his two children. The youngest was born in Israel during the Gulf War. He was barely a day old when the SCUD alarm sounded in the hospital, rendering him deaf. Ze'ev's ex-wife, who was non-Jewish, resented him for insisting they move to Haifa, blaming him for their son's injury. Ze'ev was the first of many Israeli scientists I was to encounter in America. Another told me frankly that he moved to America in 1989 because he couldn't stand the constant fighting.

Upon returning to Michigan, I quickly fell into a comfortable rhythm writing my dissertation. I turned night into day, waking up at 5 PM, working out, spending time with Roy, Chris, and Leroy; then by midnight, when the dorm quieted and everyone went to bed, I locked myself in my room to write, usually staying at it till 9 AM. The long quiet nights evoked memories of the long nights of the Intifada, and I got to appreciate the dimmer and slower Michigan sunrises.

With graduation ahead, I again had to decide what to do with my life. The unstable situation in Palestine encouraged me to stay in the US for a few more years. I applied for jobs in the US and Canada, and traveled for interviews. I also stayed tuned to news of the Peace Process. If, ultimately, peace were to prevail, Palestine could become a viable option for my future.

I successfully defended my doctoral thesis in early 1997, and continued the research with Prof. Liu while awaiting a suitable job offer. I stepped up my flying lessons, wanting to earn my pilot license before moving out of Ann Arbor, and I did. In this last semester, I accidentally met a new student, Charlene, who had just arrived to our dorm from China. We dated sporadically for the rest of the semester. I ended up accepting a research position at a university in the DC metro area. Chris finished a year later, staying in Arizona afterwards. Among my old friends, only Leroy and Waseem stayed in Ann Arbor past their degrees.

News of the Peace Process was discouraging. Oslo's final status negotiations were scheduled to begin the summer of 1996. Instead, the summer started with Israel's new prime minister, Benjamin Netanyahu, pronouncing the Oslo Accords null and void. Netanyahu gave a voice to the "settlers" and others invested in the Occupation, who saw peace as a personal threat to their privileges. The rest of the 1990s were spent in prolonged fruitless negotiations, not regarding final status issues, but rather the terms of implementation of the Interim period. Everything was back on the table – the boundaries of Areas A, B, and C; the number of Palestinian policemen authorized to carry guns; and what powers were relegated to the Palestinian authority. Whereas Rabin's style was to quietly negotiate these matters behind the scenes, Netanyahu favored loud, glaring pronouncements. Jerusalem is a "Red Line", "forever united, forever the capital of Israel." This blabber eroded whatever goodwill Palestinians retained towards Israel.

Netanyahu's alternate strategy to scuttle the agreement was to provoke conflict. One of his first acts as Prime Minister was to authorize opening a tunnel under the *Haram al-Sharif* complex in Jerusalem. The tunnel, found by an archeological dig, was presumably dated to King Herod's time. Muslims feared that open access to the tunnel made it easier for Jewish extremists to bomb the Aqsa mosque, something that had been repeatedly attempted in recent decades. Given the sensitivity of the issue, the tunnel opening was inessential and could have waited until the status of Jerusalem was resolved. In fact, Rabin had issued a standing order to keep the tunnel shut during the Oslo Interim period. Naturally, the opening reignited protests in Jerusalem, protests that Netanyahu used to "prove" to Israelis that "Palestinians did not want peace," strengthening his own power within the Israeli system.

In a way, Netanyahu's *modus operandi* was little different from Hamas's, except, as Prime Minister invested with the power of the state, his provocations were more damaging. Netanyahu restarted stolenment construction, like Har Homa on the hill of Abu Ghneim at the outskirts of Beit Sahur and Bethlehem. Within months, the green, forested peak – a rarity in that part of Palestine – was converted into a mass of concrete, ignoring cries from human rights and environmental organizations alike. Har Homa was one of the pillars of the policy of strangling Arab East Jerusalem, separating it from the Arab population in the West Bank, surrounding it with a noose of stolenments. The idea was to make it practically impossible to return the city to us once peace was concluded. Time was running out on the Oslo clock, so stolenment construction intensified. The rumor by the end of the 1990s was that many units in the stolenments were unoccupied, simply there to stake a claim on the land.

All the while, the pace of negotiations was frustratingly slow. Even Roy, who rarely followed international news, noted how Netanyahu seemed to be the main impediment. The talks were stuck for months over the transfer of 3% of the land area of the West Bank. That is about half a percent of the total area of Palestine. Given that the "3%" negotiation was not even about the final border, but a non-binding interim redeployment, the whole charade felt demeaning.

Those endless talks eroded our hopes for peace, as Netanyahu's government exacted more demanding conditions for each and every "withdrawal". The PA was compelled to arrest members of opposition groups, and implement security practices satisfactory to Israel. We could no longer have the free society we were dreaming of, but a police state, where the PA was Israel's enforcer. Eventually, Netanyahu's government, under pressure from the US and internal charges of corruption, collapsed and was replaced by that of Ehud Barak. Netanyahu's tenure highlighted another weakness of Oslo: a successful agreement needed to be made invulnerable to a change in government on either side. The only guarantee of that is rapid implementation of a final agreement, instead of a prolonged "interim period".

By the summer of 1997, I had moved to DC. Charlene and I stayed in touch over email and telephones. Making new friends was not that easy after college, especially with DC being a transitional place where few lingered. I worked with a diverse group, including several international students, but my coworkers, older and married, went back to their families immediately after work. The colleague closest to my line of work was Ernie, an Orthodox Jewish-American who devoutly kept the Sabbath. He became my mentor in computational physics. When not talking science, we chatted about the Middle East. We also banded together at conferences and lunches, as his diet was roughly as restrictive as mine.

Roy, then Chrissy, each moved to the DC area that same summer. We saw each other on weekends, but unlike the old days when we lived nearby and could get together daily, their living in downtown or the opposite side of the Beltway made it impractical. Chrissy became a congressional aide for a well-known senator. Later, she joined the foreign service, returning to DC frequently in between her stints at foreign embassies. Roy had gotten an engineering job with one of the government laboratories. Soon after, he married his girlfriend from college. I traveled frequently to Michigan, playing Monopoly with my nieces, and visiting Charlene and my old friends in Ann Arbor. By 1999, Charlene finished her studies and found work in the DC area, so we got to see each other more regularly.

1998 marked the 50th anniversary of the *Nakba*. While world leaders like Bill Clinton joined Israel in celebrating its birthday, we were quietly remembering the forced expulsion of our parents and grandparents from their lands and homes. Interested in learning more, I became engrossed in Walid Khalidi's encyclopedic *All That Remains*, a volume that detailed each of the 418 Palestinian villages erased in the Nakba. Village by village, I read about its early history, its life before 1948, how it was depopulated, and the fate of its land and buildings. It was too depressing, the story too sad, for me to continue. Ancient villages listed in early Islamic censuses – ones with Crusader names, Biblical names, Canaanite names – all reduced to rubble, their people sent elsewhere. Cemeteries destroyed or turned into parks. Massacres committed to terrorize the people and make them flee. It was too much to handle.

"Everyone has the right to leave any country, including his own, and to return to his country." So states Article 13 of the Universal Declaration for Human Rights, which continues: *"Everyone has the right to freedom of movement and residence within the borders of each state."* The declaration recognizes the natural and inherent right to return to one's home, whatever the reason for leaving. The right certainly applies to Palestinian refugees from the Nakba, as individuals. No entity has the authority to negotiate away a human right. Oslo, however, put the Right of Return on the table, to be traded for other "agenda items", a foothold in East Jerusalem, for instance.

In the background during the 1990s was the news of Holocaust reparations, with establishments in Europe – countries, banks, museums, forced to pay for assets belonging to Holocaust victims. At first, I was pleased to hear of these attempts at partially correcting a grave injustice. Then I learned that, in certain cases, the money was not returned to the actual victims or their descendants, but to special funds, some controlled by the Israeli government, adding to the billions of dollars it received in international aid.

It seemed Israel wanted it all ways. The country was founded on violent seizure of our land and property to house refugees from Europe. Israel continually denied, not only our right to return or receive reparations, but more importantly, their responsibility for our expulsion. Through reparations, it sought compensation for property European Jews had left behind when they came to Palestine. Not satisfied, it also demanded compensation for property the Arab Jews had left behind when they voluntarily emigrated to Israel. As for my grandfather's land, Israeli leaders were unashamedly calling on Arab countries to set up a fund to compensate us for property lost in 1948. Were the Arabs responsible for our expulsion? Did they enjoy the property, for over half a century, that they were being asked to compensate us for?

Several groups in the USA organized activities to commemorate the Nakba. I attended an event at the National Mall displaying a large embroidered quilt, containing one panel for each of the destroyed villages. Activism for the Right of Return heightened, partly because of the 50th anniversary and the ticking of time as the first-generation refugees were aging, but also because of the ticking of the Oslo clock and the real possibility that this right will be forfeited if we did nothing. Disillusioned from my SAMAR experience, I had no interest in activism. Still, feeling obligated to make a symbolic gesture, I added a virtual Nakba memorial to my personal website. Nothing elaborate – a black page with the following statement:

> "Called *al-Nakba* in Arabic ("The Catastrophe"), 1948 marks the destruction of over 400 Palestinian villages, accompanied by the expulsion of nearly a million Palestinian Arabs from their homes, and the subsequent takeover by Israel of most of the land area of Palestine. This page is here to keep the memory alive. Only by remembrance can we hope to prevent the catastrophe from happening again."

One day my boss – the elderly, respected Professor Greider – called me into his office. "Are you crazy?" I had no idea what was going on. He had visited my personal website. Calling the content of my page "controversial", he asked me to unlink my personal website from my professional website, and further advised me to remove that page altogether. He even suggested that my Jewish colleagues might be offended by it. Those who would, missed the point. The commemoration of a historic event, and insistence on a basic human right, is an apolitical activity and should offend no one, regardless of their faith or political loyalties.

I disconnected my personal space from the professional site, but kept the memorial page alive. I felt discomfited at the rupture between my personal and professional lives. I am not a machine programmed to compartmentalize. I am a human being with different aspects to my identity, yet I am whole, I am one. I had misunderstood the meaning of individual freedom in America. Freedom of expression does *not* imply true intellectual freedom.

What bothered me about Greider's advice was his labeling of the Nakba, a well-documented historical event, a "controversial issue". The Nakba was not only the story of my parents, it was a present reality. Seeing the character of my country transformed under my eyes, it was only a matter of time before what little had remained for us vanished, too. If I silenced my fears, was that going to prevent them from materializing? If I kept them to myself, would that stop the transformation of the land? With talk of "Transfer" in Israel, the possibility of a repeat *Nakba*, driving us out of the West Bank, was all too real. I wrote of Palestine in hope of preserving the little that was left.

Interestingly, a year later, my Ph.D. advisor, Professor Liu, who formerly kept out of politics, was agitated at the Wen Ho Li incident. He privately expressed his concern that no matter how long an immigrant served America, he would still be regarded a foreigner. The screen separating Liu's personal and professional lives, like mine, was rupturing under the pressure of external events.

By the summer of 1999, I needed a long vacation. After two years of excellent work, I remained at the bottom of the pay scale. My job offer had promised a green card sponsorship, but the fine print conditioned it with getting promoted beyond my postdoc. Meanwhile, knowing I had incentive to stay, my department offered a meager salary. Other places making offers, aware of my "non-resident alien" status, also lowballed me on the salary. I felt exploited. Later, my foreign students were to suffer similar fates, with no one offering work at a salary commensurate with their skills. I was in debt from my college years, having charged some tuition payments to credit cards. While the stock market was booming, and everyone talked about the prosperous Clinton economy, what little I made was barely enough to make partial credit card payments on top of the rent.

Frustrated with my job and the exploitative US immigration system, I revived my interest in returning to Palestine, taking a month-long visit to assess the opportunities. With the election of Ehud Barak in Israel, optimism resurged, despite the passage of the original Oslo deadline. The promised Palestinian state was nowhere in sight, but final status talks seemed moving and the negotiators agreed to extend the deadline another year, to May 2000.

My Michigan friend Will, who was always interested in visiting Palestine, decided to join me for the first week. We met in Amsterdam at the end of July and continued to Tel Aviv. We were out of the airport an hour after landing. Oslo had simplified international travel for the time being. As usual during the Closure years, we first headed to Jerusalem, going to Ramallah the next day.

Ramallah continued growing, the construction spurt unrelenting. Out of the ground, new buildings like trees grew. Older ones taller, as floors piled higher. A dazzling sight. What wealth built those stone towers!

The City suffered. Crowded. Cars, people, and buildings left little breathing space. Our street had a constant stream of traffic. Walking and driving became dangerous activities. Traffic lights entered Ramallah, but few heeded them. Gaunt children sold chewing gum at the intersections, and they did not take "no" for an answer. Trash everywhere: people tossing it on the streets; construction leaving its junk. Construction dust. And the noise. From early morning to nightfall. The drilling, the hammering, the machines. Thankful construction of that building to the right ended, they began digging for another to the left, and again … the drilling, the hammering, the machines. Concrete monsters that swallowed the Trees. Occasionally, a goatherd was seen wandering, seeking what remained of the shrubs and grasses that covered the Land.

Day or night, the streets flooded with people, mostly strangers. I could feel the population exploding, guessing the city had quadrupled in size since the beginning of Oslo. Being one of the Palestinian-controlled areas closest to Jerusalem, Ramallah began to house PA offices, foreign consulates, and non-governmental organizations (NGOs). It also attracted businesses from besieged East Jerusalem, people returning from abroad, international visitors, and investors. The framework of an international capital was laid atop the formerly sleepy small town. I saw a city promising and prosperous, but my recognition of it was fading.

I lost track of the new stores, restaurants, and cafés. Seemed like business was good. *Rukab Ice Cream* was crowded. I frequented *Kan Bata Zaman*, a new bar with good atmosphere and decent food and drinks, going with Will, with Sandra, and later with Abdul-Jabbar. I swam with Sandra and her two sons at a pool in one of the new hotels. Pulsing with energy, Ramallah seemed like an ideal place for small enterprise.

I learned, later, that only Ramallah enjoyed such growth. Villages were hit hardest, especially after Israel diverted the main roads from them. Villagers crowded cities like Ramallah for work. One wondered where the funds for new construction came from. Foreign Aid Projects were clearly marked as such. Otherwise, I only heard speculation about the source. Expatriates investing their savings; PLO funds; someone skimming off the foreign aid. I wondered, because the people I knew could barely afford an apartment in one of the new buildings. The money seemed concentrated in few hands, while most people had gotten poorer. Salaries were low, unemployment high. The chewing gum boys risked their lives to earn their living. During my stay, one of them got broken bones when he was hit by a car. Foreign investment might have expanded Ramallah, but only a small section of society was helped.

Whereas Ramallah was a crowded, booming city, the Palestinian part of Jerusalem was the opposite: dead, deserted, and shrinking. Drawing the curtains in my hotel room on the morning of my arrival, I was greeted with broad Israeli flags draped on the roofs of several old houses in this core East Jerusalem neighborhood. The government had taken them under dubious claims. (After lengthy legal battles, some houses returned to their Palestinian owners a decade later.) Jerusalem was depressed. The Old City still saw tourists, but that was it. As elsewhere in the West Bank, new roads had been cut, names changed, and appearances manipulated to project the image of a Jewish city. Several of the Bakers' children had gotten married. The new couples, unable to find housing in Jerusalem, nor to obtain building permits, were forced to move to Ramallah. The move endangered their Jerusalem residency. The Israeli government was confiscating blue ID cards at an alarming rate.

Israel's double-pronged Jerusalem policy was all too clear: Aggressive stolenment construction near the city to expand its Jewish population, while pressuring its Palestinian natives to leave. Immediately after East Jerusalem's annexation, Israel unified it administratively with the Jewish West Jerusalem, meaning the Palestinian population became a minority and had no voice on the city council. Like every other Palestinian Jerusalemite, the Bakers had to pay the same taxes as Israelis, but did not receive the same government services. The roads in East Jerusalem were visibly worse, and schools and hospitals underfunded.

For years, Palestinian Jerusalemites overcame the strain by reliance on trade with the West Bank, especially the nearby cities of Ramallah, Bethlehem, and Hebron. East Jerusalem was the economic heart of the West Bank, the link connecting the northern and southern parts of the West Bank. The Closure not only deprived Jerusalem businesses of their West Bank customers and employees, it crippled this entire symbiotic economy. Ramallah was able to reconstruct itself with incoming PLO money and foreign aid. Other parts of the West Bank, and Jerusalem in particular, suffered.

Apart from its economic significance, Jerusalem is the religious center of Palestine. Palestinian Christians and Muslims could no longer go to Jerusalem any time they wanted to pray in the holy places. Israel occasionally issued a limited number of permits on religious holidays, a far cry from free access to places of worship. More absurdly, Bethlehem, in a Palestinian-controlled area, became inaccessible to the northern West Bank. Christians wishing to reach it from Ramallah were condemned to *Wadi an-Nar*, or Hellfire Valley (Hinnom), a narrow, dangerous, and accident-prone route that circumvented Jerusalem down the eastern slopes, halfway to the Dead Sea. Throughout the Oslo years, the number of internal borders kept rising.

Soon after my arrival, I took Will on a grand tour of Palestine. My brother Adnan was visiting with his family, so was my sister Sandra and her two sons. Together, we hired a van with Jerusalem plates. I had no permit, so I hopped in the back, with the kids, wearing sunglasses. As most Palestinians there are used to bright sun, few wear them. Will rode next to the driver. At the checkpoint, the soldiers looked inside, then motioned us to go. We headed down to Jericho and the Jordan Valley. The fortified stolenments, surrounded by barbed wire, astounded Will. Passing Jericho, we saw the new Oasis Casino, one of the PA's first investment projects. Palestinians with a more religious bent were unhappy about the presence of a casino. In Jericho, we saw resorts and hotels under construction, as well as a new cable car to the Mount of Temptation.

The desert appeared dryer than ever.

Heading north along the valley, we stopped briefly in Bisan, renamed Beth Shean after its depopulation in 1948. We toured the Roman ruins, entering an arena where gladiators fought, perhaps against lions. Close to Bisan, we stopped at Tiberias, where we strolled along the waterfront, past parks, beaches, and hotels. From there, we headed through Nazareth to Ras an-Nakura, the underwater caves at the northwestern tip of Palestine. The place was almost deserted. The attendant welcomed us and, recognizing our language, gave us brochures in Arabic. The brochure gave a "history" that went back to Biblical times, as if to establish a Jewish claim on this natural site. Nature's caves bedazzled my nephews and nieces. Will managed to photograph a radar installation on the border with Lebanon, a giant "NO PHOTOGRAPHY" sign within the frame.

In Akka, we took a boat tour on the Mediterranean. From the boat, past Akka's thick walls, we could see as far as Haifa. On board, a group of young women, some wearing the Hijab, spontaneously started singing and dancing. Back in Akka, the Arab part had the feel of a slum, left in shambles, and littered with trash. Onwards, I found Haifa had expanded. New construction and industries, on a grand scale, new hotels and parks on Mt. Carmel, and beautiful new gardens extending along the slopes, above and below the Baha'i shrine. The view of the harbor was as magnificent as ever. Will and I debated whether two distant cooling towers he noticed indicated a nuclear reactor. I thought they were part of the oil refinery. Again, the Arab areas in the city had the feel of a slum. The visit to Haifa made me wonder why Ramallah had few parks, and why people in my culture are so careless about littering public places.

The rest of Will's stay, we drove around Ramallah, visiting my old school and so forth, Ramallah having few tourist attractions. We hung out at *Kan Bata Zaman* bar, where Will savored Taybeh Beer, from our local brewery in the neighboring village of Taybeh, while listening to Cheb Khaled's cheerful Algerian music. We spent another day in Jerusalem, visiting the holy places, and shopping in the Old City streets. Will appreciated the bargains he got on souvenirs, but coming from a Protestant background, was somewhat shocked at the commercialization of religion. The spiritual Jerusalem of his imagination came face-to-face with the living Jerusalem, in which people exploited religious symbols to make their living. I felt the same dissonance, though I had known Jerusalem my whole life. The way I looked at things had changed.

The day before Will's departure, we went to Yafa and the beach. The taxi took us by way of Jerusalem. At the outskirts of Jerusalem, we saw the remains of an Arab village destroyed in 1948, probably Lifta. Some houses still stood, with collapsed roofs and shell holes in the walls. Prophetically, Will noted that our preference to building near hilltops was nowadays a military disadvantage, as a helicopter could easily hover facing the buildings and shoot straight. In Yafa, we first visited the Old City, with its gorgeous view of the coast. Afterwards, we went to swim in Bat Yam. Clean, salty, and warm water, moderate waves, blue sky, clear white sand. I missed the Mediterranean.

Driving back through the sprawling industrial suburbs of Tel Aviv, not far from the Ramat Gan Safari Park, the driver pointed at a half-destroyed shack on a neglected plot of land. "This used to be the village of Yazur. The only thing that remains (God keep it away from you) is the cemetery." Somebody spray-painted the ruin in Hebrew and Arabic:

"This is a Holy Place. Cemetery of Yazur."

Five decades have passed, and the destroyed villages have no shrine, memorial, nor even a stone that says: "Here lies the ruins of the village of al-Birwa (or Hunin, or Lifta, ...); population: XYZ; destroyed: 1948." People descended from that place deserve to have their origin remembered. Commemorating the past is not about politics, but about honoring the lives of people, human beings, who have endured this destruction. We erect memorials for terrible events, like the Holocaust, to remind people of the worst of human nature, so the future can avoid it. So why not memorials for the Nakba, for the villages destroyed, and the people displaced? "Never Again," should apply to injustice everywhere.

Cities surviving the Nakba were left to rot, turned into slums in the engulfing Jewish megalopolises. According to my parents, before 1948, Yafa was Palestine's most populous city and cultural center, with wide avenues, vibrant public squares, theaters, and libraries. Since then, Israel squeezed Yafa's remaining Palestinian population the way they more recently squeezed East Jerusalem's, relegating their neighborhoods to decay. By 1999, and after laborious efforts organizing, Yafa's Palestinian residents won only two seats on the seventeen-member joint Tel Aviv-Yafa city council, though their numbers far exceeded that ratio. They have been systematically denied city council permits, necessary for everything, from opening a store to repairing a house. Just as in Jerusalem, Arab houses built without permits were quickly demolished. I learned all that from Elias, one of the two Arab council members and an in-law of Adnan.

I found these newspaper headlines from early August noteworthy:
- "Unidentified ship throws toxic waste in front of Gazan shores."
- "Israel buys three submarines capable of delivering nuclear weapons from Germany, and receives first one."
- "Egypt loses a soccer game 5-1 to Saudi Arabia." Egyptian President Mubarak, wanting those responsible punished, ordered an investigation.
- "Poll: Palestinians don't trust Israeli PM Barak."
- "Israel building more settlements." (No wonder concerning the poll results a few days earlier.)

The day after Will left, I heard a big hubbub outside, and repetitive shooting. It turned out that the foreign minister of Syria had criticized

Arafat, calling him some obscenity. Arafat responded with an open letter harassing the Syrian minister. The Palestinian police also held a procession brandishing weapons and shooting in the air. Their actions posed no challenge to distant Syria, but seemed intended to intimidate people in Ramallah and show us "who's boss". It became obvious to me that, even if Oslo birthed a Palestinian state, the struggle for basic human rights, like freedom of expression, would still be far from over.

I wanted to know what starting a business here was like. Alarmingly, I heard rumors that PA officials unofficially inserted themselves as partners in new ventures, hoarding a 30% share while contributing nothing besides the required permissions. Everyone secretly complained of PA corruption. Squandering the confidence of the people, they left an opening for Hamas.

Elias, Adnan's in-law, thought the PA's corruption was temporary, by reason of absence of the checks and balances that were bound to come with a democratic state. I did not share his optimism. From my diary: "If the situation persists like this (PA corruption and lack of respect for basic freedoms), there will never be a democratic state, if we end up with any state at all!" We did not struggle for almost a century, and endure an Intifada, for a state run like other Arab countries, where citizens lack basic freedoms.

In retrospect, to succeed in our quest for independence, we needed to create an atmosphere of brotherhood and mutual respect, and foster a spirit of self-discipline, dedication, and community. Social growth is more critical than military, legal, or diplomatic achievements. We initiated such change during the First Intifada, but Oslo reshuffled everything, yielding us a divided, stratified society built on self-interest. The PLO newcomers, whom we looked to as "our leaders", lacked the Intifada culture we had developed. Their eyes, unused to the bright Palestinian sun, saw the glow of dollar signs, instead of the deeper wealth of the untapped human resources at their disposal.

Instead of leading the change, the PA let the factions do the organizing, further deepening societal fractures. We could be sending city youths to villages to volunteer and learn about their culture. We could be taking better care of our environment, cleaning up the cities. The PA had no plan for putting us to work on such uniting goals. Interestingly, the Zionists built their movement on the idea of sending immigrants collectively to the land, to reinforce those values necessary for a cohesive state down the road.

Once, I went with Sandra to the Ramallah Festival, a tradition during Jordanian times that was revived under Oslo. Free outdoor music and theater shows were held every night. We found the place packed, mostly with men. There, I ran into Sajid who had now returned permanently with the PLO. He was volunteering as an usher here, not an easy job among that hectic crowd.

An Arabic band from Nazareth played first, followed by a Native American dance troupe. I enjoyed the show, but was dismayed at the audience's behavior: constant chatter, snide comments, noise, chaos, and silliness. If they did not enjoy the show, they did not allow others to do so. During the intermissions, the giant screens were tuned to Palestine's official TV channel, where a commercial for "Halal meat", cloaked in the Palestinian flag, followed one for *arghileh* tobacco. In the audience, ten-year-old children smoked cigarettes. The ushers did nothing about it. Rather, children were even selling cigarettes.

Judging from the youth of the audience, the majority were children during the Intifada. They spent years without an education because of the forced school closures. That night, I saw how Israel's policy gave birth to a generation that knew no discipline.

Cellphones, unknown until recently, had quickly become a fashion. Useful as they were, people sported them more as status symbols bringing an inflated sense of self-importance. Besides the question of cellphone etiquette, debated all over the world, their use in Palestine directly supported the Israeli economy. The Palestinian cellular company at the time obtained the numbers and equipment from Israeli companies, so the Israelis were ultimately profiting from our fashion statements. Not limited to cellular, Israeli products packed the Ramallah markets. Electronics, soft drinks, foods.

I thought Ramallah was still a nice place to live. Prophetically, I wondered how long it would remain that way. As of this 1999 visit, enough Trees remained to color the city green. Apart from the Big Gaping Hole left by the attempted construction next-door, the *Sanasil* in my neighborhood were untouched. Those terraces were a wonder. Every stone, however imperfect its shape, had its place among others, and the wall held together. I walked along the well-trodden paths on the hillsides. Everything seemed bigger when I was younger. Back then, I could spend a whole day on one hillside. Now I crossed it in a few minutes, feeling compelled to go back, instead of stopping here and there to admire little things along the way. Why? People nearby? Afraid they might think it weird to see an adult on the hills? Perhaps I became addicted to this American artificial way of living, from climate-controlled workplaces, to air-conditioned cars, to insulated homes? I found it more fun to cross the hills than walk on the streets, and crossed them often, hoping the undeveloped spaces in my neighborhood would remain empty. It was a futile dream.

One night, I stayed up reading then drifted into a state between sleep and waking, the dawn *adhan* keeping me from falling into a deeper sleep. I finally got up to admire Ramallah under the light of the full moon. Roosters were crowing, dogs barking, and birds warbling, as of old. I admired Ramallah's pink sunrise again. The chickens were up, pecking for food, by the time I went to bed. That was my last glimpse of the old Ramallah. On my next visit, the morning sunlight was reflected from the facades of high-rises.

Sandra and I visited the various restaurants and ice cream places. Some were frequented by internationals, studying Arabic at Birzeit, or working at one of the foreign missions and NGOs. After being a relatively unknown small town, Ramallah became an international city. I frequented a newly-opened internet café in downtown, well-equipped and inexpensive in US terms.

Nights, I went out with friends. We once hurriedly left a bar when a fight broke out. I relished the thought that those same ballooning egos automatically deflated at Israeli checkpoints.

Indisputably, the best dance club in town was *Rumors*. Playing mostly Western music, it was packed with young women. To keep the ratio even, and quell the rowdiness seen elsewhere, the club allowed men entry only when accompanied by a woman. Luckily, between my sister and cousins, I had no difficulty finding a companion. I liked how music was subdued enough to allow conversation, and lights not totally dimmed. Abdul-Jabbar was amazed to know such a place existed in Ramallah, really digging it.

Late one night, while walking with Abed back from a club, we passed an *arghileh* coffeehouse. From the window, he pointed out several "personalities in the resistance", top people in the PA. Driving him to Ein Sinia via the Birzeit road, we passed a vast mural of the Aqsa mosque with the words, "I will not forget you, Jerusalem." I wondered if those leaders smoking *arghileh* had Jerusalem on their minds. I drove back on the main road, by Beth El. At the border with Ramallah, I encountered shooting, as masked youths threw stones at Israeli soldiers. I pushed the gas and sped away. Beth El had grown faster than Ramallah, and now a concrete wall encircled it, presumably to prevent infiltration or attack. A nucleus, a prototype laid during a time of peace, yet destined to grow into a Wall.

That night, I dreamt I was walking along Jerusalem's city wall under a full moon. The Old City's buildings were all fractured, about to collapse if no one acted. I felt frustrated, as though I was the only one caring to save the city. I awakened clearly equating the fractured buildings with our divided society.

I wanted to go to Jerusalem. The PA now handled the permits. I simply registered my name at their Liaison Office. A few days later, I picked up my permit. It was that simple, especially when compared to the daylong ordeals of 1993. Not everyone got permits, of course. That was up to the Israelis to decide. The PA only served as our friendly conduit. I appreciated the simplified procedures, but felt that by doing that service, the PA was legitimizing Israel's harmful Closure policy.

With a three-week permit, I visited Jerusalem repeatedly and went to the sea at Bat Yam once more. The new roads connecting the stolenments were completed, while Israeli checkpoints isolated our inferior road network from that universe, and the outside world. Military camps remained at the entrances, ready to shut the prison gates. Militarized stolenments like Beth El corked us into our tiny bottles. Surrounded, only having police and militias to defend our cities, we stood little chance whenever the Israelis decided to reoccupy our islets. The PA police checkpoints at the entrance to cities, supposedly to protect us from settlers, were usually unmanned. We lived under siege, with Israel's hand on the noose.

More headlines:
- Photo of an Iraqi woman mourning the death of yet another child from malnutrition caused by the US sanctions.
- "Iraq forced to pay Israel five million dollars in damages for the SCUD missiles launched during the Gulf war."
- "Egypt asks Israel to eliminate its nuclear weapons after the peace process is over."

The wall around Beth El reminded me of how much fear drove Israeli society. Fear of us claiming what was ours, perhaps? A whole security industry, of world renown, evolved to exploit and service that fear: an advanced military, intrusion detection, fences and walls, individual handheld weapons and the numbers of people carrying them, bomb squads, search parties, intelligence agencies, and computer security. This industry was an entrenched interest profiting from the absence of a true lasting peace. Rather than wage peace, Israeli society adapted itself to living in a culture of perpetual fear. Their insistence on "security" in negotiations belied the country's original sin. Deep inside, Israelis sensed that the fences, searchlights, army patrols, and bomb squads were their only birthright.

Ramallah had a growing cultural life. The Khalil Sakakini Cultural Center, honoring the Palestinian educator, opened in a renovated old house with traditional architecture. The entryways and windowsills disclose stone walls some three feet thick. In addition to hosting occasional plays, movies, and recitals, it houses a small art gallery. I watched a documentary with Sandra called "Tales from Arab Detroit". The event was well-attended, and everyone was orderly and respectful – a good crowd. The movie was funny, and well-presented. I thought it gave an accurate perspective on Arab Americans. It also made me realize that, as much as Ramallah was my home, so was Michigan.

I saw little of my friends, who were busy working. After the years of strikes during the Intifada, some family businesses opened – by choice – until 11 PM daily, as if to compensate. I could not tolerate such a lifestyle. On the last day, I found out that my old friend Jawad had been badly injured in a car accident a year ago, and was still undergoing treatment. That saddened me, especially since no time was left to visit his family.

By the time I left, all of Ramallah was engrossed in the Arab World Soccer championship. Palestine's team, playing for the first time and with no experience, made it to the semi-finals after tying Syria. That night, people celebrated all over town, with flags, car horns, fireworks, and gunshots. The sport bars were crowded.

I seriously considered moving back. I had vague career ideas: something computer-related, or perhaps working with my father. An appealing idea was to continue my employment with the university part-time, but be based in Palestine, taking advantage of internet and teleconferencing advances. At the same time, I saw past the growth and the optimism. In reality, the situation was unstable. The Oslo clock had already run out, and if the negotiations failed to produce an agreement within a couple of years, no one could predict what was to happen. I preferred to wait for the outcome of the "Peace Process".

My last night in Ramallah, after I was done packing, Abdul-Jabbar stopped to say goodbye. He was out to dinner with his father and Faisal Husseini, a lead negotiator. Dad invited them to stop by and they did. Impressing me with his expert knowledge of Jerusalem, Husseini quickly got to the point. The business my father managed in East Jerusalem co-owned another property close to the West Jerusalem border. Without the agreement of all owners, the company was unable to renovate the building or use it. Husseini warned that the property fell in an endangered zone, where Israel was confiscating properties for the slightest excuse, so it cannot be left looking abandoned. Besides my family and Abed's, Husseini was the last person I saw in Ramallah that visit. A couple of years later, he sadly died. Days after his passing, Israel closed the Orient House, the symbol of Palestinian representation in Jerusalem. They dared not do it while he lived, because they knew he was one leader with Jerusalem on his mind.

I tried sleeping but could not, so stayed up talking to my parents until the airport taxi picked me up at 2:30 AM. The ride was fast on the empty new roads, the searches at the airport horrendous. Every time they asked me "where did you stay?" "Ramallah" – that raised a flag and they repeated another tedious search. They opened every bag, emptied everything – took everything apart. When it was time to put things back together, they left me with two empty suitcases and piles of stuff. Like Will said: "we shouldn't have worried about packing the bags in the first place."

I read the *Jerusalem Post* on the plane. Burger King had opened a branch in Ma'ale Adumim. Arab American groups protested, and Burger King decided to close it. *Now*, the Israelis were angry, demanding from Jews *and* Christians worldwide to boycott Burger King "for being 'anti-Semitic'". The fact that only Jews were able to access the branch in the stolenment did not bother them. Discrimination is one-way in their eyes.

Upon returning from my trip, I became inwardly focused. I quit following the news and even cancelled cable TV. I had to decide what to do with my life: to stay at the university? To find another job? To go back to Palestine, and if so, to do what? I had to see where to take my relationship with Charlene. Naturally, she was not thrilled when I mentioned the idea of going back. What did I want from life? Did I know? *Why was I living my life as if it was an interim period?*

I read intensely, becoming engrossed in an Arabic novel I picked up from a Ramallah bookstore: *Memory of the Flesh*, for the Algerian author Ahlam Mustaghanmi. When I was there, I had gotten a harassing anonymous email from "A1 Internet Café" in London, challenging me: "if you like your country so much and feel very strong [sic] about the Palestinian cause and the suffering of your people, please ask yourself what the hell you're doing in the USA."

What did this troll know? For Heaven's sake, when that email was sent, I <u>was</u> in Palestine, thinking and making plans for going back. No one had a right to attack me that way. Besides, life is not so simplistic. I could be helping Palestine from abroad, while some, though physically there, were not necessarily helping the cause. Furthermore, by 1999, my thinking had broadened. I believed I was benefiting all of humanity with the science I was researching. Primitive concepts like flags and borders were eroding in my mind.

Still, what if I went back? Quoting Mustaghanmi (my translation):

> "What scares me is not that people there may not recognize me, but that I won't recognize that city .. those alleys .. and that house. The most difficult thing is to face memories with a contrary reality."

It was never easy to face the changes in my hometown every time I returned. Seeing the terraces and fields of my childhood disappear was heartbreaking. I almost felt like a tourist on that last trip.

I questioned life itself. Slowly sipping a cup of tea on the balcony, walking up hilly paths, watching a woodpecker or a groundhog – that is life – that is what is important. But fighting for so-and-so, defending some arbitrary political idea, embarking on gigantic endeavors – and then we die – so what is the point? That cannot be life.

> Mustaghanmi: "We cannot make peace with all the persona inhabiting us ... we must sacrifice one of them so that another one lives."

There is the rub. Which of my personalities to sacrifice? The citizen of the world, or the Palestinian? To go back, build my country and improve it? Or to live a quiet life in the USA? If I went back, my memories were going to face a contradictory reality. Could I accept the changes taking place? Do I have a choice but to accept?

The last few months of 1999, I became engrossed in the Nakba. A map I brought back from Ramallah vividly depicted the Catastrophe by marking all Palestinian villages in red (destroyed in 1948) or green (remaining). What was once a dense network of villages had shrunk to a few surviving pockets. More than half the country had been depopulated. Seeing the systematic devastation was depressing. I read Mahmoud Darwish, and history. It felt imperative upon me to keep the memory of this tragedy alive. Israel was using all its means to sever our connection to the land, to our ancestors, and to our history. We are not a people without a land. We did not come from nowhere. The memory is for us to guard against the erosion of time, like a fragile painting in darkness and decay. Inspired by a black-and-white photograph from 1948, I began painting the Exodus from Yafa, with people trapped along the harbor, cramming into tiny boats to save their lives.

I also obtained the National Geographic Magazine collection on CD-ROM, and found it interesting to read articles about Palestine before 1948, and even before the British Occupation in 1917. The snapshots of the vibrant life Palestine had spoke of a people with deep roots in that land. Recording customs of Muslim villages in Palestine, one article detailed their unmistakable similarities with Biblical traditions. Color plates of the hills near Bethlehem from the early 1920s illustrated a lush carpet of green grass and brilliant wildflowers. There was no "desert" for Zionists to "bloom". One author had the freedom to drive from Yafa to Beirut, and then to Aleppo in Northern Syria, in the span of *one* day. A lost age when borders were more porous, or simply non-existent.

Early in year 2000, Charlene and I got married.

With the wedding, moving in together, and buying furniture, we kept busy. For a while, I paid little attention to news of the outside world.

By May 2000, the negotiations between the PA and Israel were stalled. More than a year had passed since the expiration of the Interim period's original deadline, but no final agreement was in sight. Arafat and Barak traded threats of unilateral actions, symbolic declarations on our side, annexing territory on theirs. Meanwhile, Israel was driven out of South Lebanon by Hizbullah fighters, after 20 years of occupying Lebanese territory. The images of Israeli tanks on the run re-ignited people's fantasies of a successful armed resistance in the West Bank and Gaza. I was more skeptical. Lebanon suffered tremendously for its success. Were we willing to withstand the damage? Did we erect all those Buildings to suffer aerial bombardment? We had no air raid shelters, nor defensive structures of any sort. People had invested in peace. The PA was busy building a capitalist economy, not preparing for war.

Dad, ever optimistic, convinced Basman to reestablish his life in Ramallah. So Basman moved back in June 2000, along with his wife and their two-year old son. They stayed in the middle floor of my parents' house and reopened the family store.

President Clinton opted for the spectacle of a Camp David to press for a deal. Looking at the "final status issues" from ground level, we were far from an agreement. Jerusalem was inaccessible, the stolenments larger and more numerous than ever, and the Right of Return no more than a dream. Meanwhile, a key Israeli demand was our signature on an "end of conflict" document, meaning what we might get at Camp David would be it. There was simply too much at stake, too much to be accomplished.

For two weeks in July, I held my breath, daily checking news online. Those leaders' decisions were to have a huge impact on our lives. My Palestinian friends worried that Arafat was going to write us away. There was no real news, only rumors of what was under discussion, and occasional trial balloons. Before leaving to the USA, Arafat kept repeating his optimistic signature message: "The day will soon come when young girls and boys from Palestine will raise the Palestinian flag on every church and mosque in Jerusalem." Meanwhile, the US media was distracted by the superficial: the handshakes and postures, who entered first and who talked to whom. The Israeli negotiators made a point of stopping negotiations on Saturday, after our negotiators carelessly conducted business on Friday. Camp David was high on symbolism and showmanship, but low on substance.

From what I read afterwards, what was offered at Camp David was little more than the permanentization of Oslo's Interim period. No real sovereign Palestinian state was on the table. Israel would not allow that state to have a military, meaning we could not defend ourselves and our children from the constant threat of re-occupation. There were limits on the new "state's" control over its own airspace, borders, and water resources.

231

This purported state differed little from the PA's government, except its territory might be expanded to include a few more villages, some desert tracts, and symbolic tokens of Jerusalem. A slither of refugees might be allowed "back", not to the homes that were taken in 1948, but to the new tiny entity in the West Bank or Gaza. It was not clear how our religious rights in Jerusalem would be preserved. In return, we had to relinquish our rights, give up our heritage, and sacrifice our memories.

We had no incentive to accept a "peace" barely better than the Occupation, an occupation we almost ended had the Intifada continued.

Jerusalem loomed large as Israeli proposals severed it from the Palestinian "state", stressing the centrality of the city to Judaism above anything else. (I find it pointless to compare the strength of religious connections to a place shared by all three religions.) As the West Bank's economic solar plexus, ripping Jerusalem away disables the nascent state, while leaving the Palestinian citizens of Jerusalem a minority in their own city, subject to discriminatory taxation, licensing, and practices.

I thought of my father's East Jerusalem business. If Israel entirely retains the city, it suddenly becomes in a different country from its owners. Will Israel eventually confiscate it as "absentee property"? An American proposal awarding most of East Jerusalem to the Palestinian "state", with the exception of the Old City, is no better. The business stays in our country, but with the Old City in Israeli hands, tourists will opt for Israeli hotels, restaurants, and shops instead. Given the dependence of East Jerusalem's economy on tourism, the city's survival is at stake.

The plans acceptable to Israel failed in their details to offer any guarantees of peace for Jerusalem's Arab residents. It is not a question of this one neighborhood or that extra inch. Rather, it is commitment to the principle of treating us as human beings and assuring our basic rights. For the final agreement to be viable, it has to guarantee our security in the same way it guarantees Israel's, so that the encroachments of the past will not be repeated.

The three words "Barak's Generous Offer" condensed three falsehoods: it suggested our basic rights were theirs to offer, with 'generous' inserted to make Palestinians look insane for rejecting it, while actually "offering" little material change. The "90% of the West Bank" in Barak's proposal excluded the large areas annexed to Jerusalem, and a sizable security zone in the Jordan Valley that completed our encirclement. Israel was to keep the large stolenment blocs near Ramallah, Bethlehem, Nablus, and the western West Bank, and the agricultural land in between. These "fingers" splinter the Palestinian state's territory into four disconnected blocks, plus Gaza. The fingers and the Jordan Valley zone retain a large Israeli foothold over the West Bank's water resources, assuring their continued control and exploitation.

I was thankful Arafat refused to sign. For whatever reason he entered into Oslo, the deals presented at Camp David were not something he wanted to affix to his legacy. He got a hero's welcome in Gaza for refusing to give up our natural and historic rights. Meanwhile, following the US press, I saw him trashed and vilified for "never missing an opportunity to miss an opportunity," the acrid soundbites and snide witticisms showcasing Israel's investment in public relations. Pro-Israeli opinions swamped the op-ed pages. Clinton publicly blamed Arafat for the failure to reach an agreement at Camp David – an unprofessional position for the self-declared "honest broker" to take.

Over the dozen years preceding the summit, Arafat had led the PLO to make major concessions over key issues. Noteworthy were the rejection of armed struggle, the acceptance of a two-state solution, recognition of Israel, annulment of sections of the PLO charter, and full cooperation with Israel since the signing of the Oslo Accords. After all those concessions and compromises, little was left for us to offer, apart from ending the conflict. One could retrospectively fault him for making those concessions *a priori* with little in return, but certainly not for rejecting the unfair Camp David deal.

At the same time, Al Gore chose Joe Lieberman for his running mate. Lieberman's faith did not concern me. His voting record did, him being the strongest advocate for Israel in the Senate. I tuned in to his Larry King Live interview. Larry asked what I thought was a reasonable question: "The US is a major player in the Middle East Peace Process. Given your background and your support for Israel, do you think that will make the US appear less of an honest broker?" Instead of reassuring us the opposite, Lieberman summarily dismissed the question with a "Larry, America is pro-Israel!" Perhaps he was truthfully describing long-standing US foreign policy, but that dismissive attitude was no way to address concerned voters, especially those disagreeing with that policy.

At the end of the summer, I attended a rally in DC organized by *al-Awda* (the Return), the Palestine Right to Return Coalition. "The Return" felt the most threatened of our rights in any two-state peace deal. By this time, I was well-established in the USA and unlikely to return to my parents' homes in Ramleh or Yafa, even if I had the chance. However, for people languishing in the poverty of the refugee camps, exercising that right was vital. Furthermore, I glimpsed a larger picture. If we forego our right to return to our homes – a basic human right – we set an international precedent. Any country could then expect to attack a neighboring country, expel its population, wait a few decades, and then be blessed with a territory free of its people. The Right of Return for us is not only a right, but an obligation. By insisting on it, we concurrently uphold the rights of other weak and downtrodden people. No one has the authority to sign it away.

Camp David failed because the entire Oslo framework was designed to fail. Expending so much time and effort on the Interim stage left little energy for serious negotiation of the final status. It also left Israel room to entrench the Occupation and expand the stolenments. Controlling 100% of the land and confident of their military superiority, Israel approached Camp David from a position of arrogance, as if we had more to lose if talks failed. With the Intifada and other resistance silenced by Oslo, Israel had little incentive to make further deals, the working arrangement during the Interim period suiting it well. Hence, the Interim became the Permanent.

Palestinians the world over felt the flood of disappointment at the failure to reach Peace. Those who had given Arafat the benefit of the doubt at the start of "the Process" were now convinced of their error. Thanks to the Closure, people were worse off than in 1993. Unemployment was high, while a few fortunes were being made from foreign investments and corruption. It was a nervous time of disillusion and uncertainty.

13

Aftermath

Oslo's collapse left Palestinians an inheritance of road closures, stolenments, a retarded economy, and fragmentation of the Land. The PA had no Plan B. Israel, however, prepared well for a conflagration, both militarily and by mobilizing Israeli and American public opinion against us. Israeli citizens, who had been isolated from us since the early 1990s, believed what their leaders repeated about the absence of a "partner for peace". I read afterwards of a mock-Arab city in the desert, codenamed 'Chicago', that Israeli armed forces had been using since 1998 to train for urban warfare. In other words, Israel was already preparing to reinvade and reoccupy the Palestinian cities in case of Oslo's failure.

Chafing from years on the sidelines of Israeli politics, Ariel Sharon exploited his ill-repute to orchestrate a spark that would relaunch his career. To Palestinians, Sharon was a household name from his tenure as Israel's Defense Minister in the early 1980s, when he led Israel's invasion of Lebanon. In mid-September 1982, Israeli troops under his watch surrounded the disarmed Palestinian refugee camps of Sabra and Shatila near Beirut. For three days, they gave cover to hostile Lebanese militias, who entered the camps and murdered several thousand people, mostly women and children. An outcry within Israel, and an investigation finding him personally responsible, culminated in his demotion to "Housing" minister, where he presided over stolenment expansion. For both these reasons, he was loathed in Palestine.

I was instantly alarmed when I read in mid-September, 2000, that Sharon intended to visit the Haram-al-Sharif in Jerusalem, what Israel terms "the Temple Mount". His stated goal for the September 28 visit was to "talk peace". The mere presence of this walking war criminal at one of Islam's holiest sites, near the anniversary of the Sabra and Shatila massacre no less, spoke anything but peace. Even without the thousand policemen escorting him, the visit felt threatening in light of past Jewish extremist attacks on the mosques, related to the movement to resurrect a "Third Temple" at their exact location. The plot was clear. Resisting his entry would be "evidence" that "Palestinians do not want peace", turning more Israelis away from the faltering peace process. Yet, allowing him free passage extends a precedent for eventual takeover of the mosques.

Worried about the consequences of this provocation, I checked news often on the websites of *al-Quds* newspaper and the Israeli daily *Ha'aretz*. Despite the magnitude of the threat from Sharon's visit, no one stopped him. I never understood why Israel's Prime Minister Barak gave his political opponent the green light and armed police cover. After all, Barak had attached his own name to the Peace Process in the form of "Barak's Generous Offer". If the peace collapsed, he stood to lose, politically. Palestinians, meanwhile, seemed intent on resisting Sharon's unwelcome break-in.

As planned, Sharon's police army entered. Palestinians amassed there met them with stones. The police responded violently. The next day, a Friday – the Muslim holy day, the police shot and killed seven unarmed Palestinian protestors at the mosque, wounding scores. Protests erupted throughout the West Bank and Gaza in response to this Israeli violence, leading to more Palestinian casualties, fifty murdered in the first five days, according to the Red Cross. Sharon's plan unfolded like clockwork.

At the time, I had a preplanned month-long trip to China, to meet Charlene's relatives. I left days after Sharon's Haram violation, worried about my parents, Basman and his family, and my friends. In China, I could get little information about events in Palestine. The evening news was in Chinese, and I needed translation. Occasionally I visited an Internet café, only to find my inbox swamped with emails from friends trading news items.

A horrendous medium for that purpose, email at the time was almost my only connection to the outside world. I could barely keep up with the long forwarded articles. Some emails opened to gruesome photos of wounded and killed children. The lack of frequent communication with my parents added to the stress. Still, my month-long stay in China was a calming vacation from what was to come.

My presence in Palestine during the First Intifada had lifted my morale. There, my friends, neighbors, and the entire community were united in our goals and in our understanding. Despite the instability and the daily harassment and intimidation we endured, we found consolation in the fact that we were not alone. Observing the "Second Intifada" from USA, as an immigrant, was a different experience. The media was hostile and far from accurate in its reporting, sometimes serving as a mouthpiece for the Israeli government. The average American, including some of my friends, were ignorant of basic facts about the Middle East.

Sarab, whom I had run into at the Right of Return event in mid-September, advised me to subscribe to al-Jazeera, a nascent Arabic satellite news agency. I installed a dish and was immediately assailed by live feeds of the horror Israel was visiting on my country. The news, even when stripped of al-Jazeera's annoyingly incendiary tone, upset me, more so for my inability to do anything about it. Sharon's policy was to instigate our anger – the reason he went to the mosque in the first place. We needed to channel that anger into productive pursuits, but had no response plan ready. Instead, the hours of watching al-Jazeera, on top of the loads of forwarded emails, incapacitated people like myself. That's the trouble with the 24-hour news cycle. People feel they are informed, but end up with less time to act on that information.

Though the media was quick to call it the "Second Intifada", I hesitate – from my own experience of the First – to call it such. The original Intifada was a spontaneous struggle that erupted with the objective of repelling the Occupation. The mass uprising involved almost everyone, and we consciously limited our arsenal to stones. This conflict, however, was a survival response to a preplanned Israeli assault. Ordinary people could not participate on a wide scale (for one thing, the presence of the PA in the cities minimized direct confrontations with Israel). Meanwhile, the PA police found it necessary to use the light firearms they had to defend themselves, giving Israel the pretext to use tanks and helicopters. Incidentally, I couldn't overlook the irony of "Apache" helicopters rounding us up into reservations.

Consequently, the toll of casualties was tenfold that of the first Intifada, averaging about ten Palestinian lives lost each day. One-third of those were children. Perhaps some participated in protests, but many were innocent bystanders – even babies made the list.

> A video played on the news:
> A child crouches in fear, huddling
> His dad's arms a shield, protecting
> Shopping bags from their hands fallen
> Sounds of gunfire — a brief barrage
> Child goes limp, dad soon collapses.
> There lies a child of twelve,
> His name, Muhammad al-Durra.

Facing a shocked world, the Israeli military evaded responsibility, first blaming the "crossfire", and then accusing Palestinians of the murder. Refuting those lies distracted, even for a moment, from the real tragedy. This brief video clip, another fragment documenting Israeli brutality, told a deeper story. This human story I only understood a dozen years later, after the birth of my own daughter. It could have been anyone in the eye of the camera, in the cross-hairs. The individual who has no escape. A father's heroism, protecting his child and allaying his fears in the face of certain death. That is what has captured the hearts of the world. That is our true story.

To the backdrop of a mounting death toll, negotiations inched along. By then the "Process" had lost the headlines. The near-deal at Taba in January 2001 was moot. Barak was two weeks away from an election against Sharon. The Intifada had escalated beyond the abilities of Arafat and Barak to stop it, Clinton was out of office, while Bush was uninterested in peace. Sharon emerged as the masterful politician, positioning the pieces precisely to his favor. In February 2001, stirred by his campaign of fear, Israelis elected him to be their Prime Minister.

Before the elections, Barak's army had relocated the checkpoints some distance from the West Bank's edge, separating Palestinian villages from their lands. On the same day, Clinton praised Barak for his "courage" and "efforts towards peace," calling for "both sides" to make peaceful gestures, as if the two sides were equivalent in terms of control, responsibility, and firepower. By then, Palestinian casualties outnumbered Israeli ones tenfold.

For months, I was treated to daily images of the consequences of Israel's superior firepower. Facades of houses and apartment buildings riddled with bullets. Holes where tank shells ripped through walls. Images of the dead and wounded. With my parents in Ramallah, I couldn't ignore the news. PA buildings, a primary target for shelling and helicopter attacks, are strewn throughout the city, including one next to our house, and another down the street. I called to check on my parents whenever something was reported in the vicinity. After the murder of al-Durra, Basman became convinced that it was no place to raise small children, especially with another child on the way. His family moved back to Michigan by Christmas 2000. Their move to Ramallah, just before the ill-fated Camp David, was in retrospect a miscalculation.

My nerves wore thin. One night, the news reported the death of an elderly woman at a checkpoint, where the ambulance taking her to a Jerusalem hospital after a heart attack was delayed. "It could've been my mother," I thought. The barrage of images: Israeli soldiers dressed in what looked like camouflaged space suits, peering from tanks and aiming their guns at children in tattered rags throwing stones. It was the first war of the twenty-first century, the robocops battling stone-age rebels. Could be a scene from "*Stargate*" or "*Star Trek Insurrection*", except no renegade fighters from a technologically advanced civilization came to the rescue.

Israel used the Intifada as an excuse to assassinate Palestinian activists on their "wanted" lists. One activist after another fell down to helicopter fire, booby traps, and outright sniping and shelling. Israel invariably labeled the targets of its assassinations "Hamas bombmakers", though none were tried, let alone convicted of "Hamas bombmaking". The victim's family or innocent bystanders were sometimes lost in those attacks, especially when the victim's car or residence were the target.

After Sharon's assumption of power, his army dug a system of deep trenches across Palestinian roads in the West Bank, isolating us from each other. My friend Waheed, who was by then teaching at Birzeit University, told of the hour-long ordeal he needed, walking across the hills, under constant threat of Israeli fire, as cars could no longer navigate the 10-min drive. Some villages had their water cut off. They had to import it by truck, at high cost, or walk long distances to haul it.

George W. Bush did not even pretend to the "both sides" rhetoric, his refrain echoing Sharon's worldview: "Palestinians must stop the violence." Israel's tanks and helicopters were simply "excessive force" used to quell Palestinian "attacks". The daily violence of the Occupation was ignored. The Closure, checkpoints, and sieges could not be enforced without violence. The violence of detentions, home demolitions, permits, and other forms of state oppression is quieter and more gradual than the few headline-grabbing suicide bombs, even though the former impacts far more people.

Israeli terminology predominated in the US media. Palestinians were typically described as "armed", "militants", or "gunmen". Israeli soldiers, who were literally *armed, militant gunmen,* were portrayed as "returning fire", or acting in "self-defense". A Palestinian attack on Gilo, a stolen-ment built on land taken from the West Bank town of Beit Jala, was reported as an attack on a "Jerusalem neighborhood". Presenting in short soundbites devoid of context, the US media created a world in which the Palestinian struggle for freedom was "violence", while Israeli oppression was "retaliation". Even the "liberal" NPR, in a media study I read, was five times more likely to report Israeli deaths than Palestinian deaths, and more likely to mention the names of the Israeli victims. This deflation of the numbers of Palestinian casualties and personification of the Israelis fundamentally distorts the narrative.

Israel's information war spread far. Ernie, my close colleague at work, often parroted the Israeli propaganda he had absorbed from mailing lists and Israeli news outlets. I liked the guy, but was astounded at his unquestioning attitude towards those statements he repeated, some downright racist. Expecting more from someone with his intelligence and scientific skepticism, I was too naïve to understand the power of fake news.

The high proportion of children killed by the Israeli army were "explained" by the soundbite "Palestinians send their kids to die" (3.2 million Google results in 2010). Besides diverting responsibility, this racist, callous, and morally-bankrupt argument suggests Palestinian parents love their children less than other people, designating us a "primitive" race that engages in human sacrifice. The South African Apartheid regime had used exactly the same argument after gunning down child demonstrators.

For one thing, we never *sent* our kids anywhere. The Palestinian children were killed in their streets, marketplaces, and neighborhoods. Some were shot at their own doorstep, or even inside their homes. We had not invaded anyone's land, but were defending our cities, so our streets turned into battlefields, and our residences into targets for planes, tanks, and artillery. Israeli cities, safely behind the checkpoints and barriers, had not witnessed the urban warfare of the sort they unleashed on us, so their children had been mostly shielded from the firing.

The racist statement implies another, more sinister, assertion. Supposing a ten- or twelve-year-old child *did* throw stones. Does that justify his being shot?

It is every human being's right to protest and express a desire for change. Those forcefully occupying our land, imposing their will while stripping us of rights, cannot expect an indefinite silence. They cannot simultaneously be the victor and the victim.

The conversations with Ernie dragged on. Every day brought new events that got one or the other riled up. It was futile, yet eye-opening. Not only did we have different news sources, making us disagree on facts, but we had even deeper disagreements regarding values. When I brought up international law, he responded: "International law doesn't matter." When I brought up the immorality of the Occupation, he retorted: "Morality doesn't matter." Ernie's justification for the Occupation was that "Israel fought for the land and won it." By his own logic, the only acceptable way for us to restore our lands is to fight for them. Yet, when we do throw stones, my friend decries "Palestinian violence". When our militias use firearms to defend their own homes, it is "terrorism".

The first conversation with Ernie upon my return from China centered on Sharon's provocative entry into al-Haram al-Sharif. Ernie expressed his concern about the Palestinians killed on the mosque compound, quickly adding that it was a result of "the hail of stones falling on the Jewish worshippers" at the Western Wall, adjacent to the mosque. In his own words: "If I was down there that day, I would not hesitate to grab my guns and go on a shooting spree." This coming from an elderly, highly-respected scientist. If the stoning of worshippers justified going on a shooting rampage, how then ought we have responded to Baruch Goldstein's attack on the Hebron mosque? Getting wronged is no license to kill innocents.

Fact-checking in contemporary newspaper accounts, I found no mention of a "hail of stones" on Jewish worshippers except when quoting Israeli officials, the reporters themselves affirming that the stones were directed at Israeli police. According to the Guardian from Sep. 29, for instance, "Young Palestinians heaved chairs, stones, rubbish bins, and whatever missiles came to hand at the Israeli forces." From the next day's edition, "Dozens of police, including the Jerusalem police chief, were hit by stones." There were no reports of Israeli casualties besides the armed police force.

Looking at the pattern of events, Sharon's main policy was gradual escalation, so as to normalize Israeli violence. First the trenches were dug; in a few weeks those faded from the news, and even Palestinians got used to them. The trenches accepted, Israel stepped up to temporary invasions of PA territory;

> then invading PA territory to "arrest" (really kidnap) wanted Palestinians;
> invading PA territory, making arrests, and demolishing homes;
> invading PA territory, making arrests, demolishing homes, and uprooting trees; …

In executing this diabolical version of the *Twelve Days of Christmas*, Sharon's evil genius lay in his uncanny understanding of people's attention spans and tolerance limits. A severe escalation might have provoked serious international condemnation. A series of small provocations, however, taken at intervals commensurate with the news cycle, were likely to go unnoticed.

In May 2001, I was shocked to hear that F-16 jets were used to attack buildings in Gaza and other Palestinian cities. This was not a situation of war. Palestinians were civilian residents within the area Israel's military controlled, and lacking any kind of air defenses, were completely vulnerable to air attack. In the first F-16 attack, a high-rise building was brought to rubble, killing a dozen people. I watched hundreds of people running on the street amid billowing dust and smoke, not knowing the planes' next target.

The Arab masses protested, world leaders condemned. Colin Powell threatened to investigate whether Israel violated restrictions on foreign military aid specifying use for self-defense, not against civilians. For two weeks, Israel kept a low profile until criticisms quieted, then resumed using F-16s against civilian targets on a regular basis, killing dozens. Images of rescuers digging under mounds of rubble in search of survivors and remains became commonplace.

Perhaps that explains my disgust when I hear of Israel sending a "rescue team" to countries struck by natural or man-made disasters. From earthquakes in Haiti and Turkey, to the US embassy bombings in Africa, the Israeli team was there to promote a manufactured image. "Israel is an expert in digging in the rubble," or "Victimized by terror so often, Israel is used to rescue missions." The rescuer cloak magically renders invisible the terror they inflict on others. Had they cared for human life, they would have stopped periodically bombing Lebanon and Gaza.

Sharon's cabinet included members from the most extreme parties in Israel, including Rehavam Ze'evi, whose party's platform insisted on peace only through military victory, consecrated settling the land, and avowed Jerusalem the eternal united capital of a *Jewish* Israel. For the sake of that Jewish purity, Ze'evi openly promoted the "Transfer" policy, sending Palestinians on another Trail of Tears. The rest of the world had coined the term "ethnic cleansing" (itself a euphemism) to describe such policies. With the multiplicity of cameras this century enjoys, the 1948 "Transfer" script – expulsion through terror under the fog of war – gave way to the slow implementation, making life so miserable that Palestinians would choose to relocate. Our survival on the Land was at stake. My concerns about a repeat Nakba reignited. My friends dismissed that possibility. Looking at reality, the "slow-motion" version was already in progress. Finding it impossible to lead a normal life under occupation, people were leaving, like my brother Basman. Others, like myself and my friends Archie, Tigran, Wasel and Abdul-Lateef, had flown overseas to study, and remained there. Those who stayed in Palestine continued enduring countless hardships.

The Sharon government expanded home demolitions. Additional buildings were destroyed by air raids and tank shells. The Ramallah police station next to my old school, from which Israeli soldiers routinely shot at our classroom, had switched to PA hands since 1996. An Israeli rocket totally demolished it during this Intifada. On my next visit, I found a parking lot in its place. A historic house visible from my bedroom window was also flattened, the red-tiled roof collapsed within a perimeter of scattered building stones. The damage was particularly heavy in Gaza, which had one of the highest population densities in the world, where large families crowded in tiny apartments. The destruction of an eight-story high-rise, for whatever reason, deprived three-hundred souls of their homes. New refugee camps came into being to house the new wave of Palestinians rendered homeless by Sharon's demolitions.

By the end of 2001, Israeli fire had claimed the lives of 904 Palestinians, and caused 16,600 injuries, according to the Red Cross. Something like 40% of the injuries resulted in permanent disabilities. The hospitals were overwhelmed with casualties. There were frequent blood shortages. Israeli blockades made ambulance travel more difficult. Sooner or later, Sharon's government hoped, harried by homelessness, food and water shortages, economic bleakness, and sheer Israeli violence, more Palestinians would choose to leave.

I was frustrated at the world's failure, or inability, to stop this onslaught, or was it a lack of will? As in the conflict-ridden former Yugoslavia, the rest of the world watched. Unlike Yugoslavia, the rest of the world only watched. No UN peacekeepers intervened. No-fly zones were not even suggested. Neither were weapons embargos. US Aid continually replenished Israel airplanes, armor, and ammunition. The condemnations and symbolic gestures from Arab governments were no help. The large crowds of protesters in Arab and Islamic countries often had to battle their own governments' security forces.

Meanwhile, the Bush administration had a single-minded focus on Iraq, bombing it frequently from the no-fly zones, while siding completely with Israel in their war on us. This deepened the perception of America as anti-Arab and anti-Muslim.

I recall news from the mid-1990s about US immigrants from Croatia and Bosnia training in the US, then going to fight the Serbs. No one stopped them from helping their extended families. As for Palestine, Bush declared Hamas a "terrorist organization" (though they had never attacked Americans, nor anyone outside of Palestine). Under this blanket declaration, a pro-Palestinian radio station in the DC area, and several US charities were shut down. Among them was the Holy Land Foundation, a large relief organization that had assisted victims of the Oklahoma City bombing, the ethnic cleansing in Bosnia, as well as floods and earthquakes around the world. It was alleged that they supported Hamas by aiding the families of suicide bombers in Gaza. The entire affair struck me as politically-motivated. An organization that gave out tents and blankets to the thousands of Palestinians made homeless by Sharon's demolitions, would inevitably help the occasional family of a suicide bomber. A charity should not be in the business of barring people from its aid.

At the same time, numerous American "charities" supported the Occupation using tax-deductible donations. One in New York state delivered bullet-proof vests to the settlers, as well as rifle scopes, so they could occupy our lands and attack us without fear of retribution. It is "charity" to donate military equipment to settlers living illegally in subsidized luxury villas, but "support of terrorism" to donate tents, flour, and water to impoverished children in the refugee camps.

By the end of 2000, former Serbian leader Milosevic was on trial for war crimes. A group of victims from the Sabra and Shatila massacre brought a war crimes lawsuit in a Belgian court against Sharon. The case was accepted, but Sharon refused to stand trial, avoiding travel to Belgium. When he became Prime Minister, and because of that, the case was ultimately dismissed. This dismissal to me defeats the purpose of war crime laws: a head of state has more power to commit further crimes.

On campus in the Washington DC area, I got to attend a Q&A for Sen. George Mitchell, who gave his name to one of the few feeble diplomatic initiatives. After several months of investigations, by which time the Intifada was well underway and more damage done, the Mitchell Report came out, stillborn, another addition to the mountains of sterile documents proposing solutions to the Middle East's problems. Mitchell highlighted the construction of stolenments during Oslo as a major cause of mistrust. It recommended steps to be taken so negotiations would restart. Sharon added his own prohibitive precondition to implementing those recommendations – the "total cessation of violence."

The purpose of investigations and reports, seems to me, is to excuse inaction. The Mitchell Report, and what documents followed, looked like an obstacle course designed to thwart a peaceful solution, under the illusion of a process. Mitchell was the first of a series of American envoys (Tenet, Zinney, and others), each devising a plan to get the parties back to the point where the implementation of the previous plan could begin. The number of unnecessary conditionalities multiplied. The long, drawn-out, process is the antithesis of Peace. Israel has always relied on its asymmetric military power to enforce the Occupation, seeing no advantage in a negotiated agreement. By prolonging the status quo, those "plans" in effect advanced Israeli policy. The peace talks needed to be structured such that everybody's best interest was to make them work, not the other way round. Oslo had failed because it rewarded those who violated it.

By late August 2001, Israel had assassinated Abu Ali Mustafa, the head of the Popular Front (PFLP), one of the main PLO factions. Within a couple of months, the PFLP retaliated, assassinating Rehavam Ze'evi, the racist "Transfer" minister in Sharon's government, who, ironically, was an advocate of Israel's assassination policy. He was immediately hailed a hero in Israeli circles, a stolenment founded in his name. A road was also renamed "Gandhi Road" after his ill-suited nickname, considering how he dedicated his life to opposing peace and advocating military violence and genocide. Ze'evi was the first and last Israeli to be assassinated during the Intifada. Israel, however, continued and intensified its assassination policy, targeting activists big and small. The idea, learned from the way the British crushed the 1936 uprising, was to leave us leaderless.

I was alarmed at the resurgence of suicide bombings. The first suicide attack in the Second Intifada was aimed at Israeli *soldiers* manning a checkpoint. By the summer of 2001, after Israeli F-16s had leveled high-rises, the lethality of suicide bombs intensified. Two bombings grabbed headlines: one in Tel Aviv leaving 20 dead, and another in Jerusalem killing 15. The loss of life saddened me. Pizza parlors, nightclubs, weddings. The bodies fell. The aftermath, the sadness, the funerals. It was no different than what the families of our dead were going through. I was left wondering what justice was served by the killing of innocents?

Whatever aims those bombings accomplished, they hurt us internationally and divided us internally. Heated discussions arose within an activist group I was in, some members urging us to condemn all violence with no exceptions, others maintaining that our group was in no position to judge those "under fire". Some even doubted whether Israeli society could truly be deemed "innocent" – a society in which every adult served in the military, and had a choice to dissent, but chose to conform and ignore the oppression.

Years later, I read of a statistical study that noted similarities in the profiles of the bombers: most were hurting economically, came from households of eight or more, and had a family member killed, arrested, or injured by Israeli soldiers. The study in no way suggests that those suffering the same poor conditions are bound to strap a bomb around their waist. Most chose *not* to. For those who did, it was a *choice*, and they made that clear in their parting videos.

Statistics cannot capture the intangible of hopelessness. Israeli repression for sure widened the pool of disaffected Palestinians for the militant groups to fish, but it also intensified the sense of despair that drove a few to suicidal acts. During the First Intifada, economic conditions were perhaps just as dire, and Israeli actions touched everyone, but we had hope – that freedom was around the corner. There were no suicide bombings back then. Fast forward to 2002, fifteen years after the start of the First Intifada and following a decade of fruitless negotiations; the promised freedom was obscured by the encroaching stolenments, and denied permit to enter. The massing mountain of unfulfilled agreements, like the Mitchell Report, only verified that no amount of international effort was of help in securing human rights. In 1988, we struggled thinking our actions were leading us somewhere. In 2002, people simply struggled to survive. The peaceful path to freedom was barricaded.

I strained to imagine an individual amid the rubble of Jenin, looking at the destruction from the Re-invasion, having lost family members, or seen friends fall to Israeli fire. A few miles away, in Tel Aviv or Netanya, Israelis were enjoying their lives in apparent peace, going to nightclubs and beach parties, oblivious to the misery they hurled upon his world. At what point did he gather the determination to take it to them, to make them feel a small part of what his city was sustaining?

Hopelessness does not make good policy. Evening out the body count did not bring us any closer to our goal of freedom. The factions that engaged in it realized the futility of random bombings and after 2002, concentrated instead on checkpoints, military bases, and stolenments in the West Bank and Gaza.

Suicide attacks captured media attention like nothing else. Hundreds of thousands of peaceful demonstrators might get a minute on CNN, if that. But a single attack on Jerusalem could become instant "Breaking News", the reels of the aftermath replaying for hours. It was the wrong kind of attention, brought by a desperate attempt to get a deaf world to listen. Perhaps the media is complicit for glamorizing sensational violence. But then the media plays what their audiences want to see. In that sense, we all share in the responsibility because we tune in only when blood is shed.

Random violent attacks against average Israeli civilians, apart from being morally wrong, are counterproductive. Israeli society is not monolithic. The 17-year old who joins the army because he has to, is not on par with the millionaire general who runs his own company on the side. Bus explosions will not affect the Israelis running the country, who have their own chauffeur-driven bullet-proof limos. Instead, those attacks unified Israelis against us.

Just because Israel calls itself a "democracy", responsibility for the Occupation doesn't rest equally on individual citizens. More to blame than any individual are the economic interests exploiting the Occupation. The most efficient path to freedom is to turn their profits into financial losses.

The settlers, secure in their subsidized and government-defended housing, gain directly. So do the land speculators and construction companies building the stolenments, Occupation Roads, and the Wall. The force needed to maintain the Occupation is to the advantage of the armaments industries in both Israel and the US. Some Israeli businesses exploit the occupied markets and underpaid Palestinian labor. Israelis outside those segments have little to gain from it. The fact that Israeli government agencies needed to advertise in Israeli newspapers stressing the vitality of the West Bank's water for Israel, highlighted the lack of Israeli mass support for the Occupation.

From that point of view, the real enemies of Palestinian freedom extend far beyond Israel's borders. Certain Palestinians, too, profit from the Occupation and the ensuing conflict. It was rumored that the cement for Israel's Wall was purchased from a certain someone within the Palestinian Authority. Churches, among others, had sold land for the stolenments. Corrupt Palestinian officials sapped resources from the struggle for their own personal benefit. Mayors of Palestinian cities who allowed developers to contravene building codes were as culpable. Uprooting trees and destroying our own environment, in return for petty profit from a building, does the work of the Occupation in making our cities unlivable and pressuring people to leave.

A boycott of Israeli products was logical. Every purchase not only helped the Israeli economy, but through taxes, directly helped the Israeli government and its occupying military. International corporations also profited from Israel's Occupation. So did the New York bankers lending Israel, the US industries shipping militarized US tax dollars to Israel, and the CEO donating – tax-free – to settler organizations. Those palpable financial interests could be shaken by organized international boycotts and divestment.

I became aware of such a boycott during the Second Intifada. Unfortunately, it lacked focus and was thus less effective. Too many companies populated the list: Coca-Cola, Johnson & Johnson, Nestlé, almost all brands of cosmetics, Starbucks, *etc.* The connection to Israel for some, such as owning an Israeli subsidiary, was too tenuous to motivate people. I thought it better to select a few companies at the forefront of the Occupation and at the same time vulnerable to the decisions of individual consumers. Caterpillar clearly had blood on its hands for making the armored bulldozers that leveled Palestinian homes, but was no easy target given its sales did not depend on small consumers.

I abided by the boycott anyway. I stopped drinking Coca-Cola, all the better for my health. I switched from Kleenex to store-brand tissues, and from Nescafé to other brands of instant coffee. I never cared for Starbucks to begin with. It felt slightly better to be doing something, but I doubted that my individual boycott hurt those companies' bottom lines. Coca-Cola and Kleenex were still on supermarket shelves when I checked. I wrote the companies one by one explaining my boycott. In most cases, I only got canned responses thanking me for my feedback. Coca-Cola went a step further and claimed that the company's operations in the West Bank benefited everyone, including Palestinian Arab workers, sidestepping the issue of siphoning Palestinian water. It was an utter waste of time. Perhaps the only benefit of my boycott was giving me conversation starters, like explaining to a friend why I refused a Coke when offered one.

Companies on the boycott list had significant ownership by Arab investors. At the height of the Intifada, when Israeli bulldozers were flattening Jenin, Citibank lent Israel one billion dollars to build the Wall.

Citibank had large investments from Gulf countries, who reportedly owned 25% of its shares. Those Arab shareholders could have had a say about the loan, but they favored their own personal profit from the transaction. American corporations making weapons for Israel also have Arab investors. (The Saudis were reported to own over 5% of the Carlyle Group.) Again, they chose personal profits over anything else.

Instead of identifying the real enemy and stressing economic resistance, the leaders of some Palestinian factions opted for headline-grabbing attacks on innocent Israeli civilians. The persistent image of Palestinian children confronting tanks with stones was now diluted with the aftermath of suicide attacks. Far from hurting Israel, the suicide bombing bestowed it otherwise unwarranted sympathy, united Israeli opinions against us, and gave the occupiers an untold number of talking points. Every measure Israel took to repress our population was now "justified". "The suicide bombers built the Wall," I often heard from Occupation-supporters.

Perhaps it was no coincidence that Hamas was funded by Gulf countries. Whenever a suicide bomb exploded in Haifa or Tel Aviv, oil prices shot up and Gulf countries made windfall profits from oil sales. Defense contractor sales multiplied, and Citibank profited from its loans to build the Wall. This is the way it worked. The victims and their grieving families, whether Israeli or Palestinian, are collateral damage in this international game for profit.

14

Body Counts

CLICK, CLICK.

It was my first time using a typewriter. Miraculously, the anachronistic, dust-coated specimen in the copy room still worked. I needed it for my application for US immigration, required to be typed on carbon paper, no less. Apparently, they had missed the memo about the turn of the millennium.

Click, click.

Character by character, I painstakingly filled the form on behalf of Charlene and myself. With Palestine in turmoil, I had made up my mind to stay in the USA. I dreamed of becoming a US citizen one day.

Despite a misguided foreign policy and a xenophobia that sometimes extended to immigrants, I found much to admire about America, particularly its ideals, heterogeneity, and inclusiveness. I liked my American friends. I appreciated the individual freedom absent from much of the rest of the world. I respected the clean environment and the Americans who cared about it. I wanted to stay.

One sore spot nagged me. Of the US taxes I faithfully paid every year, part was diverted to fund the Israeli military. Typically averaging *three billion* dollars a year, this "military aid" was bolstering the Occupation. My own earnings were being misdirected to a foreign country, paying for munitions to threaten my loved ones, and to destroy my country of origin. It was obscene. I contemplated refusal to pay taxes, I wrote letters to my congressman about it, but there was no escape. The money kept flowing. For the average American, the federal budget is a political issue, to be decided by elected representatives. For Palestinian Americans, aid to Israel is personal.

I struggled to understand the point of that aid. After Sadat made peace with Israel, and aligned Egypt with America, US aid to Israel ballooned, as a "reward" to the Israelis for making peace. The peace on the Egyptian front and the additional weapons from the expanded aid enabled Israel to invade Lebanon just a few years later. US aid therefore had a destabilizing effect on the region, rather than the purported goals of "defending Israel", or "maintaining the balance of power". Assuring Israel's militarily superiority only made it refuse to compromise and disregard the consequences of its aggressive actions. Counting on steady and unconditional American support, Israeli leaders had no incentive to seek peace.

American aid to Israel made more sense considering domestic politics. Apart from pleasing the pro-Israel lobby, US aid to Israel, like most of the US military budget, ended in the coffers of the US "defense" industries – corporate welfare. My friend Will thought a goal of the aid was to have Israel test cutting-edge weapons in a combat situation. The geniuses who dreamt such a policy had no qualms about the people their "tests" hurt. Those gifts touched the lives and liberty of millions in Palestine and Lebanon, and everyone could read "Made in U.S.A." on unexploded shells.

This was June 2001. I was in Chicago for a conference, and Will, who was living in Indiana now, swung by for a day visit. He was shocked at the recent attack on the USS Cole. What did "security" mean, if the world's strongest power could be attacked thus? Having been to Occupied Palestine, he could see why people in the Middle East resented American support for Israel. In addition to military aid, the US covered diplomatically for Israel at the UN. By the end of August 2001, Colin Powell boycotted a UN conference on racism "because of language critical of Israel," despite voluminous documentation of systematic discrimination in Israel.

Writing in my diary after that conversation with Will: "The nightmare of terrorism is difficult to prevent solely by enhancing security. The next strike can come from anyone, anywhere. The US is on the wrong track confronting terrorism by increasing control and surveillance of its own Arab and Muslim residents, while completely ignoring the root causes of anti-American sentiment abroad."

The very word "terrorism" is a loaded expression. It is invariably used to describe the violence committed by those out of power. The violence of those in power is systematic, institutionalized, and sweeping, but is accepted or ignored.

Collapse

For Labor Day, Charlene and I made a road trip to Canada, visiting Niagara Falls and Toronto, then over to Windsor to visit Adnan. It was a relaxing time, during which I hardly watched any news. One book kept me up all night: *Sacred Landscapes* by Meron Benvenisti. Drawing on recently declassified Israeli documents, he retells the story of our expulsion and the deliberate destruction of our villages in 1948: how, under the guise of "slum-clearance", Arab Yafa was demolished to make room for Jewish-only neighborhoods; how Arab cemeteries inside Israel were left to neglect, or used for roads, parking lots, parks, and trash dumps; how the official Israeli definition of "historic places" was designed to protect modern Zionist buildings, while allowing native Palestinian structures to deteriorate with time, eventually to be demolished for development; and how meanwhile, "antiquity" laws prevented exploration or preservation of the destroyed Palestinian villages, and handicapped Palestinian archeology in general.

That summer, Ernie kept me informed of the controversy surrounding the Haram-al-Sharif area in Jerusalem. His sources were accusing Muslims repairing a room underneath the Dome of the Rock of "removing bucket loads of dirt" without any "proper" archaeological oversight, meaning Israeli-government oversight. Meanwhile, the Israeli government had seized the 8th-century Umayyad palace just outside the Haram – built by the Arabs along with the mosques. The Israelis converted the Umayyad palace to their "Temple" museum, with virtual reality visualizations of their historic, or rather planned, Temple. Nightly, light and sound shows projected images of the Temple on the walls of the Haram. My Palestinian circles were outraged about that. To me, the "archeological crimes" felt like minor issues, possibly distractions, in comparison with the ongoing Judaization program of Jerusalem and Israel's war against its Palestinian residents. Destroying thousands-of-years-old artifacts of people now dead (whether Jewish or Muslim) paled in comparison to destroying the livelihoods of the hundreds of thousands still alive.

Those thoughts kept me company as we drove back on Sunday, September 9. Fortunately, my job allowed me to keep my own hours, as the Canada trip had totally upset my sleep routine. Tuesday, I was awakened about 11 AM by a phone call from Chris in Arizona. He wanted to know if we were OK.

"We're fine, why call us so early?" I asked, half asleep and clueless about what time it was.

"You don't know? Turn on the TV! A plane hit the World Trade Center. The towers collapsed. The Pentagon was hit, too. I called to see if you're OK."

Still half asleep, I had no idea what the words he just said meant. It sounded too far out to be real. Sure it was all a dream, I turned on the TV, and the images reeled, over and over.

By the time I remembered it was a Tuesday, I figured it was too late to go to work. No matter, as my coworkers were all glued to the one TV in the building. A strange day, full of emotion, and shock, and puzzlement. By the time Chris's call woke me up, it was all over. We had to reconstruct what happened from the chaos of images and news. The planes hitting the towers, people running on the streets amid billowing dust and smoke. Reports of the Pentagon getting hit, and some strange story about a 4th plane falling down in Pennsylvania. What was going on? I called to check on Roy, who worked near the Pentagon. He had not gotten home, as the roads in DC were hectic, the Metro closed, and no one knew what to do. He finally made it extra late in the afternoon.

The crowds running on the streets of New York resurrected images, just months earlier, from Gaza and Nablus after F-16 strikes. Meanwhile, frenzied news commentators stressed how historic this attack was, and how the world had changed forever. Despite the magnitude of this atrocity, it was neither the first time nor the last time that people murdered so many others. Such utterances struck me as the illusions, or should I say hallucinations, of a country whose mainland was spared bombardment in the past century. World War II had seen far greater horrors. Iraq had endured losses of 300,000 people in a few weeks of the 1991 war, and multiples more from the ensuing sanctions. What is "unique" about mass murder?

The most pressing question on my mind was "where next"? Was this the first strike of a war? Living close to DC, we naturally worried. Who did it was another mystery. No one admitted responsibility. Suspicion was narrowed down on al-Qaeda, but the attack looked so well-executed and well-planned, I doubted that could be the signature of a ragtag band of terrorists hiding in caves in Afghanistan. Then the pictures of the hijackers streamed in: nineteen individuals, all Arabs. I watched in disbelief. I wondered how they decided which passengers were the hijackers, especially we knew nothing of what happened inside the planes. Did they simply pick all the Arabic names on the passenger lists? Were I a passenger, would I have been listed as one of the hijackers? The "evidence" trickling from the news was anecdotal. Could having a pilot's license be held against me? How about forgetting the Arabic-language novel I was reading in the car?

From grief and shock, my instincts turned to self-preservation. The tone of the round-the-clock television broadcasts was alarming. I vividly recall a Fox news reporter standing in front of the mosque in DC behind the headline "America's Fifth Column", warning of "sleeper cells" – people already here, who looked beyond suspicion, but were going to unleash terror one day. It sounded like an excuse for the xenophobes to crack down on immigrant communities. Opinions called for deportation of visitors from Arab countries, and others for internment of Arab Americans. "We" needed to give up some of our freedoms to make sure an attack like this is not repeated, the "we" in question shackling Arab and Muslim citizens. Emotions were raw and, in the first few days, innocents were shot, including someone wearing a Sikh turban mistaken for an Islamic headdress. I was glad when respectable commentators spoke up against those attacks, asserting that "Taking things into your own hands by attacking innocent people makes *you* a terrorist."

Even so, I thought it was only a matter of time before someone knocked on my door. My parents compounded the situation by calling me on the phone, only to lecture me about "keeping a low profile" and "not saying anything over the phone." I was sure that eavesdroppers hearing these warnings would think I was up to something. As it turned out, I never got contacted by the FBI. Either they were so competent as to know everything about me, and thus know I was a harmless human who minded his own business, or they had no clue I existed, perhaps because I entered the US on my Canadian passport.

September 11 was hailed as "an attack on our freedom," but the real attack on freedom took place in the weeks and months after the event, as the US government stepped up its surveillance, searches, and infringement on our rights. The "Patriot" Act was quickly passed to give the government extra-constitutional powers. They could tap phones and read our emails without judicial oversight, learn what books we checked out from libraries, or detain someone without a court order. Americans assumed these measures would largely be directed at terror suspects, but the law had no such restrictions – any American could be subject to these unconstitutional measures, and the government would prevent them from knowing they were being investigated. Activist groups were being infiltrated and monitored, people reported on their neighbors simply because of differing political views, and electronic billboards flashed "Report Suspicious Activities", without defining what a "suspicious" activity was.

The Arab-American community suffered a greater share of the consequences. Countless people in the Detroit Metro area, including friends who never got involved in activism or politics, were interviewed by the FBI without a pretext. Undocumented immigrants from Arab descent were rounded up and deported, tearing families apart. Those who came here escaping politically oppressive regimes were sent back without regard to their safety. (Ironically, the 9/11 hijackers actually entered the USA legally.) Arab students on campus had to visit the Immigration office every so often for a process called "Special Registration", where they got fingerprinted and had to demonstrate they were full-time students. (In an interesting twist, Palestinian students were exempted from Special Registration, a tidbit that surprised, and irked, my colleague Ze'ev. Chatting at a conference in 2002, I gently reminded him that Israel got the credit for Palestine not being recognized a country.)

In the scheme of things, I was lucky. On Sep. 11, my green card application was still pending. Finally in February, out of the blue, Charlene and I received letters requesting we report to the INS office. Not knowing what to expect, we were pleasantly surprised when the immigration officer stamped permanent resident visas on our passports. A week later, INS issued a renewal visa for one of the hijackers, and all hell broke loose. The agency was criticized and investigated, then reshuffled, while pending applications suffered an indefinite hold. We narrowly escaped with our green cards.

The news from that period was cloaked in fear, fear being the drug that kept us tuned in. Those with agendas to push, particularly the neo-conservatives in the Bush administration, exploited this atmosphere and heightened it. The enemy vacuum created by the fall of the Soviet Union was now a thing of the past. The "War on Terror" became the new Cold War, justifying open-ended wars on small countries, and more significantly, bloated defense budgets. "The enemy could strike again, anytime, anywhere." "Chemical and biological weapons, ..." "Al-Qaeda potentially has access to nuclear material." While that filth floated about, newspapers distributed readiness supplements to stoke our worries. It was the nuclear fallout shelter craze of the 1950s all over again. In the end, the warnings and "readiness" instructions amounted to the world's most elaborate duct tape commercial.

Perhaps the initial media estimate of 50,000 dead in the World Trade Center was an honest mistake, but this first impression stuck, heightening the state of fear. The "terror threat meter" was unveiled, seen on electronic billboards and airport elevators. Never green, the color code fluctuated like a toddler's piano playing an eerie Halloween tune, seducing us to succumb to the restrictions on our freedoms, and the Wars. All the TV faces exhorted us to "rally around the President," leaving no room for dissent, or even skepticism. The DC area was blanketed in a sinister atmosphere. The Saturday after the attack, Charlene and I drove to the Pentagon to see the damage for ourselves. We weren't the only ones with that idea, and traffic was stuck as police had blocked the roads that provided the best view of the damaged side. Finally we made it to a side street where we parked and walked up a hill a good distance away. We could only see smoke rising from a corner of the building. It was sobering that the headquarters of the world's strongest military was attacked.

The two events that stunned the DC Metro area, though, were the anthrax attacks and the Sniper, both of which made 9/11 appear as a first step in a coordinated attack. The anthrax letters passed through the same postal distribution center used by my local post office. Afraid to check the mail, we switched to online billing on everything, and sent electronic Christmas cards. The Sniper struck about a mile from where we lived. One victim fell at a shopping center we frequented, another at a gas station we used. No one knew where the next strike was going to be. For the rest of the year, we stopped going out, especially at night, shopped less often, and hid in the car when filling up with gas.

Long before September 11, I was convinced that US policy in the Middle East was heading in a disastrous direction. I was disturbed at the ignorance Americans had of the rest of the world. My friends paid little attention to foreign policy, thinking it had no impact on their lives. How wrong! The movie *"Memento"* vividly illustrated how someone with a strong grievance, but lacking knowledge of the past, could be easily manipulated to do someone else's bidding. In the collapse of the twin towers, those with agendas found the murderous grievance with which to manipulate a population ignorant of what happens outside the borders. In the aftermath, I naively hoped that Americans would realize how ill-served they were by the decades of damaging US foreign policy. More naively, I hoped that now that Americans experienced destruction firsthand, they would oppose meting it upon small, defenseless countries. Instead, the emotions unleashed by the attacks pushed people in the opposite direction. Rather than hold their President accountable for his disastrous policies, Americans thirsted for an outside "enemy", first lining up behind a war in Afghanistan, then another in Iraq. America's need to "look strong" caused the death of tens of thousands of innocent Afghans and Iraqis whose only fault was being born in the wrong place, at the wrong time. It seemed to me a desecration of the memories of the September 11 victims to exact such "revenge" in their names.

Terror does not stop terror, only breeds more. It does not convince people on the other side to change their ways, only makes them more radicalized. The September 11 attack was no way to address the numerous legitimate grievances against the errant US policy in the Middle East, if that was ever its purpose. As events had shown, it only made Americans mistrust and even hate Arabs and Muslims more. As for the American response, it was equally misdirected, and hence counterproductive. "Shock and Awe" only multiplied America's enemies. The Iraq War ultimately created ISIS. Today's wars create tomorrow's enemies, in an endless pyramid of terror.

In the months following the attack, Israeli spokesmen masqueraded as "terrorism experts" on TV. The Palestinian suicide bombs, borne out of decades of an inhuman Occupation, were held in parallel, to garner sympathy and acceptance for Israel's oppressive measures. In reality, Israeli actions bred terror where none existed. My parents were living peacefully in the coastal cities until Zionist terror drove them from their homes. The First Intifada was a principled, nonviolent, resistance movement that Israel met with violence. It took a quarter-century of occupation to breed the first Palestinian suicide bomb.

For months, those "experts" pushed for the Israelization of America. "Retaliate, bomb, use nothing but force, and keep your citizens living in fear so they support the government's belligerence." Behind this posturing was the Israeli government's intent to intensify their own war on Palestinians without stirring an international response. The number of Palestinian casualties multiplied after September 11. With the eyes of the world on New York and on the American wars, Sharon took full advantage of the reporting darkness.

Ernie was getting on my nerves for interjecting Israel into every conversation, every occasion. A colleague from another university visits us. Chatting upon arrival about his flight and airport delays, Ernie interjects that "security in US airports is laughable compared to Israel's." The coffee room another day. Someone mentions the fear that the Sniper's attacks have stirred, and that activates Ernie. "In Jerusalem, you have to be careful when taking out the garbage; you never know when a bomb is hidden in the bins." I was never sure if his exaggerated statements, rather than evoking sympathy with Israelis, deterred people from Israel's path. Who wants to spend the rest of their lives in such fear?

Re-Invasion

Charlene and I were hoping to visit Palestine but the plans were derailed by the Intifada. In early 2002, my mother fell down and broke her hip. She had an emergency surgery at the Ramallah hospital, but ultimately needed a hip replacement that could not be performed there. With the unpredictable conditions and Closure, it was not possible to get it done in Jerusalem, either. So my parents decided to come back to Canada for the surgery, where we planned to meet them over spring break.

Apart from email discussions with my friends, I mostly withdrew. Nothing could be done. I continued watching al-Jazeera, now split between coverage of Afghanistan and coverage of Palestine. I had not attended a single protest except for a Christmas vigil at the end of 2000, in solidarity with the people of Bethlehem. Since the 1991 Gulf War, I had become convinced of the futility of protest in this country. After a particularly bloody F16 attack in Feb. 2002, however, I joined a small protest downtown organized by *al-Awda*, the Right of Return organization. I had no illusions that this protest, or any other, would accomplish anything. Rather, it was a form of therapy, and networking. Holding signs and chanting slogans, with other like-minded people, released the pent-up stress from watching the daily injustices. I got involved in *al-Awda*, attending meetings and helping organize events.

By March, the Israeli army had besieged all Palestinian cities. Tanks massed on the borders of Areas A, signaling a major offensive. At that time, the Arab countries were preparing for a Summit in Beirut to unveil a Saudi peace proposal going back to the basics – immediate peace with Israel from all the Arab countries in exchange for a full withdrawal to 1967 borders. Unsurprisingly, Israel rejected it. Since 1967, the Israeli government had two overwhelming goals: keeping the West Bank under its control, and retaining Israel's Jewish character. The Israeli mantra during the Peace Process was "maximum land, minimum Arabs." Israel grudged returning any territory, simultaneously refusing to grant the Palestinian residents citizenship.

I was in Canada for my mother's surgery in the spring of 2002 when Israel launched its re-invasion of Areas A in the West Bank. The tanks rolled while the Arab leaders assembled in Beirut, as if mocking their peace plan. The invasion was far from smooth-sailing, as the PA police and the militias of the different factions put up the best resistance they could muster. The light weapons of Palestinian fighters, against tanks and airplanes, only slowed the advance. Within hours, Israeli tanks were arrogantly roving the streets of Palestinian cities, leaving a trail of flattened cars. The defenders were cornered into tiny enclaves: the old city of Nablus, the Jenin refugee camp, the Church of the Nativity in Bethlehem, and Arafat's headquarters (the Muqata'a) in Ramallah.

Sharon's reign of terror had begun. My family and I were stunned at the images and stories in the news: a scene, imprinted in my memory, of a tank pinning an ambulance against a wall, slowly crushing it with the medics inside; Israeli soldiers shooting at medics rescuing the wounded, and in some cases at reporters; a woman in labor rushed to the Nablus hospital in the early morning, only for their car to be showered with a stream of bullets; a deaf boy walking, shot dead for ignoring the order to stop. It was madness.

While the tanks grooved the streets, the army began house-to-house searches, presumably for weapons and arrests. The entries were violent. A caretaker watched my parents' house while they were in Canada. He approached the soldiers with the key, offering to unlock the door. The house had two front doors for added security, both made of iron, with the outside one supposedly bullet-proof. The Israelis shot a bullet right through both doors and across the room, leaving shrapnels in the opposite wall. Lucky no one was inside rushing to open the door. Maya later sent me a photo of the tank-crushed cars dumped in the Fig Tree Lot.

Those months of fear and intimidation drove Veronica and her family, who lived on the outskirts of Ramallah, to leave for good. They emigrated to Florida. The "Transfer" was working. One by one.

Within hours of their invading Ramallah, we watched the tanks roll through the stone fence and into Arafat's compound, where one building after another collapsed under fire. TV cameras fixated, above piles of stones and rubble, on the one building left standing, with Arafat inside. It was the age-old Israeli approach – coercion and brutality. Meanwhile, at the Arab "Summit" in Beirut, the Syrians and Lebanese – who nursed a personal enmity for Arafat – refused on dubious grounds to televise his address to the summit. Excelling in the art of absurdity, the Arabs, in a Summit addressing the intense situation in Palestine, silenced the besieged Palestinian leader. Those were, supposedly, our friends and allies.

Arafat instead turned to the media and broadcast his speech to the world, reaffirming his support for peace, and for the Arab peace plan specifically, but insisting he would "die a martyr", if necessary, resisting on his own land. He may have failed us in signing Oslo, but he did capture our spirit at that moment – the just resistance against a colonial power that dealt with the occupied only from behind the barrel of a tank. Millions flooded streets around the world in support of Palestine. Something in the defiant spirit that refuses to yield to the forces of oppression appeals to free people everywhere. The worldwide protests put a damper on the tanks. Sharon hesitated to kill Arafat, opting instead to keep him besieged.

While this unfolded in Ramallah, we watched the pockets of Palestinian resistance in Nablus and Jenin hold out against the disproportionate Israeli military. The Israelis feared entering the densely-built old city of Nablus through the narrow streets, where they could easily be ambushed. I read later that they resurrected the tactic the Irgun had used in conquering Yafa half a century earlier. Boring holes through the walls, they crossed the city from house to house. In the end, the hastily-organized Palestinian popular resistance, combining fighters from different factions as well as ordinary citizens, was unable to stop the well-trained and well-equipped army. The Israelis captured the old city, killing eighty Palestinians in the process and wounding more. Hundreds were arrested for defending their homes.

Jenin held out, its resistance concentrated in the dense refugee camp at the outskirts, home to 13,000 people. By the beginning of April, the Israeli army had massed 1000 soldiers to attack it, closing the entire area to reporters. Al-Jazeera sporadically aired phone calls and brief video clips from camp residents. Resistance fighters were confronting the army boldly. Israeli soldiers attempting entry fell into an ambush, resulting in the death of 13 Israeli soldiers.

We watched for ten days a besieged Jenin, deprived of water, food, electricity, and medical supplies. As the medieval siege tightened, the trickle of news from inside quieted. We held our breaths, expecting the worst. Finally, with the continued resistance of Jenin sapping the attackers' morale, Israel unleashed one of its deadliest weapons – the D9 Caterpillar bulldozer. Built like tanks, with their drivers protected in reinforced, bullet-proof compartments, the mechanical behemoths ran amok through the refugee camp, flattening everything in their way – houses, cars, and people. No one realized the extent of the damage until later, when access to the camp was restored. Satellite views showed a contiguous area of about 40,000 square meters, formerly home to 4000 people, that was erased in its entirety.

Based on the number of Palestinians missing, Palestinian human rights sources estimated the number of deaths at five hundred, prompting the PA and the Arab media to call it a massacre. Israel vehemently denied it was a massacre, claiming that many of the missing had actually been arrested, and that "only" fifty Palestinians were killed, as if fifty human beings were not enough. (That same month, a suicide bomb killing thirty Israelis in Netanya was termed the "Passover massacre" by Israeli media. Apparently, Israeli society values a human life according to the faith it professes.) Israel succeeded in barring the UN, both from monitoring the event in real-time, and from conducting a fair investigation afterwards. In reality, the truth about Jenin was buried in the rubble. While the whole world watched, no one moved to stop Israel from committing further atrocities. Sharon had a free hand.

Facing this genocide alone with no outside support, the people of Jenin resorted to their last weapon. Israel could stop reporters and medical supplies from reaching the town, but it could not stop those with nothing left to lose from braving the siege. They left Jenin after seeing their friends and families disappear right underneath their crushed homes. It was the last stand of a desperate, besieged, people driven to the edge of a cliff, who refused to go down, alone.

Meanwhile, Bethlehem was steadily falling to the Israeli army. The defenders were trapped in the Old City, then cornered in Manger Square. If defeated, they knew their fate would be certain death, or a lifetime of detention. In a land where churches offered shelter to anyone seeking the sanctity of their walls, Bethlehem's defenders sought refuge in the Church of the Nativity, birthplace of Jesus. The oldest church in the world still in use, it was built in the 4th century AD, almost like a fortress, connected to the outside world by a tiny door. Inside its thick walls, they hid for their lives.

In 2004, I visited Bethlehem and saw the remnants of the siege. The Israelis had installed automatic machine guns, aimed at the church, that were laser-triggered by anything that moved. Birds easily set it off. I saw the centuries-old stone riddled with bullets. The defenders could not go out into the courtyard, and used the underground crypt to move. An autistic altar boy was one of the first casualties. He simply went into the courtyard to ring the church bells, as was his duty.

The siege lasted several weeks through May. The Vatican and other religious bodies pressured Israel not to attack the church. The defenders were running short of food and water. Several people were killed, and the living had to share the space with the rotting bodies. Finally, a deal was struck. Israel would allow the defenders to walk free, but they had to leave their families in Bethlehem and be exiled to Gaza or foreign countries. In the same deal, Arafat's life was spared, but he could not leave the Muqata'a.

By that time, we were back in DC. I became more involved in activist groups, including *al-Awda*. We hastily organized a large demonstration in coordination with other local groups. 100,000 protesters covered the

National Mall on April 20, during the siege of Bethlehem and the aftermath of Jenin. It felt good to see such a crowd in support, but that night, apart from CSPAN, we barely got half-a-minute of news coverage.

As if to undo the damage, a week after our protest, a pro-Israel counter-protest took place on the steps of the capitol. Buses brought participants from outside the Metro DC area to boost the numbers. With the AIPAC lobbying conference in town that week, members of Congress appeared at this counter-protest to avow their unwavering support for Israel. Peeking at it on CSPAN, I was disgusted to see our own senator rousing the crowd, fist up in the air, cheering for Israel, while Jenin counted its dead.

Israel sold the 2002 invasion as part of the worldwide "War on Terror". It was really a War *of* Terror. The PA was disarmed. The weapons were for doing the dirty work of the Occupation, not for resisting it. A disarmed PA was less able to control the different factions, and random acts of resistance, such as the launching of homemade rockets, proliferated. While Arafat was under siege in Ramallah, the leaders of Hamas were safe in Gaza, building strength. More than anything else, the 2002 invasion strengthened Hamas. Perhaps that was the foremost aim of the invasion: to destroy Palestinian unity.

The diplomatic impasse continued. Bush's "Roadmap", which promised Palestinian statehood by 2005, was yet another document added to the piles of worthless documents. One more unneeded layer obscuring peace.

When pondering the intensity of this Intifada, with higher casualties and more widespread destruction than the one I experienced, I understood it was a different generation fighting this revolt, one that grew up confined to the ghetto. The only Israelis they saw were soldiers. The main Israeli product they tasted was violence. Simultaneously, the Closure and the Roads have rendered us invisible, shielding our humanity from the next generation of Israeli fighters. I wondered about the upcoming generation of Palestinians, those who were little children during the Second Intifada, growing up under the shadow of the Wall, hearing of Jenin? They hardly encountered actual Israeli soldiers, but rather tanks, armored bulldozers, drones, and Apache helicopters. The face Israel revealed to them was that of brutal, mechanized, robots spewing destruction. What is the ultimate outcome of this despicable human experiment?

With the re-invasion complete, activism in DC area congregated on the impending Iraq War. We marched, and marched, and marched. Leave it to an Iraq War to disillusion an activist. The better part about it was getting to meet activists from a wide swath of backgrounds. The lady who is so opposed to paying taxes to the US government, she sells homemade pins at protests in DC to make a living. The Jewish American student who took one of the Birthright Israel free trips, then slipped away to the West Bank, volunteering to help Palestinians in the villages. The Iranian man, my age, who escaped to Turkey on horseback in the 1980s, because his coming of age meant certain death from getting drafted to fight Iraq. His American former girlfriend, who ended up moving to New York City and starting a band. ... The world events, and especially America's role, mobilized so many in America to get involved. Perhaps that was the one silver lining amid the destruction and the body counts.

People care!

Among those who cared was a certain American activist who stood in front of a bulldozer. Rachel Corrie gave her life to stop the demolition of one more Palestinian home in Gaza. It meant nothing to the Israeli bulldozer driver that she was a US citizen, or that she was human. Within the driver's cubicle of an armored Caterpillar, humanity had evaporated.

Rachel lives.

She's personified what it meant to stand up for what she believed in.

15

Stranger

SPRING, 2004
Into the Dark of Night

Long plane ride. Seven hours from Dulles to Frankfurt, a layover, then another five hours to Tel Aviv. The last time I visited, in 1999, was at the height of the Oslo "Peace Process". I found people optimistic, hopeful that the decades-old conflict would come to an end, so they could enjoy normal lives. Some emigrants had returned, and Ramallah was booming.

This time, I didn't know what to expect. The high point of peace had lasted only briefly, after which this slither of land slipped into a violent conflict, erroneously labeled "Intifada", after Sharon's offensive entry into the Aqsa mosque. Over the last four years, I remotely followed the violence, filtered by the TV and the worldview of the broadcasting channels. The loss of life saddened me. My heart jumped every time I heard of an attack on Ramallah, picking up the phone to check on my parents. My heart jumped, too, when I heard of a suicide bomb in Jerusalem, for in addition to the carnage there, a "reprisal" Israeli raid on Palestinian areas was sure to follow. "Breaking News" once came of Israeli Apache helicopters attacking a certain PA office in Ramallah, a couple hundred yards from my parents' house. I called home immediately. My elderly mother answered the phone. She was alone, my father away in Jerusalem that evening. It was dark, the bombing having knocked down power for the whole city, and Mom couldn't reach any candles from her wheelchair. I could hear the sounds of distant explosions.

Traveling with me, and not knowing what to expect either, Charlene was looking forward to her first visit to my home country, continually postponed since the Intifada's eruption. Despite my reassurances, she was apprehensive, worried for our safety. My own secret fear, however, was the negative first impression she was sure to form when she saw the destruction and felt the danger. I somehow imagined arriving to a Ramallah in ruins – the TV images of Arafat's bombed-out compound dominating my memories.

One year to the next, we waited for the situation to improve. Instead, things kept getting worse. After the massacre of Jenin and the siege of the Church of Nativity in Bethlehem, Sharon's government began building a wall, to keep Palestinians enclosed within their cities-turned-prisons. I had seen images of that Wall. Tall, medieval, threatening. Being somewhat claustrophobic, I dreaded coming face-to-face with it. What would my reaction be? With events spiraling towards the worst, we finally decided there was no point in waiting any further, no "good time" to go.

Our first challenge was getting an Israeli visa for Charlene, since she was not yet a US citizen. After inspecting her application, the embassy official blankly informed us that it would likely be denied. When we asked why, she explained matter-of-factly, "for the reason that she is married to a Palestinian." Apparently, they take pride in discrimination. To get her visa, Charlene returned to the embassy alone, wearing a big cross, and posing as a tourist interested in Jerusalem's Holy places. It worked.

Two days before our scheduled departure, Israel assassinated the top spiritual leader of Hamas, Sheikh Ahmed Yassin. The suspense went up notches. After hours watching news, phone calls home, and lengthy deliberations, we decided to risk it and go. The newspapers served on the plane were far from reassuring, quoting Hamas's threats of retaliation, Tel Aviv airport noted among the chief targets. More worrisome was Israel's planned response if Hamas took the bait and retaliated.

We felt rather uncomfortable on the Frankfurt-Tel Aviv flight, aware that I was one of the few Palestinians on a flight packed with Hebrew-speaking passengers. I felt the eyes of suspicion and looks of scrutiny, our immediate neighbors frequently casting glances. An elderly man had taken the adjacent window seat. Traveling alone, he looked kindly and harmless. Twice, he asked to borrow a pen to fill out his paperwork, and twice, we loaned him ours with a smile. Upon landing, while we waited for the airplane door to open, he attempted to strike a conversation. "First time to Israel?" I made the idiotic mistake of saying "no" and, little by little, he gleaned just enough to deduce I was Palestinian. The door opened. At the bottom of the stairs, a number of airport security guards waited. Descending just ahead of us, the old man nodded to a guard, and the next thing I knew, the guard jumped in my way. For the next 15 minutes, we were interrogated right there on the tarmac, not allowed to board the bus to the terminal, while other passengers looked on.

Finally at the terminal, we were led into the infamous "Arab Room", now reduced to a small corner of the airport. Despite all that she heard about Palestine and the conflict during our years together, Charlene was shocked at the way they treated us in that room. After the tiring twenty-hour trip, we were made to wait three-and-a-half more hours. At first, she thought they were taking their time to methodically check our passports. It was obvious, though, that the airport was empty, and the border guards were hanging around chatting and doing nothing. We were starving but no food was accessible on this side of passport control. At some point, they stamped Charlene's passport and handed it to her, only to snatch it back from her hand when they learned she was married *to me*. Eventually, they escorted us out of the airport, and into an Israeli taxicab (with the fare on us). Handing our passports to the driver, they instructed him not to return them until we were inside the West Bank. Whizzing past the airport lights and the distant lights of Lydd, the taxi dropped us off at a remote checkpoint closer to the airport, but an hour away from Ramallah. In the dark of night, we immediately had the sinking feeling of stepping into a prison.

An Invisible Occupation

From that checkpoint at the West Bank's edge, the way to Ramallah wound through dark valleys on the western slopes, alongside new Israeli stolenments (the so-called "settlements"). The Jerusalem taxi my father had sent had thankfully followed us. Ed, the driver, was clearly worried about taking that route at night. A photo of two young children hung from his rearview mirror. Though lit with bright lights, the stolenments wore a gloomy face, reverberating with the tense quiet of hiding indoors. Each stolenment was surrounded by barbed wire enclosing a large swath of land. The entrances were guarded by armored personnel carriers, or tanks. Instead of the toughness they were meant to project, in their walls and fortifications, I read fear.

A while afterwards, we reached an older (and not so well-paved) road connecting Arab villages. At the intersection stood a deserted Israeli guard tower, which, in the gloom of night, looked more like a haunted Transylvanian castle. "This is the checkpoint where a Palestinian sniper killed ten soldiers. They closed it down now." An eerie encounter for our first night.

Fortunately, the older road entered the town of Birzeit, home to Birzeit University and to millennia-old olive presses – familiar ground. Unlike the road connecting the stolenments, which skirted the edges of habitation, this road went through the ancient village. Though the street lights were not as bright, people were outdoors, their shops open, children playing, and loud music blazing from outdoor restaurants. The whole town was alive, fear residing elsewhere. Though Ed was overly worried his Israeli license plates would invite someone to attack us, nothing of that sort happened.

After those long insomniac hours of travel, our first night back home felt depressing. The first thing greeting us as we walked through the front door was the large bullet-hole left as a souvenir by Israeli soldiers during the Re-invasion, two springs earlier.

Despite this harrowing introduction, the rest of our stay was calm and uneventful. The long-awaited Hamas retaliation did not come, though we could feel the continual suspense. My own understanding of "Intifada" was colored by my own experience in the First, when the *shabab* faced the Israeli soldiers with stones. We saw no such engagements this time. In fact, we hardly saw any Israeli soldiers in downtown Ramallah. They prefer to remain at well-defended checkpoints on the outskirts, where they control us from afar without risking their lives.

Things weren't always this quiet. When people in Ramallah spoke of the Re-invasion, their voices darkened and breaths quickened – an enervating time for them. Public buildings in the city were destroyed. What we saw on our trip was the outcome of two years of rapid reconstruction. We were told Ramallah was one of the quieter cities too. Other places, especially Gaza, Nablus, Jenin, and the refugee camps, were not so fortunate.

On the second day of our stay, I was watching CNN on satellite TV, when they announced that a 12-year old Palestinian boy was killed in "a refugee camp in the West Bank", and that was that. Not mentioning the name of the child, as usual, this time CNN did not bother to mention the location of that incident. "Some refugee camp," as in "who cares?" I listened again. We wanted to know if this refugee camp was in the vicinity so we could avoid trouble. Giving up on CNN, we thankfully found al-Jazeera, which not only identified the place as the Balata refugee camp in Nablus, but also gave the details of the incident, how the boy was playing on his balcony when the Israeli bullet did its deed.

The deceptive calm we experienced existed only because the occupying soldiers chose not to enter the city. Any time they wished to reassert their authority, they could enter Ramallah unopposed, as they routinely did to arrest "wanted" individuals. The Palestinian Authority police, just reinstated a month before our visit, were forbidden from carrying guns. People ignored their orders directing traffic. Israel found it more efficient to wall us into enclaves, leaving only small detachments at the gates.

The result of these policies can be described in one word: "suffocation". The oppression of bullets and bombs, while still there, is now the backup for the sweeping institutional oppression. Downtown Ramallah is only a few square miles in area. One can drive from end to end, checkpoint to checkpoint, in a matter of minutes, but without a permit from the Israeli jailers, one cannot leave those confines. Such travel restrictions stifle what's left of the Palestinian economy and add to the ravaging unemployment.

Palestinians, now confined to their respective cities, do not get to see their oppressors. There is no one to blame, no one to resent – no one in sight anyway. Protest and demonstrate all they want, no one is listening. While we were there, Israel was busy building its Wall in several villages at the western outskirts of Ramallah. That section of Wall was inside West Bank territory, separating Palestinian farmers from their lands and water wells. I watched on TV the Israeli soldiers violently evicting the villagers and quelling their small protests. Handfuls of international and Israeli volunteers were defending the villagers. Had I wanted to show my support as well, I could not contemplate how to get to that area with all the blocked roads, checkpoints, and walls. The blockades facilitate the preying on our lands, one village at a time.

Once, I was excited at the news that the Israeli High Court issued a decision to halt construction of the Wall. I learned the fine print only after seeing things with my own eyes. The Court ordered a halt of "construction", but not a halt of "preparations" – a seemingly benign term that allowed for such things as expropriating land from villages, demolishing Palestinian homes standing in the way, digging ditches, and laying concrete blocks in place, but on their side. The second fine point was the local nature of the rulings. While "construction" halted in Abu Dis, it continued full speed ahead elsewhere. Hundreds of miles of wall are planned for the West Bank, and Israel's "High" Court only lets us battle them inch by inch. This system of "justice" seems more like a way to extort, in court and legal fees, the remaining life-savings of the threatened villagers, in effect making the victims finance their oppressors.

Once the Wall is completed, it will be an even more absurd situation. People in the Palestinian prison-enclaves will be left to rot without a visible culprit on the scene, while Israelis go about their daily business unconcerned and can "forget" about the Palestinian nuisances in their backyards. Occupier and Occupied, separated, no longer seeing each other.

Checkpoints and Walls

My longest road trip was a 24-hour drive from Michigan to Florida for spring break. For the entire distance, no one stopped us. Here, two Israeli checkpoints now block the 10-mile drive from Ramallah to Jerusalem. Though checkpoints were nothing new, on this last trip I found the procedures surreal, a far cry from the time we drove to Jerusalem in the family car.

We now dismount from the taxi at the first checkpoint near Qalandia; once through, we take another taxi to the second checkpoint, walk through again; then we take a third taxi to Jerusalem. The taxi drivers refuse to drive through the checkpoints, as they won't earn a cent for the time spent waiting in long lines. So the short trip takes over an hour, assuming we are lucky enough to get permits. Many who need them to work, study, or go to a hospital, are not so lucky.

Dominated by a concrete military guard tower, a typical checkpoint divides into a pedestrian entrance, and two car lanes: one with a long wait for Palestinian cars and a special open lane for Israeli cars. The zones are separated by blocks of concrete topped with barbed wire. Placement of the checkpoints appears arbitrary. The second Jerusalem checkpoint stands amid a Palestinian residential area in Beit Hanina. The guard tower looks into the second-floor windows of an adjacent house. On the other side, a small car dealership straddles both sides of the dividing line.

I thought my permit would relieve me from the tortuous, four-hour ride along Hellfire Valley to Bethlehem. Taking the shorter road through Jerusalem (normally a half hour end to end), the trip still took us three-and-a-half hours. We went there on Good Friday with Archie, who was visiting for Easter. We had stayed in touch, meeting on my trips to California, so it was nice to reconnect here. Soon, we found out that Israel bans men younger than 45 years of age from entering Jerusalem before 2 PM on Fridays, the Muslim day of prayer. The soldiers at the second checkpoint refused us entry, but allowed Charlene in. Never mind that my ID said "Christian," that our final destination was Bethlehem, or that my permit was issued for reason of "Christian religious holiday." The whims of the person with the rifle override logical arguments.

Determined to go, we waited, a line building behind us. Some balked at the line and left with the intention of walking around the checkpoint, perhaps across the fields. Others warned us from following suit, pointing out the Israeli patrols on the side roads. That day, as on nearly every Friday for the last four years, Palestinian Muslims were denied the right to pray in Jerusalem, and, this time, Palestinian Christians were kept from praying, on Good Friday, at the site where Jesus walked the *via Dolorosa* 2000 years ago. Standing there, with memories of the Baha'i

Temple in Haifa fresh in my mind from the previous day, I grasped the jarring dissonance in Israel's claims to "protect" minority sects like Druze and Baha'is, while simultaneously persecuting religious *majorities* like mainstream Christians and Muslims. (More absurdly, the soldiers who stopped us at the checkpoint were Druze.)

About 1:30, they finally let us through, and we were shortly aboard the third taxi ride of the day, to Bethlehem. Unused to being stopped *leaving* Jerusalem, I was surprised when we reached a closed gate. We had just passed the monastery of St. George (Mar Elias), at the outskirts of Bethlehem. I strained to recall the rustic feeling of the monastery among hills covered with lush pine forests and olive groves. Denuded into stone forests, these hills now boast towering stolenments. The one on the right, close to the ancient village of Beit Jala (Biblical Gilo), is now Gilo. On the left, we see Har Homa, built in the middle of the "Peace Process", while Israeli negotiators demanded the privilege of annexing "existing settlements" to Israel. The land for Har Homa was sold by the Greek Orthodox Patriarch, deepening the rift between the leadership of the Orthodox Church in Jerusalem, and its Palestinian congregation.

Amid this surreal desertified landscape, with the two stolenments in view, just left of the road stood a substantial military installation, comparable to a border crossing. It gave the Qalandia checkpoint the look of an impromptu "garbage-can" roadblock. We dismounted, then walked down a long narrow pedestrian path parallel to the road, encaged in barbed wire, and studded with surveillance cameras. The path followed the perimeter of the building, away from the road. Making a final turn, we emerged into a long tunnel, at the end of which, the soldiers checked our papers (twice). On the other side of the street, we saw a line of about 15 young Palestinian men with their faces to a wall and their hands behind their heads. Apparently, they had attempted to circumvent the checkpoint.

Walking along the road, we felt a glimmer of tranquility at the sight of beautiful expansive olive groves on both sides of the street. This brief interlude rudely ended, a few hundred yards further, when we came face-to-face with a section of the Wall under construction – one slicing the olive groves of Bethlehem's Palestinian citizens to the side of Gilo and Har Homa. Tall, ugly slabs of concrete, standing on end, interspersed with tall guard towers. The Great Wall of Israeli Apartheid.

In Bethlehem, we met with Huda, a Palestinian political science student at my university who was conducting her PhD research here. She toured us for a few hours, visiting the Church of the Nativity and the old city. Her father was kind enough to drive us to Beit Sahour and the Mar Saba monastery beyond. On the road, we encountered another section of Wall under construction, this one cutting off Bethlehem from the east. Returning from the monastery at dusk, we were told that the Bethlehem checkpoint had already closed at 6 PM (hours prior our permit's end time). The only way to leave now was a risky walk across the border near Beit Jala, where we supposedly could easily find a taxi to Jerusalem.

There, we walked across a fence and onto a dark street. An Israeli military observation post was visible to one side. We inched a few steps to avoid it, only to glimpse another tower on the other side. Dogs were howling in the dark of night, and the street was deserted, except for an Israeli military jeep on patrol. We kept walking quietly, praying the patrol would not stop us. It felt like escaping a high-security prison. Archie and I scared ourselves into a frenzy, imagining a scenario where snipers shot us dead, then covered it up by planting explosives, claiming we were "would-be suicide bombers". The area was so dark and remote they would have gotten away with it.

Finally, a taxicab appeared. The driver was willing to take us to the Ramallah checkpoint, but taking advantage of the situation, asked us four times the usual fare. Happy to get out of there, we hopped in. The taxi took one of the new "bypass roads" connecting the stolenments on the southwest of the West Bank with Jerusalem. Through a tunnel underneath Beit Jala, then a checkpoint at Gilo, we reached the neighborhoods of Katamon and Talbieh, formerly Palestinian areas in West Jerusalem, but depopulated in 1948. From there, the taxi joined another Israeli-only road, this time connecting to stolenments north of Jerusalem on a long bridge flying above the villages of al-Jib and Bir Nabala. From such an elevated and walled road, there was no sign of Palestinian existence, despite our hovering right on top of it, physically. Our fantasies of escaping the high-security prison suddenly came to a screeching halt, as our driver dropped us off at the Ramallah checkpoint.

Life in the Ghetto

Near Ramallah, the Wall is still in the form a snaking stretch of electrified barbed wire shadowed by military roads, rather than the familiar giant slabs of concrete seen in other cities. A five-minute drive towards the nearby village of Rafat, situated between Ramallah and Jerusalem, brings three layers of wall into sight. A U-shaped portion juts well north to encircle the Jerusalem airport, while excluding Jerusalem's large Palestinian suburb of al-Ram. The wall then loops back to exclude next-door Rafat, and isolate it from the Israeli military camp on the other side of the village. As a result, this tiny village is enclosed by wall from three sides, joined only to the larger enclave of Ramallah by a narrow road.

Inside the Wall, these Palestinian enclaves that were formerly thriving cities, now resemble ghettoes. The physical entrapment and hopelessness of the populace can be read in the miles of graffiti coloring every building in city centers: "no to the treasonous Geneva Accords", "no to negotiations", and "we will remember the martyr so-and-so". These slogans are interspersed with thousands of portraits of Palestinians martyrs – often ordinary Palestinians who suddenly lost their lives to Israeli violence. A few steps from the Church of Nativity, we saw a brand-new poster of an 11-year-old child who was shot in Bethlehem the prior week. On the side of a store in Ramallah we saw a tattered old poster of a handsome young man. An acquaintance of mine turned out to be his cousin: "The Israelis killed him just four months after his wedding."

Before our trip, I attempted to alleviate Charlene's natural anxieties by looking up statistics, thinking I could illustrate how small the chance was of getting shot. Downloading the latest tally from the Red Cross website, I picked the most conservative number, counting only civilian casualties. Whereas, as I had expected, the chance of actually getting killed in Ramallah was low, I shocked myself with the number of wounded. Among the 250,000 residents of the Ramallah district, as many as 5000 people were hospitalized for Intifada injuries, usually from Israeli gunfire, or one out of every 50. A short walk in the crowded downtown area guarantees we will pass or encounter a handful of Intifada casualties – not so reassuring!

Adding to the sense of captivity is the Israeli economic control of the Palestinian areas. Having boycotted Israeli products in the US, I was surprised to see the same items stocking the shelves of most stores in the West Bank. I was told it was hard to find substitutes. With Israel controlling the borders, Israeli products flow easily, while Palestinian products from the West Bank face export restrictions and internal road closures. Produce from remote villages is difficult to transport to the main West Bank markets. Even when trucks can reach the village, they need permits to travel on certain roads inside the West Bank and to cross Israeli checkpoints. Thus, crops make it to the markets only occasionally, and after needless delay.

Palestinian society is not free of economic complacency. I saw Palestinians carelessly drinking Israeli Maccabee beer, when Palestinian and foreign alternatives were readily available. The same goes for Israeli coffee, soft drinks, chocolates, and other consumer products that are not so essential for a people locked in a struggle for survival.

Another avenue for peaceful resistance to the Occupation is to defy the Israeli permit and travel-restriction system. Every Palestinian wishing to travel is faced with the dilemma, effectively accepting and acknowledging Israeli rule by applying for that permit, or challenging it and bypassing the roadblocks, at great personal risks. Had a collective decision been made to boycott Israeli permits and to always bypass the checkpoints when traveling, the personal risk would be shared and the oppressive Israeli roadblocks would remain empty and rejected. Instead, the PA adds legitimacy to Israeli-imposed borders when it acts as intermediary. The permits they obtain help Palestinians as individuals, and business moves forward, but at the expense of the long-term national interest.

Visiting friends, we witnessed the work of a few of the NGOs and local initiatives filling the vacuum of institutions needed for a self-reliant society. At Birzeit University, my former Arabic teacher, Mr. Wajeeh, toured us their journalism academy. The students get to run the university's small TV and radio stations. Such an opportunity was a mere dream when I lived there. Another NGO, *al-Haqq* ("Law in the Service of Man"), conscientiously documents human rights abuses in Palestine, whether committed by Israel, or by the Palestinian Authority. We saw an exhibition on "Collective Punishments" at the Sakakini Cultural Center, featuring photographs and documents provided by al-Haqq. The exhibition illustrates how Israel controls electricity, water, and movement to make an entire community suffer, for the alleged action of one of its members. The Sakakini Center itself aims to advance culture and provide an outlet for artistic creativity. Nearby at the al-Qattan Center, my friend Waheed now shares an office with my cousin Jameel. With the travel difficulties, they had quit their respective jobs in Bir Zeit and Jerusalem. Here, they educate teachers and develop an independent educational curriculum to replace the outdated Jordanian one of my generation.

Abdul-Jabbar started a charity to help Palestinians in East Jerusalem resist Israeli pressures, developing and aiding indigenous solutions to the city's struggles in public health and education. Whereas Israel considers all of Jerusalem its unified capital, the Israeli municipality spends little on the Palestinian part of the city. Touring the Old City, I longed to find a single garbage bin to throw my trash, forcing me to add to the litter that gives a false image of East Jerusalem as a backward, barbaric city. At the same time, I could not escape the big Israeli surveillance cameras poised on every street corner, covering every inch, and monitoring every step of the city's quarter-million Palestinian residents. The digital age has only deepened their intrusion into our lives. Similarly for education, the Israeli municipality only funds schools conforming to the Israeli curriculum, mainly in Hebrew and meant to erase the children's Palestinian identity. Abed's organization helps the severely under-funded alternative schools, set up to teach a Palestinian curriculum. As if to illustrate Abed's point, the clock struck noon and school-children filled the streets. They attended school only half-day, to share the limited classroom space with another batch.

By and large, Palestinians in these enclaves entertain little hope of liberating themselves by means of a breakthrough in either negotiations, or military operations. Few foresee an impending end to the Occupation, a dismantling of the stolenments, or a crumbling of the Wall. For the majority of Palestinians, resistance today consists of mere survival – *sumud* in Arabic

– persistence, or in this sense continuing to exist on their land, striving for a normal life, despite all the obstacles that Israel hurls in their way.

Smuggled

Before I got the permit that enabled the Bethlehem trip, I entered Jerusalem smuggled. Ed, the driver who picked us up from near the airport, knew a way.

> Jerusalem,
> 10 miles South of Ramallah.
> We first headed North,
> Through Birzeit,
> To the deserted Transylvanian guard tower.
> A dirt road from there
> Joined with the Israeli road,
> Taking us East, then South.
> Speeding in between stolenments,
> Beth El, Ofra, Rimmonim,
> We reached the village of Anata,
> Northeast of Jerusalem –
> Anathot, in the Bible,
> From Anat, Canaanite goddess of Fertility.
> We ducked, before an Israeli checkpoint,
> Into the adjacent refugee camp,
> Through a maze of tiny alleys,
> To the back of the car dealership
> On the main road,
> Straddling the Second Checkpoint.
>
> I hopped over the fence,
> The lot attendant offered me Arabic coffee.
> Thanking him, I sipped while waiting,
> As the car retraced its path
> Through the labyrinth,
> The Anata checkpoint,

And over to pick me up.
An hour and a half after leaving Ramallah,
I was 10 miles South,
in the Old
City
Of Jerusalem.

On its streets I was wary,
Tiptoeing through side alleys,
Avoiding soldiers.
One ID check away from
Three nights in an Israeli jail.
We walked the old city wall.
It was fenced off,
The ticketed entrance at Damascus Gate,
Where soldiers checked IDs.
So I climbed the fence,
At a remote city gate –
A thief in my birthplace, or
A pirate
Following a treasure map.

Seems all we do,
In that land,
Is climb over fences
To get to places
That formerly welcomed everyone.
Places accessible, unfenced,
Unwalled!

Wormhole
The hurdles are obviously meant to make us leave, and not come back. The curtains are drawn around the rest. Hidden – swallowed by a network of new roads interconnecting new sites, while the ancient roads are left to neglect. A single modern stolenment called "Beth Horon" has displaced

the historic villages of Upper and Lower Beit 'Ur, the same biblical "Upper and Lower Beth Horon," noted in Joshua's lists as existing at the time of his invasion of Canaan (Joshua 16:3-5). The original villages are conveniently out of sight from the new "bypass" road cutting deep through the ridge.

With Hebraized place names, the West Bank is staged as an Israeli playground – growing bedroom communities and vast recreational areas, where Israelis go hiking in the valleys or kayaking in the Jordan. Names are critical to this conflict, it seems. Jerusalem has for long been known to Palestinians as "al-Quds" – the Holy City. Since taking control, Israel has been trying to impose its Arabized Hebrew name "Orashalim", referring to it as such in official documents and weather reports. In my childhood, the road signs for Jerusalem were plain: "Yerushalayim" in Hebrew, "al-Quds" in Arabic, and "Jerusalem" in English. Visiting in 1993, I noticed the Arabic then read "Orashalim al-Quds." Today, on a road sign near Nazareth, I read the obituary: "Orashalim (al-Quds)" with al-Quds in parentheses *and* finer print. What's next?! Plain "Orashalim"?

This stolenment and road construction craze exacted a toll on an already precarious environment, as arable land and water sources got depleted, and scenic hills disemboweled. There is hardly a hilltop on the West Bank today where one can stand without seeing barbed wire or an eight-meter high wall. The nearly five million Palestinian residents of the West Bank, Gaza, and Jerusalem are all but invisible. Protest all they want, their oppressor is conveniently shielded by several layers of wall.

In the Coast and the Galilee, where we prospered until the Nakba, our presence is faded and erased. Never mind returning to my parents' homes near Yafa and Ramleh. Nowadays I have to plead for a permit to see those cities, and not for overnight, my permit explicitly stating "5 AM - 10 PM". If I'm careful and attentive while driving through those regions, I might see a partially destroyed building or a cactus patch from a Palestinian farm, but many of the 418 villages Israel had demolished retain no obvious trace. As if we were never there.

Crossing the "green line" at the edge of the West Bank, one is immediately transported from the 4th world to the 1st world. ("Green line" itself is a mindfuck of terminology evoking a virgin land, ready to be "settled" and exploited.) Israel presents itself today as a megalopolis where speculators turn a buck from urban sprawl, while city centers (usually where Israeli Palestinians live) are in decay. Gone are the miles of fragrant orange groves between Ramleh and Yafa, there as recently as 1990. Instead, the Israelis welcome strip malls and big boxes. Whether in Haifa or Jerusalem, more Russian is heard on the street than either Hebrew or Arabic, and Russian is seen on street signs. I wondered what connection to the place a newly-arrived Russian had, that justified their having more access to my ancestral home than myself.

We saw the same tendency back at the airport. Droves of people from all over the world were welcomed: Europeans, Americans, Argentineans, Ethiopians, Chinese. All passed easily through the border, except the few of us who actually originated from that land, who were led aside to a separate room. There, they ignored us for hours, as if the airport attendants had more important things to do. As if, we were not even there.

I began having that unwelcome feeling during my 1993 trip, at the beginning of Oslo. Riding on one of the new Occupation Roads, as we passed by Beth Horon, I noted a small sign in Arabic marking a side road to the twin villages of Beit 'Ur. Instead of their familiar ancient domed village homes, I saw the red-tiled roofs of modern Beth Horon. Instead of the cactus plants bordering Beit 'Ur's plowed fields, I saw minefields and barbed wire surrounding the new stolenment. Is this the West Bank? Supposedly the last Palestinian foothold? I searched for any hint of our presence. Apart from that small Arabic sign for Beit 'Ur, the signs were in Hebrew and English, pointing out biblical relics and Israeli stolenments with biblical-sounding names. Suddenly, I felt a stranger in my own land, as if history ruptured and engulfed the memory of my forefathers. Thousands of years disappeared in the void, as the 1990s became connected to biblical times.

An imaginary scenario haunted me, of a tourist ignorant of history, visiting the "Holy Land", and never guessing our existence.

In the "restored" Old City of Yafa, we found a large plaque displaying a timeline of the city's "history". The timeline, which uses the name *"Eretz Yisrael"* for the land throughout, glosses over the Arab portion of that history, while emphasizing historical details concerning the Jewish community of Yafa. After 1000 AD, there is almost no mention of the non-Jewish majority of the city's inhabitants, nor is there any mention of the expulsion of Yafa's Palestinian population. My mother's roots, her childhood, and presence there are quietly erased.

That frightening feeling of invisibility and alienation I sensed in 1993 was a premonition of things to come. The rapidly expanding stolenments I saw back then were mere embryos of the megalopolises that now hungrily jostle for every inch of that congested landscape. The red-tiled roofs of Beth Horon are now eclipsed by the skyscrapers of Modi'in, the brand new stolenment down the road. The little sign pointing to the Beit 'Urs is now gone, the side road connecting them with the Occupation Road blocked, isolating those two villages from the world. The Occupation Road is inaccessible to Ramallah, either, its former entrance near the military camp by the village of Beitunia now sealed by a wall and a line of tanks. The only way for Palestinians to enter is to first cross the Qalandia checkpoint.

Tourists today have to actively seek Palestinians in order to meet any. With few exceptions, Israel is in control of historic and tourist sites, even within the West Bank. Before leaving on this trip, Charlene and I pored over travel books to identify destinations for sightseeing. I wanted her to see as much as possible of my country. It was a waste of time. Most places of interest were several roadblocks away, or beyond the Wall. With permits difficult to obtain, many among the younger generations in Bethlehem and Ramallah have never set foot in neighboring Jerusalem. Living in one of the richest parts of the world, historically and culturally, they are deprived from tasting this richness. Control of historic sites enshrines the victor's version of history. Israel thus stakes claim to the future, by ignoring or sidelining our past.

Tel Aviv

We visited Yafa for the Easter Monday celebrations, joining with Archie, Kareem, and Maya in renting a minivan (with yellow license plates and driver) to get us there. Kareem is now an accountant. In his funny accountant way he showed up at my door the next day with a detailed receipt and the exact change he owed for the lunch we had all shared in Yafa! Maya works at the Red Crescent as an ambulance medic. She has worked there at the height of the re-invasion, but doesn't talk about that part of her life.

Visiting Yafa and Tel Aviv, two things stood in sharp contrast between the two neighbors. Architecturally, we were fascinated by the vast neighborhoods of modern buildings, beachfront hotels, and Barcelona-esque style of Tel Aviv. From its outward look and its beaches, Tel Aviv projects the image of a wealthy international financial center, or a lush resort on the French Riviera.

Crossing the invisible boundary into Yafa, we found a city stranded in time, its buildings decayed and falling apart, many still bearing scars from the 1948 war. Once Palestine's largest and most modern city, with gardens and beaches and public squares, and the capital of the Jaffa orange industry, Yafa today exudes the aura of a ghost town. After evicting most of its 100,000 inhabitants in 1948, Israel froze the city's development by annexing it to Tel Aviv, then systematically denied its remaining Palestinian residents the permits for construction and renovation, at the threat of demolition. The most visible new construction favors Jewish-owned hotels and restaurants, or the renovated and now Jewish-operated "Artist Colony" complex in the Old City.

While the city itself was left to weather the ravages of time, I couldn't help notice Yafa's jubilant atmosphere, its citizens crowding the grounds of the old church, lining the streets for public parades, and later filling the parks and beaches. It was a comforting sight: despite their city's strangulation, the Palestinian inhabitants of Yafa still find the spirit to be alive and to enjoy simple pleasures.

Blocks away, Tel Aviv huddled in silence. Underneath the fancy hotels and modern buildings, the streets were empty, the beaches deserted. Stores were closed and cars parked in front of homes. Perhaps Pesach (Passover) kept everyone inside, but then these weren't the Orthodox neighborhoods of Jerusalem. Throughout our stay in Tel Aviv, we could sense an edginess in the atmosphere. Over two weeks since Israel had assassinated Sheikh Ahmad Yassin, and nothing had happened, yet. That

Hamas's expected retaliatory attack had *not* come, somehow promised it to be a major act. Everyone walked in suspense, on alert. We could sense the overwhelming fear. A security guard searched customers entering the ice cream shop we attended. We were doubly worried about an attack happening, for not only did we risk injury ourselves, but being Palestinians, we were the usual suspects and a convenient outlet for subsequent acts of revenge.

At some level, I pitied the residents of Tel Aviv. Few children were seen. Rather than enjoy their lives, they grow up imprisoned in their parents' nightmares. Despite the extreme vulnerability on the Palestinian side, I did not sense the suffocating fear I breathed in Tel Aviv. The streets of Ramallah, Bethlehem, and even strangled East Jerusalem were full of people going about their daily lives. Though they longed for a better life, they slept well at night. The assassination of Sheikh Yassin was supposed to bring Israelis security. Instead, it only stirred their fears. The walls failed to calm them. Every Palestinian shadow, every Arabic whisper, is enough to send shivers among them. Earlier in Haifa, atop the lookout on Mt. Carmel, I uttered a word in Arabic to Ed, and immediately, a group of Israelis near us scurried away, as if I was about to detonate. I never knew that "what time is it?", recited in Arabic, had such power.

Even before setting foot in Tel Aviv, suspicion filled the plane. None of the passengers could sleep, preferring to eye their neighbors, or eavesdrop on conversations, in case a "terrorist" was sitting near. So it is with the soldiers at the checkpoints. They guard their positions at constant alert, their superior firepower insufficient, their fears evidenced by the guard towers dominating the skyline. Instead of dehumanizing us with the oppressive Wall, Israelis ended up stripping themselves of humanity.

While I may not pity the Occupation soldiers, I do pity the children of Tel Aviv, growing up in this climate, not allowed to play outside or go to the beach, simply because their society insists on maintaining the domination of another people. I am saddened at the thought of them looking forward to no other future than serving in the military, perpetuating this surreal state of existence, before resuming their lives. I also pity the children of Palestine and especially the refugee camps, who are born into a dreamless world locked by a Wall. The hopelessness they must feel, opening their eyes to the inside wall of a prison they cannot escape, is something I have barely tasted in my time.

This interlocked drama of hopelessness and fear deepened the schism between an oppressive society whose *raison d'etre* is military superiority, and an oppressed one threatened with extinction and mired in discontent.

Given all this, I find it disappointing and ridiculous that international politicians are still stuck in a labyrinth of partition plans, otherwise known as a "two-state solution". Ever since 1947, the seeds of land division repeatedly crashed onto the rocks of a land that refused to be divided. A string of UN resolutions; several US plans; the PLO state of 1988; the Oslo accords of the 1990s; and recently, the impotent Mitchell Report, the still-born Roadmap, the dead-on-arrival Arab plan, and finally, the aborted "Geneva Accord"; all demonstrated the futility of division. A two-state cleavage forces us to choose between ugly snaking borders, like Israel's modern Wall, cleaner-cut boundaries that leave many on the wrong side, or forced mass migrations whose scars linger for generations. The two-state formula ignores the rights of individuals, seeking instead to bolster an apartheid system by creating an opposite apartheid system.

In contrast, and broken as its system may be, America is a dreamland: a state for all its citizens; a constitution guaranteeing equal rights and freedoms for all, regardless of ethnicity, race, or religion; the right of individuals to reside wherever they want within the country. As in America, a constitution by itself will not wipe out a century of strife, for injustice casts a long shadow.

We can dream of a world in which Jews so wishing, can legally buy land and live in Hebron, without the stigma of being called "settlers", or needing an army to impose their presence. Conversely, we can dream of Palestinians like myself regaining their parents' property in Yafa or Ramleh, and living there, if they so wished. It will take a communal healing before we can get to the point where we treat each other with equal respect, therefore we must start that project now, instead of continuing down the easy path of injustice and sorrow. In contrast with the multiplying boundaries, a unified state offers individuals freedom.

It is absurd that a country like the USA, founded on religious freedom and individual rights, pushes "solutions" cementing religious and ethnic divisions. Discrimination is not peace. Equality before the law and the right to vote are basic human rights that transcend national identity. A peace that can be imposed only by erecting walls is inherently unstable, contrary to the course of Nature.

Bridge 2004

5:45 AM	Taxi #1 arrives. Short ride to the office at the *Manarah*, where we pool into Taxi #2, shared with other passengers.
7:40 AM	Arriving at the "Rest Area" in Jericho. Too sleepy to pay attention to the road. Bridge relatively empty.
7:50 AM	Leaving the "Rest Area" on Bus #1. It's air-conditioned, and has a clock.
8:08 AM	Still stopped at the Palestinian border control.
8:31 AM	Finally, the Palestinian police return our passports after collecting fees.
8:45 AM	Stuck behind another bus, at a yellow gate in the shadow of an observation tower, waiting for the Israelis to let us in.
9:00 AM	Men on the bus use the adjacent grove in lieu of a bathroom. I wonder what the old man at the gate of that grove thinks, bus after bus.
9:06 AM	The gate finally opens. We dismount and pass, one-by-one, through a security checkpoint to Bus #2, found waiting. Bus #1 takes our luggage elsewhere.
9:10 AM	Our fifth stop at another Israeli checkpoint. Documents this time.
9:17 AM	Finally, we get to the Israeli Bridge terminal.
10:12 AM	After lines inside, and paying a bridge tax, we get the stamp to leave. They want Charlene to board a different bus for foreigners, but with no other foreigners in sight, it could be a long wait for her bus, so I convince them to let her on Bus #3 with me.
10:18 AM	Heading for the Bridge?
10:28 AM	We stop yet again (7th time) and dismount. Piles of

	luggage are on the ground. We find our bags and load them onto Bus #4, paying more fees.
10:29 AM	We cross the Jordan river, reduced to a trickle.
10:34 AM	The Jordanian terminal, our eighth and final stop.
10:44 AM	Making us wait in the bus, a Jordanian officer leaves with our passports.
10:51 AM	Where is he?
11:06 AM	We disembark to a spacious waiting room.
11:40 AM	My name called, we get our passports stamped, going to a different building for Charlene's, then hurry to Customs. It took some searching to find our luggage.
12:11 AM	We exit the terminal and hop on Taxi #3.
12:42 PM	Finally, we arrive at Sandra's house at the closest outskirts of Amman. Nearly seven hours door to door, riding seven different vehicles and making eight stops! We could have made it by 8 AM without borders.

Confession

With Huda and Charlene unable to enter the Mar Saba monastery, we opted to stay outside, admiring it from the "women's tower" nearby. Its domed buildings precariously overhung the cliffs. The four of us then threw stones over the gorge, in a tribute to the late Edward Said. A few years earlier, invitations for his lectures were withdrawn when a photo surfaced of him throwing a symbolic stone in support of Palestine. So much for intellectual freedom.

It was through reading Said that I learned to respect the power of words, and their capacity to liberate, or to oppress. Learning how word choice was used to dominate, I grew to reject Israeli terminology, like calling a stolenment a "settlement". We proudly posed with our stones, the same symbolic statement for which they sought to silence his words. This 'Edward Said Moment' on the brink of Hellfire Gorge, for me, signified my own personal Intifada against the forces of suppression and thought-control.

16

Unmuzzled

"PERFECT EXAMPLE OF PRINTING THAT SHOULD NOT BE DONE USING THE DEPARTMENT PRINTER. DO NOT USE DEPARTMENT RESOURCES FOR YOUR OWN PERSONAL PROJECTS."

2005. The admonition was scrawled in capital letters across the map. My last workday before leaving for Europe. I climbed the stairs thinking about the talks I was preparing. There, stuck on the wall facing the central hallway, next to the bathrooms and student offices, was this.

With two weeks separating my two Europe conferences, I planned to visit my parents in Palestine. Having seen how roads there had changed, I scampered the day before to find an up-to-date map. Online, I found one that would do, an Israeli map, no less, that included the West Bank and Gaza in its expanded borders. It was too dense to read on letter-sized paper, so I printed a larger copy at my workplace. Somehow the file was left in the printer memory, and reprinted when someone rebooted the printer.

Rumors all over the department had me behind it, I was told. I felt my career on the line. Someone was out to threaten and discredit me. The map's poster could have allowed the department to handle this matter privately. Instead, they favored the public charade, never mind how this finger-pointing affected department morale, or intimidated students who saw faculty members berated thus.

After eight years of service to the department, my indiscretion was made a specimen for public display, as if I was responsible for all the personal use of department printers that had ever elapsed. The evidence on the wall. Evidence of what exactly? In the copy room's pile of forgotten printouts lay the private e-mails of a well-known German-American scientist; color personal photos of an Italian-American professor; webpages in Chinese. Of all the occasional misuses of department resources, this map only is chosen for an example. The content was too inflammatory.

Of course, it had to be the one Palestinian who cared about a map of "Israel". It could not be the professor who hung a sign in his office affirming "We Are All Zionists"; not the one holding a joint appointment with an Israeli university; not the one traveling there for religious holidays; nor the one who was inviting everyone to his house in Jerusalem. All these can buy glossy maps from the stores in Haifa or Tel Aviv, so *they* have no need to print one. It had to be the one Palestinian.

With no room for us on their maps, our survival as a people is at stake, our very freedom as individuals. The word "freedom" is often used to clothe grandiose, yet intangible, concepts: the "Free World", "they hate our freedom", or "Operation Iraqi Freedom". No other word has been so abused in recent history. For Palestinians, "freedom" simply means the ability to move from point A to point B, a few miles apart, without restrictions. Freedom is to walk upon the streets of one's own city without being asked for ID. Freedom is to travel abroad for work, study, or pleasure, and return with ease. Freedom is to look far and see a blue horizon, rather than an ugly concrete Wall.

Controlling History

Two years earlier, I had posted my first review on Amazon's website, of a science book I disliked. Feeling gratified at expressing myself and helping prospective buyers, I reviewed a few more books I had recently read. Checking my reviewer page the next day, I noticed one of my reviews, for a book called *Arabs and Israel for Beginners*, was missing. When I inquired, the reply from "Bert G., Amazon customer service" claimed my review violated their guidelines. I rewrote and resubmitted it according to the guidelines, only to note its absence the next day.

The countless existing reviews violating those same guidelines bothered me. I notified Amazon about a few of those. The offending reviews were removed. That got me thinking that someone must be monitoring books about the Middle East for reviews not to their liking. "If they can do it, so can I." My freedom of expression was under attack, and I was not one to be silenced. I kept revising my reviews to pass the censors, while reporting other reviews that violated the guidelines.

In an episode of Revenge of the Geeks, I wrote my own computer program to check, daily, on my reviews, as well as on books on my watch list for new reviews. At the push of a few buttons, the program sent Amazon a customized email for each offending review specifying the exact guideline violated, and appearing to originate from one of a list of activist friends who had agreed to help me. It worked for a while. Occupation-supporters are free to write all the reviews they want, but erasing my words crosses a line. I succeeded in purging countless offending reviews, but mine kept disappearing with alarming promptness.

I was single-handedly dealing with an army of people. A friend I met on Amazon admitted he was once on a pro-Israel mailing list that alerted its members to the appearance of books and reviews critical of Israel. They tenaciously guarded certain pro-Israel books to coax innocent readers into buying them, lodging complaints about every negative review soon as it appeared. Among their most zealously-guarded books:

- *From Time Immemorial* by Joan Peters – a classic falsification of history to absolve Israel of its responsibility for the Nakba.
- *The Case for Israel* by Alan Dershowitz – a rehash of Peters' historical forgery for modern audiences.
- *The Complete Idiot's Guide to the Middle East Conflict,* by a certain Mitchell Bard, who happens to be director of the American-Israeli Cooperative Enterprise (AICE), a registered nonprofit with the stated mission: "to strengthen the U.S.-Israel relationship."

After I began protesting reviews, the last book collected one hundred new positive reviews within a week, obviously the product of an organized campaign. I searched online. Bard's organization credited itself for the systematic scrutiny of Palestinian textbooks, pushing, under the guise of stopping "incitement", to forbid teaching the correct history of Palestine. If left to him, in the name of "peace", Palestinians cannot teach their children about the *Nakba*, about the 418 Palestinian villages that Israel destroyed upon its inception, or about Palestine's overwhelming Arab majority prior. True peace, however, can never be built atop a forged history.

Meanwhile on Amazon, objective books about the Middle East received obnoxious and vehemently antagonistic reviews, using such language as "it's becoming increasingly apparent that followers of Mohammed are not human." Similar slander was reserved for such respected authors as the late Professor Edward Said. I reported these reviews to Amazon, and to be fair, they did remove the more extreme ones, but they refused my argument about the organized campaign on behalf of Bard's book.

It was futile. I was up against the information warfare apparatus of an entire country. They had at least two Amazon Top Reviewers writing large numbers of pro-Occupation and anti-Muslim reviews: "Alyssa Lepin" targeted a largely Jewish audience, and also reviewed children's books to garner "helpful" votes. "M. Robert", meanwhile, wrote clones of "her" reviews, but with a pro-Israel Evangelical Christian slant. The hundreds of books each reviewed suggest they were paid employees, or possibly pen names used by a department of review writers.

By then, I was involved in a few groups advocating for Palestinian human rights, including one on campus, Justice for Palestine (JFP). I was introduced to the group a year earlier by Zaher, an Egyptian computer science student who worked in the next building. I found his jocularity especially hilarious because he was uncharacteristically stereotypical – all other Egyptians I knew were rather serious, nowhere close to their compatriots' reputation for humor. Walking with him to the campus common area for my first JFP event, I noticed a second table near JFP's. Pro-Israel groups were handing out 'I (Heart) Israel' T-shirts. Zaher introduced me to two political science graduate students, Huda, from Bethlehem, and Wisam, who originated from Gaza but was raised in the Arabian Gulf. While chatting, I noticed that the student staffing the JFP table was also wearing an 'I (Heart) Israel' T-shirt. Huda sighed,

"That's Razeen. He's up to his tricks, but you'll like him."

I walked over and asked him about the shirt.

"It's simple. I am against the Occupation, but I have no problem with Israel itself." Mind you, this was during the Re-invasion. Razeen continued, "They portray us as wanting to destroy Israel. I wear the shirt to show that supporting Palestinian rights does not mean I'm anti-Israel."

He had a point.

I became active, attending their events and helping to organize some. Charlene joined us for evening events. Afterwards, Huda might stop with us at Wisam's one-room graduate-student housing, where we all enjoyed the superb Arabic coffee he brewed. Other times we went to an Egyptian hookah place with Zaher and his Egyptian friends. Most members were undergraduates like Jed, the energetic group leader who was always looking for new ideas. When I first met him, he was carrying a thick binder he had assembled from newspaper archives, collecting articles about anti-Apartheid activism on campus in the 1980s. He wanted to learn what worked. Closer to my age was Abram, a graduate student in physics who was such a dedicated activist I wondered where he found the time. He was almost violent in advocating non-violence as a means of resistance, getting down to in-your-face shouting, if necessary.

The group's big event was the mock-refugee camp mentioned earlier, an art display drawing attention to Palestine. We erected a handful of wooden shacks, and a mock-Wall. We couldn't afford anything life-size, so we settled for a long reel of white cloth stretched across a main campus walkway, forcing students to walk around it, and perhaps ponder how Palestinians deal with the actual Wall. Desiring the mock-Wall to serve as a forum, we provided markers, inviting students to share their thoughts. Many did. To protect the display from vandalism, we set up a schedule for members to be on duty, 24/7, for the entire two-week span of the display. Charlene and I did a weekend shift, sleeping the night in one of the shacks. The camp highlighted the dedication of the JFP students to the whole campus, and earned the group respect. It also earned it the attention of those who would rather have us silent. We were in the cross-hairs.

By 2003, I was exasperated from the continued disappearance of my book reviews. Thinking a "Top Reviewer" status would protect them, I idiotically posted a message on the JFP list inviting people to "like" my reviews. The next day, my vote tally had vanished completely. Amazon's reply to my query was that "*several* people" had sent them copies of my letter asking for votes. A small mailing list for a tiny student group, and they had it covered with multiple spies who had no better job but to read our messages and devise ways to harass us.

Intimidation

This underhanded mailing list infiltration is inimical to a free society. This was a student group advocating human rights, not an al-Qaeda cell. Some members came from countries such as Tunisia, Egypt and Syria, where their own rights were routinely repressed. It was all we could do to encourage them to speak freely and voice their opinions. Sadly, the discovery of spies on the list silenced some students and discouraged them from participating, which was precisely what the anti-Palestinian spies desired. What better way to stifle dissent than to infiltrate human rights groups and intimidate people? Our freedom of speech was at stake.

Back in 2002, an online campaign targeted thousands of members, including myself, of numerous Palestinian-rights groups. One morning, I opened my inbox to find it filled with spam. The messages kept coming, nearly 200 a day, every day. Each originated apparently from another fellow activist, the "From" address naturally spoofed. The messages contained harmful viruses, pornographic material, long pro-Israel articles, or language supporting terrorist groups. Conversely, some of my friends received similar messages faking my name as sender. When I called the FBI, they answered "Sorry, nothing we can do, this is not illegal." I was furious – those spammers were assuming my identity, and were also targeting us because of our views. Not illegal?

Enduring a month of this email-bombing, I was ultimately forced to change email addresses. I suspect the spammers obtained our addresses from a useless online petition, likely planted as a lure.

During the time the JFP list was infiltrated, the International Office on campus announced an upcoming talk by the Israeli Ambassador. We discussed the visit and our response on the list. In the exchange of messages, I facetiously wrote: "Well, we could throw eggs and tomatoes on him, but it is better to challenge his message with questions." As I stepped into my office the next morning at eight, the phone was ringing. It was the director of student activities, and he wanted to see me at his office, in person, urgently! I went. The university had gotten wind that JFP was planning "trouble" for the Ambassador's visit.

"We aren't. We plan to attend and ask questions, like anyone on campus is invited to do."

He questioned me specifically about a "plan" to throw eggs and tomatoes on the ambassador. A student "member" of JFP had forwarded a copy of my message to the director of Hillel, the umbrella group for Jewish organizations on campus, who, in turn, shared that out-of-context extract with the university. It was a ridiculous accusation, yet I assured him we were planning nothing of the sort, then endured a lecture about how, as a faculty member, my words and demeanor carried more weight. Point well taken! Still, for nothing more than a joke, the reaction was disproportionate.

The University's concern about the visit of a foreign ambassador, and a possible scene, is understandable. Different here was the fanning of those concerns by someone with the agenda of discrediting our group. It made no sense that a legitimate JFP member who disliked my comment would have taken it straight to the Hillel director. He or she could have challenged me on the discussion list, talked to me privately, or taken it directly to the university administration. The Hillel director's involvement made it clear the spies were planted specifically for collecting embarrassing communications and monitoring our plans.

On the fateful day, we held a small protest outside before the lecture. Campus police was everywhere, and we passed through a metal detector to attend. Students from the pro-Israel groups filled the room, all decked with the same T-shirt spelling the university's name in Hebrew. We took our seats, and patiently listened to the speech, which, unsurprisingly, was full of inaccuracies and outright lies. When it was time to ask questions, the organizer, pointing to a table in the back with pencils and a stack of index cards, declared that all questions must be submitted in writing. By then, I had spent 15 years on college campuses and had *never* seen any talk conducted like that. A university's role is to create an atmosphere where students feel free to discuss and challenge ideas, and ask questions. Our job is to encourage them to think critically.

We wrote down our questions nevertheless. The organizer then took the index cards and thumbed through them, discarding some without reading them aloud, for no declared reason. After several questions were asked without a single critical one, students became restless and several stood up to ask their questions verbally, only to be escorted out of the room by the police, totalitarian-style. One student, blurting that he had a question in writing, quickly pulled up a large sign bearing the query from under his shirt. Nice move that earned him a roomful of laughs, but the cowardly ambassador remained silent. As a faculty member, I could take it no more. I stood up and directed a question at the organizer. Within seconds I had four policemen surrounding me, and had to shout over their heads to be heard:

"On what basis are you selecting the questions?"

It was a simple and legitimate demand. If he's going to make up rules, at a minimum tell us what they are. He refused to answer, claiming I was disrupting the proceedings.

While this was going on, the people sitting in the front row had turned to look. Among them, I recognized faculty members from my department, their eyes wide open in disbelief.

After the printer incident, O'Brien, a friendly and respected young professor stopped by. Aspiring for ever higher accomplishment, he frequently referred to a chart that, based on his salary, revealed the worth of every minute of his time. O'Brien offered his advice. Sympathetically, he recounted how he used to get irritated at every incident in Northern Ireland, but ultimately could do nothing about it. Eventually, he let go of that to succeed in his life.

Professor Greider earlier advised, "There are refugees all over the world who cannot return. Look at the Germans who live in Eastern Europe, who ultimately began anew after years of misery."

Forget my country and start a new life. A cogent argument, but one that didn't sit well with me. Hitler's name came up, as if all our suffering is attributed to a former Palestinian Hitler. I was tired of these pointless allegories that have no basis in fact, and no comparison. Besides, what did I do but print out an oversized map of my country? It struck me that O'Brien's involvement, for a full 15 minutes in my office, had cost the department well beyond one large color printout.

To move ahead in my career, I was told, I needed to be friendly with Jewish faculty members in the department. It sounded like conspiracy theory, except I got that advice from none other than a former department Chair. My own policy was to be friendly with *all* my coworkers. I never harbored personal animosity towards anyone, regardless of their faiths or political leanings. Our views may differ on the Middle East, but I respect that. If a Jewish colleague sees my activism for human rights in Palestine as being unfriendly, it is because he blinds himself to the injustice of the Occupation.

I realize Professor O'Brien spent his 15 minutes, not because of the printout, but because he cared about my future. Still, his advice was like telling someone to convert or change the color of their skin in order to move ahead. I deserve to work for a place that respects my freedom to have my own views, judging my career purely on my job performance. Whoever taped the map to the wall had bypassed the department Chair, who was too timid to pull it down. The cost of the printout can be reimbursed in dollars and cents; the stabbed morale of the department cannot. The university President was in the room listening to the Ambassador talk when the organizer silenced us. Despite our protests, the President did nothing to defend academic freedom.

I chose not to surrender my identity.

Two years after that conversation, when I was passed over for a position I truly qualified for, I could not help wonder: did the ambassador incident register as a black mark on my record?

A Filtered Image

No wonder my American friends were misinformed about the Middle East. Searching for a book on Amazon, planted reviews guide them to the pro-Israeli books. The textbooks are skewed, and so is the media. Human rights organizations are infiltrated and monitored, their members harassed with email bombs. Dissenting voices are silenced or intimidated. Ultimately, what little knowledge Americans glean about Palestine and Israel comes filtered through these prisms.

This network of disinformation spreads a consistent message of a "tiny Israel", "surrounded by enemies", having to rely on its military might, and on US foreign aid, for its survival. Israel is the "last resort" for Jews, worldwide, whom, the propaganda highlights are *everywhere* threatened by anti-Semitism. This grim, distorted worldview is aimed largely at Jewish people abroad, to instigate them to unite behind Israel and support its policies, right or wrong. The fear is magnified – as if their criticism of Israel would ultimately precipitate another Holocaust, and hence was tantamount to signing their own death warrant.

Inside Israel, people are inducted into this worldview from an early age. Apart from government-approved school curricula, compulsory military service at age 17 drills the propaganda into virgin minds. Trainees won't make it through without a tour of the borders, getting to feel the smallness of the country, and the vastness of her enemies. The induction ceremony into the Israeli military is invariably held at a place like Masada, or the Yad Vashem Holocaust Memorial, to impress in them the fragility of Jewish existence.

In North America, certain organizations inculcate in Jews, not a love for Israel, but a cult of dependence, where the person's own future is reliant on Israel's dominance in the Middle East. Like Bard's AICE, these organizations exploit nonprofit status to extract a third of their budgets from taxpayers. AICE operates a website called the "Jewish Virtual Library", generating, collecting and disseminating pro-Occupation propaganda. Some of the featured books, like the *Complete Idiot's Guide*, are aimed at people who have no knowledge of the Middle East. Others are designed to be reference books – talking points – for activists.

The Faustian deal of a free two-week trip to Israel enables the Birthright Israel program to directly mold the minds of young Jewish-Americans, like my friend "80-camel" Hannah.

The flood of disinformation did not stop Jewish Americans from criticizing Israeli policies. Perhaps as many Jewish American organizations exist that advocate a just peace, promote the truth, and struggle for human rights. After coordinating a few events with our local chapter of Jewish Voices for Peace, JFP and JVP started a regular dialogue that brought diverse members together, forming lasting friendships. Occupation-supporters like us to believe that Jews worldwide are united behind Israel. The dissent within the American Jewish community contradicts that notion, despite the pressures that community faces to conform and toe the line.

In my first al-Awda meeting in 2002, I met Josh, a motivated and energetic activist the age of my brother Hakeem. A single dad, he brought his children with him. He was interested in forming coalitions with other groups to broaden support for Palestine. He kept at it, and was instrumental in forming the solidarity network behind the large protests supporting Palestinian rights. He also founded his own organization to expose the discrimination prevalent in Israeli law. Charlene and I stayed in touch with him long after, attending his daughter's Bat Mitzvah. Since, he had moved to New York where he now works at the United Nations.

Even outwardly pro-Israel people are not united in their opinions. Ernie himself wasn't shy about criticizing Israel sometimes. I wondered at times if he really believed what he forwarded from those belligerent lists. Perhaps he was playing Devil's Advocate to challenge my thinking. All the heated debates in the Intifada didn't stop us from being friends. We had more in common. He confessed that if it weren't for Palestinians, Israelis would have killed each other long ago because of their own divisions. He also emphasized how easy it was for extremists to polarize people and sabotage peaceful relations. I couldn't agree more. I appreciate his insight that what matters most is "What now?" Where do we go from here?

When we first met, Ernie introduced himself as a "Palestinian Jew". His father was born in Palestine, before the British occupation. After the 1929 massacres of Jews in Hebron, he moved to Brooklyn, where Ernie was born. I learned more recently that his father was buried in the Jewish cemetery on the Mount of Olives. I recalled how my own dad, in a condemnatory tone, told me how the Jordanians had cut a road through that cemetery, then built a hotel on desecrated graves. When Ernie mentioned his father's grave, I did not need to ask. I understood.

Ernie occasionally shared publications from a few "watchdog" groups. Disguised with neutral or positive names, and nonprofit status, this thought police promotes an anti-Palestinian, anti-Muslim narrative. The misnamed Committee for Accuracy in Middle East Reporting in America (CAMERA) claims over 65,000 paying members. Its front page celebrates news media corrections based on CAMERA's input, runs articles portraying Israel under attack from all sides, and vilifies those daring to criticize it. A story from Aug. 26, 2015 entitled "Praise for Carter Ignores Ex-President's Anti-Israel Obsession," accuses the former president, who has helped Israel forge a long-lasting peace deal with Egypt, of having an "anti-Israel animus, chronic errors on Arab-Israeli matters and Arab financial support." Enough said!

Rather than "correct" the media, the Middle East Media Research Institute (MEMRI) translates *select* articles from the Arabic and Farsi media. By highlighting opinions far from mainstream, the site portrays Arabs and Iranians as rabid extremists. As I learned from its public website, it attracts annual contributions of some $5 million US dollars.

Campus Watch, run by the infamous Daniel Pipes, maintains files on every public speaker of note who advocates for peace and justice in the Middle East. In addition to spying on those persons in an attempt to harass or discredit them, the group makes available synopses of their speeches, along with questions and talking points for hecklers. Campus Watch has campaigned for the dismissal of academics critical of Israel, on dubious grounds, such as expressing a personal opinion outside of class in a social media post. So much for the "land of the free", if one can speak freely only at the expense of their jobs. Campus Watch's agenda, evidently, is to cleanse American universities of critical voices, so students go through college hearing only the Israeli point of view.

White-out

A historical map in a Palestinian textbook, labeling the whole area "Palestine", as it was called during the Mandate, was considered "incitement" by Mitchell Bard's organization. Yet the Google map of the West Bank (not considered part of Israel under international law) has Hebrew names everywhere, with roads numbered according to their Israeli designations. The boundaries of Jerusalem in the National Geographic Atlas are the enlarged boundaries that Israel redrew in 1968, again in violation of international law. Road signs in the West Bank nowadays more often omit the Arabic. Official Israeli-speak calls the West Bank "Judea and Samaria", rewinding time 2000 years. Applying Hebrew names to our locations is nothing less than claiming ownership, the real "incitement" against peace.

Faced with our disappearance from the map, I developed the hobby of editing all the maps I acquire. Scratching out the word "Israel", I replaced it with "Palestine", as if this small irrelevant gesture was going to correct history.

Curiously, I later learned I was not alone in this hobby. Scanning internet hoaxes on Snopes.com, I found one calling for a boycott of Walmart for selling a globe (made in China) with the word "Palestine". Apparently, Israel's entourage is not content with the erasure of Palestine's physical existence, but feels compelled to police every store, map, and atlas. Don't I have a right to buy my daughter a globe with the word "Palestine"? Why must everyone conform to their worldview? If anyone rejects that globe, they have no obligation to buy it. Why boycott the entire chain?

Rather idiotically, Snopes defended Walmart for taking those globes off the shelf, oblivious and insensitive to the overarching assumptions. There was no question on the minds of Snopes editors that Palestine *should* be taken off the maps, only that the email was being unfair to Walmart. The nefariousness of the episode went over their heads. The obliteration of a nation was of no concern.

I revisited the English-language World History textbook we used at the Friends' School in Ramallah, the same version that Americans my generation had studied. The section on the Middle East was jarringly Israel-centric, with headings like "the state of Israel faced a hostile Arab world." No mention of the cause of Arab hostility, or of any wrong-doing on Israel's part. The Nakba is presented as "Palestinian Arabs fleeing their homes," without the context behind their exodus, or the role of numerous massacres in driving them away. Israel was no actor in that textbook, only a victim. Elsewhere, the section on the Roman Empire depicts present-day Israel as the restoration of Jewish presence to Palestine after 2000 years of diaspora. The section on World War II portrays Israel as the logical culmination of the Holocaust – the savior of Jews from future repeats. Coverage of other places, such as Iraq or Iran, is more nuanced.

The hotly-defended Peters book ridiculously claims that Palestinians moved to Palestine from elsewhere in the 1920s and 1930s, to take advantage of the "prosperity" brought about by the new Jewish immigrants from Europe. This flies in the face of all facts, centuries of census data, Palestinian family trees, my grandfather's passport and land deeds. Besides, until the British occupation, the whole Middle East was one country and people could travel freely. Jews, as well as others, took advantage of that to come to Palestine.

I found it disturbing that even respectable sources spread misinformation. In January 2001, National Geographic Magazine ran an article on Ashkelon, one of the major cities of the Philistines. The article describes modern excavations and details the history of Ashkelon from its founding till its destruction by the Mamelukes in 1270 AD. Leaving a huge gap, the timeline continues "But Ashkelon is rising anew. A modern skyline of highrises now soars behind the ruins. In the past decade throngs of newcomers, mostly Jewish immigrants from Russia and Ethiopia, have relocated to a reborn city." Omitted were the centuries of habitation in al-Majdal Ascalan, the depopulated Palestinian village on the site. Lingering in the misery of Gaza's refugee camps, where they were driven under fire to make way for the "modern skyline", the Palestinian inhabitants were rendered not merely invisible, but non-existent. The statements of the Israeli archaeologists went to press without any fact-checking.

Nearing Oslo's "final status" deadline, Israel organized a widely publicized campaign called "Jerusalem 3000". On my 1999 visit, flags decked the city proclaiming the 3000th anniversary of the "City of David". Besides the mystery of calculating the exact date of King David's reign, a millennia or two of pre-Israelite history were ignored. The "City of Salem", the Canaanite god of Peace, had existed for at least 5000 years. The letters exchanged between its king (Abdi-Heba) and Pharaoh Akhenaten of Egypt (c. 1350 BC) were excavated at the latter's capital at Tell el-Amarna. The Bible admits the city's existence, not only before King David was born, but before Joshua ben Nun conquered Canaan:

> "At Jerusalem, the men of Judah were unable to drive out the Jebusites who lived there, and to this day Jebusites and men of Judah live together in Jerusalem."
> (*Joshua 15:63*)

In other words, Jerusalem was always a multi-ethnic, multi-cultural, multi-religious city. At the time of Jesus, Jerusalem was inhabited by Romans, Greeks, Philistines, Persians, Egyptians, and others, as well as Canaanites and Jews. All these people co-existed. So what's the point of "Jerusalem 3000"?

"Israel's National Food"

When I was a student in Ann Arbor, I was upset that the local deli (Palestinian-owned, no less) had stuck an Israeli flag in their falafel tray. A label underneath read: "Falafel, Israel's National Food." An online search for that slogan in 2010 turned up thousands of images of falafel sandwiches with Israeli flags. What is the point of making flags, photos, and websites, claiming the traditional food that we have cooked and enjoyed for centuries? The majority of Israelis, originating from Europe, brought knish, schnitzels, and matzahs. They learned and adopted falafel from us, as they did with hummus, *halaweh* (renamed halva), and *baqlawah* (renamed baklava). An Israeli flag in falafel is as absurd as a British flag in sushi, but more sinister, considering Israel had displaced Palestine in its entirety.

The falafel craze in Israel could have been a great opportunity for reconciliation, had Israelis admitted their love of Palestinian food *without taking ownership*. Like renaming places on the map, the flag on the falafel is all about staking a claim. Their acquisition of Palestine can never be complete without also owning our culture, and our cuisine. To admit enjoying our food is to admit our existence and our history, belying their entire worldview. In their militaristic world, liking our food is a weakness, akin to Holofernes succumbing to the wiles of Judith. So they have to plant a flag to enjoy the falafel.

Just like its need for a modern language, Israel needed to manufacture a culture to connect the diverse backgrounds of its immigrants. By claiming Palestinian dishes for a "national food", and adopting the *tabla* and the *daff* in their music, Israelis assert their belonging to the place. World Jewry complacently accepts this new "Israeli culture," with its peculiar mix of the biblical and the modern, because it gives them the illusion of having "roots" in an ancient culture that continues to thrive, uninterrupted. They can enjoy listening to Middle-Eastern-like "Israeli" music while eating their hummus, and feel that Israeli culture was native to the region. All the while, the thousands of falafel flags betray their insecurity about that connection.

> "Every assertion of our non-existence, every attempt to spirit us away, every new effort to prove that we were never really there, simply raises the question of why so much denial of, and such energy expended on, what was not there?"
>
> — Edward Said, *After The Last Sky*

The Nakba left a deep void in the Israeli psyche. With that vacuous foundation, Israel is forever trapped in the mantle of vigilantly defending the alternate reality its founders have manufactured. Suppressing truth has become a compulsion. They campaign against books for fear people will read them. They establish nonprofits to embalm their falsified version of history. They infiltrate activist groups because they abhor the power ordinary people possess to challenge lies. They deck the city with "Jerusalem 3000" flags precisely because they know Jerusalem is *not* theirs. Try as they may to hide it, Israel's European origin is evident in the melody they have adopted for its national anthem.

17

Wall

FALL, 2005
Tormented Geography

On my first daytime flight over Palestine, aboard the Royal Jordanian to Italy, having just completed a short visit to my hometown of Ramallah. Behind me, on a desert plateau, the airport diminishes into a hazy sea of yellow and pink. Amman looms in the distance – a vast expanse of stone buildings intermingled with trees, blanketing the peaks east of the Jordan River. Jordan's capital city clings to a precarious strip of green between an endless desert to east, and a desert valley to the west, in which the ghost of a river is highlighted with a trace of green. It takes only two seconds in the sky to cross this border that has tormented land travelers for 40 years. The barrenness gradually erodes as the plane climbs high above the West Bank hills. These uniquely layered ridges – the result of millennia of terracing and human care and habitation – are lined with thousands of olive and fig trees, living in perfect adaptation to this delicate ecosystem and dry Mediterranean climate.

Whereas Jordan's population concentrates near Amman, the rugged topography of the West Bank induces fragmentation over a wider network of small towns and villages. Perhaps I would have seen the Wall had I looked harder, but I was in awe at the beauty of the landscape, and in shock from the sheer number of Israeli stolenments. No more than tiny dots mounting the hilltops, their strategic locations place them in control. The Palestinian towns, though larger, are surrounded like soon-to-be fallen enclaves in the Chinese game of Go.

It is easy to tell the two apart. The Palestinian urban areas are hectic conglomerates of buildings, sprinkled randomly along a network of narrow ancient streets that intertwine with the landscape – the products of centuries of natural growth and evolution. Up close, the varying heights, ages, and architectural styles of buildings give these towns an organic feel. The Israeli stolenments, in contrast, appear overnight creations built according to plan, the buildings all identical and the streets perfect geometrical forms. I ask myself, spying one through a puff of cloud, is it perhaps the stolenment floating atop the clouds, thinking its unnatural existence will last forever?

The West Bank's western outline is sharply delineated, as in a map, by the clouds that linger over the coastal plain but dare not tower above the hills. From this coastal plain, my parents hailed. My ancestral homes in Yafa, Lydda, and Ramleh are now engulfed by the sprawling periphery of Tel Aviv, their acres of fragrant orange groves replaced by belching factories and stacks of apartment buildings. Peering through the clouds, the deep hues of green and blue reminded me that the lands Israel engulfed first – the Coast and the North – were the richest lands in Palestine. From here, my parents' generation trekked on foot, in the middle of the night, over 30 km of hills to Ramallah or Nablus; from here, they fled on small fishing boats to the refugee camps of Gaza and Lebanon.

The clouds end just shy of the water's edge. Beyond, the sea steadily intones a symphony of indigos and aquamarines under a cloudless sky. I can clearly see the coastal cities: Tel Aviv, Herzliyya, Netanya, Caesarea, Khdeira, and all the way up to the bend at Haifa – prime real estate. I steal one last look at the sharp coastline, realizing this is as close as I can get to Yafa this time. Unsatisfied with the choice lands, the Israelis pushed forth in 1967, chasing us over the rocky slopes of the West Bank and the sandy deserts of Gaza. Since, their ruthless stolenment policy fundamentally altered our landscape, squeezing us out.

All I can do is look from this altitude at the beautiful land, deeded to my grandfather, that my feet are forbidden to touch. Ironically, I do so from aboard an Arab airline that makes daily flights to Tel Aviv – the same airport that boasts: "All are welcome here," but it's understood, not Palestinians.

Neither can I set foot in the city of my birth, Jerusalem. I had the temerity to walk over to the PA liaison office and ask for a permit to visit the Holy City. Rather than make such requests to the Israelis, thanks to Oslo, we now have a select layer of intermediaries. After ignoring me for 10 minutes while they traded gossip and munched on their falafel sandwiches, one of these PA officials finally gathered enough pity to ask what I wanted.

"I like to apply for a Jerusalem permit."

All of sudden, the entire office was stunned with silence. I got blank stares, as if I just descended from outer space.

"And what is the purpose of your visit?"

"I want to pray at the Holy places."

Again, they gave me a "get-out-of-here" look.

"You know, son, that *they* do not give permits, except for medical reasons? Do you have a medical reason?"

I should have pleaded insanity as my medical reason, for in that part of the world "freedom" and "right to worship" are insane desires, but I decided to preserve my dignity and leave. If the PA is unwilling to champion our rights, then neither should I give them my blessings by asking them to intercede.

My friends afterwards reassured me that getting a permit meant little. Those who had them were still denied entry, as the borders were closed for the Jewish holiday season.

Ernie's presence in Jerusalem made matters worse. Since he bought a house there last year, he was inviting everyone to visit. Remembering the plight of my relatives the Bakers, I secretly resented the ease with which my friend, who had never lived in the city before, could buy that house. Being friends regardless, we agreed to meet in Jerusalem when our trips there overlapped. Apparently, such a simple plan is too surreal for that land. A son of Jerusalem, I am unable to visit for a day, let alone buy property or live there. Born in Brooklyn, he is welcome, and looks forward to a quiet life of retirement in a place where expenses are low, oblivious of the things going on just a few miles away, behind the Wall.

For me, the idea of a two-week visit is depressing enough to make me think twice. The flight to the Middle East, with a stopover in Europe, takes two days for the round trip. With no airport accessible to Palestinians in the West Bank, I'm forced to fly to Amman, Jordan, then take a torturous route across the "Bridge". That's one more day on the Bridge, another returning, plus a third in Jordan visiting relatives. With five days of hauling suitcases aboard airplanes, buses, and taxicabs, I only have nine days out of the fourteen to spend in Palestine with my family and friends. Of those, I'll need to spend a day or more renewing paperwork and applying for permits.

I braved the journey despite this knowledge, proud of my defiance, given Israel's efforts to discourage us from doing so. In reality, all I accomplished was contribute money to the governments of Israel, Jordan, and the PA in the form of entry, exit, and document renewal fees and taxes. That, and feed the usurious taxi drivers, who charge for their good offices with the powers that be to hustle you through the checkpoints.

From Ghetto to Safari Park

The first change I encountered was the brand new concrete Bridge, under which flowed not a drop. In my childhood, we crossed over a tattered wooden bridge that rattled when the bus hurried above a deep, gushing river. Now the river is sucked dry by Israel's extensive industrialization and unnatural population growth. The Jordan Valley and eastern West Bank slopes, needless to say, are barren. The wide swath of reeds, that I recall have surrounded the riverbanks, is shrunk to oblivion. True, I am visiting in September, before the first rain of the season, but never before have I seen that region in such a dehydrated state. Somehow this parched scene reminded me of the Water Ministry's ad from 1989, justifying the Occupation with the dire need for water. That thirst didn't stop Israel's import of one million Russians in the 1990s – to a land of eight million.

Nearing Ramallah, I was met by miles of Wall, its snaking path swallowing more land for the spreading stolenments. Often the Wall hugs

309

Palestinian urban areas, rising adjacent to the last house, circling a town or village, leaving little or no connection to the next town. Last year in April, I was stunned at the sight of those 30-foot concrete walls isolating East Jerusalem and Bethlehem. I was concerned to see walls springing in the western part of the West Bank. I saw "fences" near Qalandia and Rafat, complexes of electrified barbed wire and military roads. Embryos, then – now full-blown Walls. The eastern slopes, however, were a free range where one could see far, and move. Today, the Wall is about to seal the eastern entrances to Ramallah as well.

Peering past a half-completed section, I spied a stolenment, Ofra perhaps, or Rimmonim. I pondered which side was the *outside* of the Wall? No simple question for a place with three-dimensional topology. Are those "settlers" imprisoning us, or imprisoning themselves?

We passed the Qalandia checkpoint, permanently installed in the early 1990s, now transformed into a gate in the Wall, as if that was the plan all along. As if the Wall's path had been long delineated, awaiting the money for construction, and the violent conflagration to justify it. The Wall here, barely a year old, was already plastered with graffiti and murals, in all languages. People expressing their solidarity, and their dreams. One mural caught my eye, a silhouette of a little girl, holding a bundle of balloons, as if yearning to fly.

That was my dream, too!

The scene reminded me of a silly booklet by Israeli leader Netanyahu, justifying the Occupation for reasons of "security" (while ignoring the human rights of the millions under occupation). Simply put, the shorter border with Jordan is easier to defend than the longer border with the West Bank. Fast forward to 2005. Adding to that border the wrinkled path of the eastern and western Walls, Israel now has a perimeter four times as long as the West Bank border to defend. The Wall echoes the hollowness of his words.

Security is obviously not an issue here, for any would-be "trouble-maker" is likely to find a way to overcome the Wall on his mission. What's at stake rather is land, water, and resources – physical entities that walls can delineate, divide, and lay claim to. But that is not all.

Walls are suffocating, especially ones noosed so tight. With no room for cities like Ramallah to grow, they squeeze upwards, overshadowing the same narrow streets, driving land prices beyond reach. Cornered and strapped, more people visit the foreign embassies seeking immigrant visas to whichever countries will let them breath fresh air, and not pester them with "permits".

Ramallah felt enclosed from almost all sides. I only needed five minutes to drive from my parents' house to reach one Wall, then another five minutes to get to another. There was no way out. I asked if anyone could smuggle me to Jerusalem, but there were no takers. Not the Bakers, and not even Ed, the driver who smuggled me on the last visit. Israel now confiscates any car caught smuggling someone without a permit. Never mind. At some point I lost my desire to go to Jerusalem. After all, little to see there pleases: confiscated Palestinian houses, a belt of stolenments, and Israeli flags. But then perhaps, that is their goal in isolating us from the city: to make Jerusalem so remote that we stop caring to visit, let alone return. Time is on Israel's side. The more disconnected we stay from Jerusalem and Haifa and Yafa, the less we will have at stake in them.

Having heard all the hype in the USA about Sharon's "courageous" pullout from Gaza, I now know better. The stranglehold on the West Bank intensified. Last year was a holiday in comparison. Though Israeli soldiers were visible everywhere, I did go to Haifa, Akka and Yafa. This time I see few soldiers, yet Israel's overbearing presence is more palpable than ever.

Suddenly, I saw with clarity the unfolding arrangement. Rather than driving millions of people into concentration camps, raising a worldwide outcry and possible intervention, Sharon quietly built the concentration camps around the millions. Rather than "ethnically cleanse" the land by the shedding of blood, he suffocates us quietly by turning off the tap, and tightening the noose. Less land and water, he hopes, will eventually reduce our population. All the while he is praised as a "man of peace", presumably for spraying a few of his extremist followers from water hoses, underlining Israel's racism even in its methods for crowd control.

Perhaps "safari park" is more apt a phrase than "concentration camp" for the Palestinian enclaves. The Walls and Gate near Qalandia reminded me of the gated lion habitat at the zoo in Ramat Gan. Surrounding the herd of wild Palestinians with a gigantic cage, the zookeepers can guard the perimeter with minimal interaction. The treatment of Palestinians at checkpoints and border crossings is meant to reinforce the dehumanization. Yelling orders, punishing us for not standing in line, and violating our bodies. Our remaining "incorrigibles" convince them of our wild nature. For the average Israeli to relax peacefully on a Tel Aviv beach, we have to be confined.

Meanwhile, the "Palestine Authority" merely added a stamp of "authority" on Israel's agenda. I went to the PA to renew my Palestinian "passport" and trade my Israeli ID for a Palestinian one. The procedures were quick, to be fair, lasting less than an afternoon. Yet in the end, I received the exact same ID but with an updated photo and a different-colored cover, from orange to green. It had the same number, same layout, writing in both Arabic and Hebrew, down to the same discriminatory line which specified my religious affiliation. Again, I was told I could not use the new "Palestinian" "Passport" to travel, because it first needed "entry into Israeli computers". So I ended up applying for a separate Israeli permit to go to Jordan. All the same, new uniforms, same old oppressors. In fact, no Palestinian whom I met in my nine-day stay refrained from cursing the PA.

Squeezed

I arrived in Ramallah to a house saturated with the fragrance of the guavas Mom had arranged in a basket in the hallway, a seasonal treat I could not taste on my summer visits. That night was *Eid es-Salib,* the holiday celebrating the discovery of the Cross. The Orthodox club was having a fire, so I visited. There, I saw Mr. Shami, my old teacher. He had retired from the Friends' School and was applying for immigration to the US, to follow his children. Kareem was there, tending the fire. He is engaged to a woman from Ramleh, an Israeli citizen. Well, not officially. He had to postpone the ceremony because he was refused entry. (With all the closures and denied permits, it took two more years before they could have the wedding. That was only the beginning of their ordeal. Israel had imposed restrictions on Israelis marrying people from the West Bank.

Neither could she enter the West Bank, nor could he stay overnight in Ramleh, that is, when he could visit at all. They waited years for him to obtain Israeli citizenship, so they could live together.)

The next evening, we heard gunshots. Someone having a wedding, apparently. It could be the Israelis entering to arrest people like they'd done repeatedly the week before. Nobody knows. Nobody cares. The sound of gunfire became normal, automatically filtered out of people's hearing.

Construction filled Ramallah. The city doubled in size since I last saw it a year and a half ago, thanks to migrations from other places devastated by the Wall. Al-Tireh, once isolated, now looks like a city center. My parents' house is eclipsed by the stacks of high-rises all around. I hardly recognize my hometown anymore. Abdul-Jabbar took me to see Ramallah's new *Mall*, a multi-story glass-and-concrete building. It boasted the first escalator in town. Buildings are replacing trees, as land prices unimaginably rise from the scarcity and competition of a constricted land. Those with money are happy. The rest, the majority, are left to wonder where the money is coming from. Is it foreign aid being squandered? Is it PA officials selling their influence? People are talking about Fateh purchasing votes during the elections, while others talk of Hamas paying 'salaries' to women who wear the Islamic dress.

I am disgusted by the rampant materialism. I grew up regarding America as the more materialistic society. Up close, I saw the greed, driven by corporations and an insatiable consumerism. But I also sensed the ideals and aspirations of individual Americans. Ramallah today seems to be moving forward with no other purpose but amassing money. Trading land and stocks in a highly unregulated market, it is capitalism unbridled. The only principle is a principled disregard for all matters of planning, environment, culture, or good taste. The city is allowed to explode out of proportion, with ten-story buildings springing alongside narrow one-lane streets, tall buildings blocking decades- and centuries-old historic landmarks, with no semblance of style. Trees, views, and breathing space are a thing of the past, as if the Israelis haven't taken enough of those from us. Traffic congestion, noise, and pollution are out of control. The character of the city is disregarded.

The quaint "resort" town of Ramallah, famous for its fresh air, beautiful gardens, and rolling hillsides, is now a stone forest with people busily dodging each other on the streets. This "prosperity" does not touch everyone, but only the enterprising few, while the rest smolder in poverty and refugee camps. Is this the society we want to build for ourselves? The confinement that the Wall and stolenments impose on us contributes to this overcrowdedness. Yet can't we help ourselves? Can't we exercise town planning? Make the streets wider before building? Enforce zoning laws? Keep green spaces? Why do we have to blame the Israelis for all our misfortunes? Can't we take *any* responsibility for ourselves?

My last day in Ramallah. This is my first visit without going to Jerusalem. I did not even go to Birzeit – the farthest I made was Rafat and al-Tirah. Our parameters are getting smaller. I did not go to the Sakakini Center. I felt a laziness, a lack of desire to go anywhere, borne by the claustrophobic closeness of the space.

Suffocated

A month after my return to the US, the whole world expressed indignation over the Iranian president's comment about "wiping out Israel". While his utterance was yet another instance of the cynical use of Palestine by a self-serving politician, I noted that none of those countries condemning Iran had so firmly and vociferously condemned Israel's actual and physical erasure of Palestine. Nor did they condemn Israel's Wall with the same vehemence, nor has the Security Council met to take action against it.

While the Iranian presidents' words made world headlines, just a few days earlier, Sharon had quietly announced plans to import yet another million "Jews" – presumably to counterbalance the "demographic threat" that Palestinian babies pose to this 21st-century Herod. The talk within Israel of "demographic balance" and "the Palestinian birth rate" revived the words of Pharaoh:

> "Then a new king, who knew nothing of Joseph, came to power in Egypt. He said to his subjects, 'Look

> how numerous and powerful the Israelite people are growing, more so than we ourselves! Come, let us deal shrewdly with them to stop their increase; otherwise, in times of war they too may join our enemies to fight against us, and so leave our country.'" (*Exodus* 1:8-10)

Whereas Sharon was more likely to act on his threat – as he had physically done in the past decade – his statement attracted almost no attention from the world. As if it was his absolute prerogative to bring more armed "settlers" to this already-overcrowded place, to suck what is left of the water table and displace Palestinians from the tiny remaining enclaves. While claiming to the world that there was "no room" for Palestinian refugees – the rightful owners – to return, Sharon wanted to ensure leaving no room for those Palestinians who yet remained. I read online about rabbis being sent to Peru to convert indigenous tribes to Judaism. What next? Will we hear in 2030 about an Israeli mission to Mars to evacuate the "Martian Jews" to Israel?

Discontent with the Palestine Authority had been building for a decade. The Wall only made it worse. It was clear during my visit that Hamas was slated to win the elections scheduled for January. I followed news upon my return. Hamas candidates carefully stripped their platform of extremism and ran primarily on ending corruption. Having seen the corruption for myself, and heard the rumors, I could tell it was a good strategy. Some in America were surprised at the results. I could read a Hamas victory on the near-completed Wall.

The occasional American headlines suggest the Wall is but "one of a set of issues." No one locked in its twisted, tangled, writhing clutches can downplay its gripping hold over Palestinian lives. The overwhelming feeling I witnessed in the West Bank was suffocation. Whereas Americans have the luxury of forgetting about the Wall until its next appearance on CNN, Palestinians have to endure its ugly sight and its inescapable hegemony every hour of every day. Like the stolenments, it swallows the land, sometimes deep within the border. Houses, olive trees, and fertile fields alike fell to its insatiable appetite. It separates the village from its meadows, the family from their farm, and the house from its neighbors. The road to Jericho cost me an extra hour on a dangerous route, while a brand-new, Israeli-only road was kept Palestinian-free by military watchtowers. The closest I got to Jerusalem was standing at a hilltop south of Ramallah, and peering over the ugly Wall at the skyline of the City I love, but cannot touch.

After one of the Gaza "Wars", I ran into Gregory, an eminent Israeli-American scientist at a conference in Berkeley. We had interacted professionally for years and followed each other's work, but late at night at the Berkeley Lab Guest House, meeting accidentally at the deserted vending machine lounge, we could chat about things other than science. He was one of Israel's "Soviet Jews," though he stayed in Israel only as long as it took him to secure a US green card. Previously, he held a professorship in Novosibirsk. With the chaos following the fall of the Soviet Union, and the rise of nativist groups, he felt his family was in jeopardy for their Jewish faith. He had long adopted a Christian name, which he still uses to match his thick Russian accent. Few know his real name is Yakov.

As usual, when conversing with Israelis or former Israelis, we have to first prove our innocence. Convicted by virtue of our identity! Hamas, rockets, suicide bombs. We have to convince them we are not *that* type of Palestinian, then prove again that we are *not* the exception.

That last message was lost on him:

"Palestinians voted for Hamas, which means they want to destroy Israel."

How to explain that Palestinians are more than simply "Hamas"? That we have an identity independent and unrelated to Israel? That we are, first of all, human beings?

Americans sometimes take for granted things like law, constitution, freedom of movement, justice, freedom of religion and worship, freedom of assembly, and freedom of expression. For the last 40 years, Palestinians under Israeli occupation enjoyed *none* of those things. The complete absence of such basic rights meant a dearth of possibilities for securing a peaceful restitution. Israeli courts were a farce, with Israeli law siding permanently on the side of the occupier. A militant rabbi was sentenced to six months of community service for murdering a Palestinian, while Palestinian youths were routinely sentenced to years in jail for throwing stones. There was no constitution to appeal to. Protests encountered a violent response, often involving live bullets. Elected mayors and intellectuals were assassinated, the remainder imprisoned, without trial, while schools and media outlets were arbitrarily closed. Oh, did I say bookstores blown up?

The world system failed in stopping the Wall. The International Court ruled it illegal, but who's enforcing? In the absence of ordinary means for securing justice, and as the Wall extended section by section, Hamas and the military resistance it embodied became inevitable. Headlines after the PA elections, purporting that "Palestinians voted for terrorism" involve a not-so-innocent play on words. The Occupation itself, far deadlier than isolated terrorist acts with its disenfranchisement, land confiscation, and genocidal Wall, is utterly ignored.

This trip has opened my eyes to one thing: "peace", at least the sort intended in the "peace process" of the 1990s, is an illusion conjured by the strong to subjugate the weak. Whenever the weak happen to gather enough feeble strength to protest and rebel, this is called "violence". There is no such thing as "peace" as long as there is oppressor and oppressed, occupier and occupied.

I cling to my vision. Throughout human history, the most enduring entities were multi-ethnic and tolerant societies: China, the Islamic empires, USA, and the Roman empire. Narrow Nationalism – the ideology that the surface of the globe should be fragmented into hundreds of culturally and linguistically "homogenous" fiefdoms – had its heyday back in the 1800s and early 1900s, a mere scratch in the long film reel of human history. Nations in Europe clamored at the turn of the century to merge into one entity, after realizing that Nationalism had brought nothing but endless warfare from Napoleon, to the World Wars, to the countless local conflicts all over the world. Dividing an already tiny slither of land to create two countries along narrow ethno-religious lines is swimming against the currents of history. A multi-ethnic, religiously-tolerant society is the *only* assurance of long-term peace.

Balance Sheet

The world immediately imposed penalties on Palestinians for electing Hamas. Foreign aid stopped, borders closed, Israel arrested elected Hamas legislators, and Hamas retreated to Gaza. There, the population remains almost hermetically sealed, for more than a decade and a half, with gunboats obstructing the shore, and drones patrolling from the sky. Periodically, Israel launched wars against Gazans, presumably to "destroy tunnels" (which the starving population needed to bring in food and necessities from Egypt), or to stop the launching of rockets that were their only audible SOS to the world. From social media, I watched videos a cousin of mine living in Gaza had posted, of Israeli planes bombing buildings, smoke filling the city. Under siege with no escape. International activists organized a flotilla to bring desperately-needed food and medical supplies to Gaza, only for the flotilla to be violently intercepted by the Israeli navy.

It was in one of those wars that I noticed the international oil prices soaring at the commencement of the Israeli attack. Some $15 a barrel, give or take, to the benefit of every oil-exporting country, and the oil corporations. For an Arab Gulf country with an output of 10 million barrels a day, that increase in oil prices meant a cool $150 million each day. The more days the attack lasted, the more cash stacked from liquid shit, while human blood soaked the sands of Gaza and mountains of Lebanon. A month-long war at a $15/barrel markup earns them $4.5 *billion*. At the end of the war, the oil countries might pledge a hundred million to help in Lebanon's reconstruction, the mere cost of doing business.

Chris' friend got a job in Iraq to work on "reconstruction". He was paid ridiculous amounts, for risking his life. The contractor who hired him made more money, and up the ladder the money bags multiplied. Every conflict has people profiting from it. Perhaps the ones defying solution are simply too profitable to end.

Wall construction is profitable. So is the import of "1 million Jews" every decade, boosting the housing and road construction industries. If their presence leads to more tensions and fighting, so much the better for Israel's warfare industries, and for America's as well. While Israel was attacking Gaza and Lebanon, the US accelerated shipments of "smart bombs" to replenish Israel's arsenal. The business interests couldn't care less whether the lives lost were Lebanese, Palestinian, or Israeli. They couldn't care less if they were Iraqi or American. The sums are too great for them to worry about something as a trivial as human life.

Forever a Jerusalemite

At the other end of that flight from Amman in 2005, I attended a conference in Erice, Italy. A week in the ancient city on the peak, with a stunning view of the rugged Sicilian coastline, helped me forget the pain of walls for a while. Not entirely. For lunch on my last day, I returned to a restaurant with large picture windows facing the sea, aiming to imbibe the view in quiet solitude. On the next table, an elderly couple entertained a young Italian man: not sure if he was their host, or perhaps tour guide. I couldn't help overhear their English conversation. The old man was saying, in a thick, unmistakably Israeli accent, how this view reminds him of *"kHaifa"* and Mt. Carmel (using the Hebrew pronunciation of the city name). I wished I could close my ears. I wanted to forget them and enjoy the view, but the old man, reminding me of Ernie, started every other sentence with "In Israel …". It was enervating. Can Israelis sit at a table for ten minutes without invoking "Israel"? Haifa being out reach for me pushed the conversation from irritating to painful.

Two days later at Rome airport, about to board a flight back home to America. I was in a good mood despite the long security line, mentally listing gifts I wanted from the duty-free. The line was moving. Sounded like the usual questions. "Did you pack your bags yourself?" "Did anyone give you anything to carry?" A minute at most, then on to the next. My turn came. As soon as the security officer looked at my Canadian passport and US green card, she left with them. I stayed there waiting for my documents while the line behind me kept moving. After a while, she came back with her supervisor, looking as if they snagged a big catch.

"Stand aside here, please"

It was my place of birth, again, I knew it.

Though I had been living for sixteen years in America, had no accent, no beard, was not carrying anything, nor involved in any illegal activities, I had the suspicious label *"Born in Jerusalem"* to accompany me for the rest of my life.

"Where were you born?"

"Jerusalem. It says so on the passport." (Duh!)

"And which country is that in?"

How do I explain? "Palestine, but I guess your government doesn't recognize it as part of any country. It is currently occupied by Israel."

"And at the time you were you born, what was its status? When were you born?"

I was born under occupation. Did he need to rub it in? No one in the world recognized Israel's annexation of Jerusalem, which meant I was *not* born in Israel. Do I need a lawyer every time I wanted to board an airplane?

I tried to remain calm despite my resentment at being unfairly singled out, but his sheer stupidity was getting on my nerves.

"It's written on my passport. Why do you ask when it's all written in front of you?"

"Sir, I am just asking you. What country was Jerusalem in, at the time of your birth? Why does your green card say Jordan instead of Israel?"

Canadian passports, like American ones, allow "Jerusalem" without specifying a country. When I got fingerprinted for the green card, the clerk at the INS office asked me to enter a place of birth. "Jerusalem," I replied, but he could not find it on a long list of recognized places. I tried explaining, but his English was not good. So I finally gave up and entered "Jordan", the birthplace my green card inherited. If the governments couldn't agree on my status, why should I be the one to carry the onus?

"Look sir, I did not choose my birthplace. Why are you singling me out? Why are you letting all those people pass, but stopping me? Isn't it just because I was born in Jerusalem?"

I could not take it anymore. This ordeal was adding insult to injury. Not only was I barred from my birthplace, but I was condemned to a lifetime of discrimination at every international airport because of it. It was not enough that Palestine was taken, but I needed to explain why its occupier's name was not listed. All I wanted was to get back home to my wife. I had no interest in making the political statement this security officer, for whatever reason, was apparently trying to elicit.

"No, I am not singling you out. This is for security reasons because this is a US flight. Now you're the one making a scene in front of these people."

"In the USA this sort of profiling is illegal. Besides, I want these other passengers to see how you discriminate against me wherever I go, just because I was born Palestinian."

For once, I wanted to let it all out and express what's wrong with the system. Of course, this performance earned me the super-detailed last-minute search at the gate that a rebellious Palestinian deserves. At the same time, I wished I could change my birthplace like people change names – some 'Anytown, Ohio', or 'Timbuktu', or 'Fiji', or anywhere in the world where normal people come from, and could go about their business without getting harassed. Can't I enjoy one normal flight?

Flying across the Atlantic that day, it suddenly occurred to me that Israel is not alone in oppressing Palestinians. The entire world system is based on the mutual recognition of countries, states, each of which controls a definite territory. Our sheer appearance at an international border point challenges the world system that has negated us. Everywhere – Europe, the UN, "developing" countries, Arab countries – we are kept under tight control, searched, and our movements watched. Borders guards, sworn to protect the states they serve, see stateless people as dangerously destabilizing. As the Rome incident, and Amsterdam earlier, prove, no foreign passport or nationality guarantees immunity from the stigma.

The simplest of acts is an adventure colored by every historical memory.

My colleagues at work, like that well-meaning Professor O'Brien, advise me to forget about the conflict. Trouble is, even if I want to, the conflict doesn't forget about me. I am constantly reminded of my Palestinian-ness, whether by those prevalent Israelis talking about the joys of "kHaifa", or by the endless airport harassments. O'Brien can easily forget about Northern Ireland. With his Irish passport in one pocket, his US in another, and "Limerick" for a birthplace, there is hardly a country on Earth where he is unwelcome. Nor does he have to apply for Jordan visas, or some other third country's, every time he wished to visit his parents. Same with the Italian professor, and the German. Not easy for them to comprehend what it means to have that suspicious label, "Born in Jerusalem," stamped everywhere you go.

18

Nature Enchained

Winter, 2007

"Bridge over *trickled* water," hummed in my head to the tune of "Bridge over troubled water," as I crossed it from Jordan. Although December was squarely in the rainy season, the river ran dry. My parents had decided to move back to Palestine, permanently. Their deteriorating health was worrying us. I arranged a two-week stop to visit them at the end of 2007. By this time, though I was successful in my career, I reconsidered the possibility of moving back to Palestine, in part to be closer them. The question was what would I do over there?

Before descending to Amman, the pilot of my Royal Jordanian flight announced "As we shortly cross the coast, we will be flying over Israel. This is Tel Aviv, soon we will pass Jerusalem on the right." No mention of "Yafa" or "Palestine", nor that Jerusalem was once in Jordanian hands. Rubber-stamping the Israeli map for permission to land in "Ben Gurion".

Passed Jerusalem. How tiny! A few streets. Couldn't tell East from West, Old City from New. It all looked the same at night – a tight spot of light, with some sprawl in a few directions. A separate blob to the east – that must be Ma'ale Adumim. That's it. Not like LA or Istanbul, or even Tel Aviv. Tiny patch of land. What is all the fighting about?

By noon Sunday, I was at the Bridge. A new "VIP" service, for a fee, has a private car take you quickly to the Israeli side. I had used it on my last visit, but this time I took the normal way. The Jordanians were organized, gave everyone a number and were processing quickly. The bus ride to the Israeli side was slow, as we often pulled over to let VIP cars pass. For $40, I could've avoided this, but I didn't like the idea of feeding a usurious system.

The chaotic heap of travelers crowding the arrivals window reminds me of the old food store at the Friend's School. You push and shove and reach with your passport, until they take it and ask you to sit – "they" being 18-year old army draftees. Kids. Upon the bus's arrival, the passengers jostle to get out first, as if they're in a hurry, when a minute later, they readily obey the 18-year-olds' orders.

So I wait. Past the security check, "they" select people for more detailed checks of hand luggage. Some poor intellectual-looking guy has two heavy boxes full of books. They make him open them and take out the books one by one.

Outside, most people take a bus to the Rest Area in Jericho, wasting even more time through the PA border. For $100, I can get a taxi to cut through the crap and take me all the way home in Ramallah. I find someone to share the ride. I muse how all those checkpoints and blockades enable this price gouging.

Driving up the West Bank hills, I notice the eastern slopes are more parched than at even the last visit. The roads have changed substantially. I strain to recognize the area around al-Ram, Anata, and Qalandia. More hills are splayed to make the Jericho-Jerusalem road wider, straighter, and flatter. The sea-level sign is forgotten on the old road. At one quarry along the way, nearly intact in 2005, a whole hillside has disappeared – crumbled into dust and cement to build the Roads and Wall. The Wall's eastern tentacles continue to spread, trampling the landscape, the environment, and the character of the land.

As if to accentuate the gutted landscape clouding my thoughts, we pass the newly-renovated, Qalandia 2.0 "checkpoint". The "garbage-can" look was swapped for a militarized Gate complex attached to the Wall. This is now one of the few access points to our forgotten enclave. With al-Ram now co-walled alongside Ramallah, there is no need for a second checkpoint at Beit Hanina. We ran into PA construction crews widening and paving the Qalandia Road.

As used as I am to being rendered invisible in this place, the signage on West Bank roads still manages to shock me. In three languages, they almost exclusively refer to Israeli stolenments. I see no signs indicating Palestinian villages, and mention of Ramallah is sparse.

Tuesday, 6:30 AM

Watching the sunrise. Tomorrow is Eid el-Adha. Basman was in town for the first couple of days of my visit. He was excited to see Ramallah's winter storms again.

I arrived home to find the view from the sunroom completely gone. A new Building is rising behind my parent's house, blocking the west side with its afternoon sun and cooling sea breeze. Only one window in the house is left with a slanted, partial, view, while the windows to the front only welcome the noisy street. To that noisy street, I stepped to take my customary panorama, guaranteed unobstructed by the Big Gaping Hole, now an unofficial trash dump. The sole surviving almond tree in the backyard is dying from lack of sunlight, and the old eucalyptus tree looks unhealthy. Did the construction crew chop its roots?

The Fig Tree's leaves, not yet fallen, are brown and droopy, and covered with construction dust. Its lot – my childhood playground – is now damaged, saddled with a dirt road for construction trucks working on the new Building. Otherwise, the Building is locked behind us, with only a steep, narrow ramp to the street. The construction crew simply trespassed on this lot, leveling a couple of stone terraces, *sanasel,* to make ramps. Everything save the Fig Tree itself is destroyed. How long will that tree last? (A decade afterwards, a fire spread in the lot burning all the cypress trees. The Fig Tree lives, its gnarled boughs proudly bearing the ravages of storms and humans.)

Few *sanasel* remain visible in Ramallah.

Ramallah had changed enough that I had difficulty directing the taxi driver to my parents' house. The old familiar landmarks had shrunk into insignificance next to the towering new buildings, new parts of town, and new associations. Street names are hardly used, thanks to the former attempts to rename streets after Intifada martyrs, ending up with multiple names for each street that no one could agree upon. Some streets have adjacent signs with different names. With historic buildings razed or left to deteriorate, and with the bulk of Ramallah's inhabitants being newcomers, all the latter recognize are the transient institutions of the PA and commerce. "This is the PA ID renewal office, that's Hotel Best Mideastern, and this is Silliman's building." None of these places existed a few years ago. I see little effort to preserve historic buildings and landmarks, add placards, or educate the public about the history of Ramallah.

The city's character changed. Gone are the trees, gone the green fields. Gone are the empty breathing spaces, gone the quiet afternoons.

Al-Manarah is closed to traffic. Good for the town center, but puts more pressure on the side roads. With most streets switched to one-way, our street is the only access to a chunk of the town, and so gets continuous traffic. Even at midnight, the stream of honking cars doesn't stop. They plan to raise a 30-story building down the street, and for that, the city wants to expand our street 1 m on each side, making away with the trees on the sidewalk, and the ones on our and the neighbors' lands. (Ultimately, the developers could not get the Israeli authorization for such a tall building, so the building went ahead, limited to some 15 floors, while the street expansion project fell to opposition by the street's residents.)

An environmental movement is desperately needed. This destruction to the land is hurting us and we will regret it long after the sudden "boom" is over, which at some point, it must. Advanced countries in Europe, USA, and East Asia succeed because of their ability to organize themselves and damp individual gain for a common good. Here, everyone is instead clamoring to develop the last bit of land left by the Wall. Sheer greed triumphs over beauty, peace, and culture every day here.

The newspaper has a section called "*al-Quds* 20 Years Ago." The time capsule this week is replaying the first days of the First Intifada. Funny how, back then, they hadn't yet coined a name for it – the leaders naively postponing our final exams till January, as if problems would be solved by then. We tend to allow a delusional optimism to stop us from doing the things that contribute to problem-solving, like working and going to school.

Back in that Intifada, it was quiet and peaceful. We could see the town and the trees. We could see the smoke from protests rising over Main Street. Now all these sights are blocked by buildings.

I don't feel this is like a Holy Land anymore. The only thing people worship here is money. "Turned my Father's house into a den of thieves."

Wednesday, 4:00 AM

The Muslim *adhan* started. Today is the Eid.

Reading *How Life Imitates Chess*, by Garry Kasparov. Strategy is more important than tactics. That's why the Israelis always win. They have a long-term strategy, we play tactics. They plan the next stolenment to the littlest detail, we think "planting a building here will generate good profit," without evaluating other consequences of that building. They plan obstacles to make life difficult for us, we push each other to get off the Bridge bus first.

Wednesday, 4:30 PM

Ramallah is quiet. Can hear a few birds, not as many as in 2004, perhaps because it's winter? Hope they didn't fly away as the trees disappeared. They're pulling out the big trees in the garden of *al-Bardouny* restaurant, now closed, to be replaced with yet another tall building. Sheer commercialism has taken over. Landmarks and trees alike sacrificed to the god of stone.

Change is a way of life. The internet is one change I embraced. Should I accept the changes of Ramallah? What does acceptance mean? The changes are there, in spite of me. I can adapt to endure them, but why should I, when I can imagine a better world? We cannot let our acceptance of change be the extinction of our dreams.

Thursday, 7:00 AM

Today it is raining – thunderstorms, too. First winter storm I see in Ramallah in years, as I usually visited summers. The town is closed for three days because of Eid el-Adha. I haven't seen anyone yet. Anticipating my visit, my parents had applied for my Jerusalem permit, expected to arrive Saturday.

Found a map of Ramallah. Now large enough a city to have a map.

Dad says the elected municipal and legislative members from Hamas are still in jail. The ones running Ramallah are underqualified Fatah appointees. Hence the chaos and lack of planning?

Friday, 5:30 AM

It is still dark and Ramallah is engulfed in fog. I take advantage of the sleepy streets for a quiet walk. Perhaps I'll photograph the remaining empty lots in the neighborhood before they disappear. I'm loving the Eid. Our street is empty. No cars, and hardly any people. Only a cat, and an old man walking with a cane. Of the hills I used to roam, few remain to extend their welcome. I climb one. In the quiet of dawn, the bird sounds ring majestic. I record them. This historic house on the street looks deserted, windows smashed and yard littered with trash. Few buildings are left with arched windows and stone so thick. Restored, it can be turned into a restaurant or museum. Its large backyard down the slope ensures the city view cannot be blocked.

The littering saddens me. Along with the historic house's lot, nothing is spared: the streets, the empty lands, and the stairs connecting two streets. Photos from my prior two trips confirm how much cleaner those places have been. Today, they're piled with empty beer cans and tiny vodka bottles, some say, scattered by PA police drinking on patrol. People attribute the litter to suspension of trash collection during the holidays. Even so. That's the wrong attitude. Why rely on sanitation workers to clean up *our* mess? If we don't litter, we won't have that problem, no matter how long a holiday shuts down the town.

I tread carefully on a downhill street, still slick from last night's rain. More photos of empty lands, clothed in green for the season. The city center is deserted, like the strike days of the Intifada. I walk down the hill past the post office. Colorful flowers overhang the wall of a nice house, urging me to click the shutter. On my next visit, that house will be no more. Gutted for another stone tower.

Tired, I head home to find fresh *ka'ek* from the bakery, with cheese and pickles for breakfast. The simple certainty of a chunk of dough, shaped into a donut, and studded with sesame seeds, is sometimes enough of an anchor to calm the fears of time.

Monday, 1:00 AM

The celebrated permit arrived. Thanks to the Christian holidays, it is valid 24/7, for a whole month, to "all Israel". I can be sleeping in Haifa and Nazareth and hanging out at night there. What a pity I'm not staying longer.

Jerusalem keeps changing. Its entry point at Qalandia is now a walled enclave with iron cages, cameras, and guards we don't even see, yelling at us in Hebrew over loudspeakers. We wait as they let us in, one by one, through successive turnstiles. Finally, I walk through a metal detector after emptying my pockets onto a conveyor belt, then show them my ID and permit through a bullet-proof window, and they wave me through. That's it. Then I take a bus all the way to the Old City. The Old City looks good and is busy. Compared to Ramallah, it is neat and clean. Jerusalem overall looks well-organized, zoned, and lovely.

I saw Abdul-Jabbar there Sunday. The big talk of town was the $7.4 billion promised us in international aid over three years, to boost the Fatah PA, which had taken over the West bank after internal Palestinian fighting drove the elected Hamas PA to Gaza. Abed thinks the foreign aid is bad for us. What do we do once that aid runs out? We will have become dependent. I wondered where all this money will go. Those with land will benefit by selling or renting to those with money. Those without property will find things even more expensive. This is not real money. All this aid is just inflating our economy, and hurting our self-sufficiency. Better for us to rely on ourselves, building a real, productive economy, not one built on consumption, ostentation, and outside injections of aid that can be withheld anytime to force our decisions.

Taking the bus back to Ramallah, a long stretch of the road, near the airport, hugs the Wall. I get to examine the ugly concrete slabs up close. Their dividing lines blur as the bus rolls by. On top is a thicket of barbed wire. My permit is Israel's way of boosting the Fatah PA. Loosen the screws a little to let us breathe. Open the cell doors for an hour walk in the prison yard, and we get excited to glimpse the blue sky, above the tightly-stacked Wall.

Tuesday, 11:30 PM

Monday, the Scouts held a parade to celebrate Christmas. I hung out with Kareem and Sajid at a café, filled with thick Arghileh smoke. They were complaining about the former Hamas government, calling them "criminals". Knowing my two friends both worked for the Fatah PA at the time, I wasn't sure what to believe. Kareem is now an accountant there. He is still battling to get his wedding plans underway.

Walking in town, I passed a mannequin dressed in risqué lingerie outside a clothing store. Interesting evolution, given that the hijab dominates the street. Talk about split personality. Arab satellite channels play music videos featuring women wearing and doing things no one does in practice. They enjoy viewing it on TV, but condemn it in real life. In Egypt, right after this trip, I passed another lingerie store adjacent to one selling Islamic dress.

I had noted this duality in Arab culture since the 1990s, when I was involved with SAMAR. I could see the cultural split between students, often bearded, who identified themselves as religious Muslims, and others who dressed more revealingly and liked music and dancing and parties. The presence of the latter pushed the religious folks to distance themselves even more from what they saw as encroaching decadence and debauchery.

Friday

Last day in Ramallah. Saturday, the Bridge closes early so I have to leave in the morning. Too short a trip. Saw few friends, as five out of my ten days, the town was closed for holidays.

Wednesday, I saw Waheed and visited his house briefly, meeting his wife and son. He was back home visiting from Illinois, where he was doing graduate work in education.

Yesterday, I went to Haifa with a cousin of mine and her friends. We had lunch on Mt. Carmel. With the congested traffic in Israel, we barely had time to reach Tel Aviv before sunset, where we had some drinks and walked on the deserted winter beach. The Israelis we interacted with were friendly. Entering a Tel Aviv supermarket, we passed through a quick security check. That's all.

The drive was the most interesting part.

With the Beitunia road permanently closed, and wanting to avoid Qalandia, we took the cactus-lined village road west through Ein Arik, Deir Ibzi', and Kufr Ni'meh. The road was narrow, but as the only access to that portion of the West Bank, it teemed with yellow "Fords", the ride-sharing taxis connecting towns. Since none of those villages had the police power to slow down traffic, they resorted to frequent speed bumps. At the end of the road, we passed through scenic Bil'in next to a Wall under construction, the subject of legal battles and site of perpetual protest.

Emerging through a checkpoint to the Israeli road, we took the new "Highway 6" to the North. Trespassing on West Bank land, it shadows the Wall, doubling as a military patrol road. This side of the Wall is painted with fields of flowers and happy colors. We saw hints of Palestinians only when passing the congested towns of Qalqilya and Tulkarm. The Wall appeared on the brink of bursting as it belted a choked Qalqilya, leaving it only upwards to expand. The open space next to the city, Palestinian land, is now on the "Israeli side" (originally also Palestinian land).

The sight of Tulkarm similarly squeezed reminded me of the poem (with apologies to Salem Jubran for updating the last line into the twenty-first century):

> "The Sun glides over the border,
> No soldier shoots at her face.
>
> "A Songbird sings at dusk, in Tulkarm.
> Nighttime,
> It feeds and sleeps,
> Peacefully,
> With the birds of Jewish kibbutzim.

> ".. A stray Donkey
> Grazes the line,
> In Peace,
> No soldier at his face opens fire.
>
> "And I, your human, the Refugee,
> – O Land of my country –
> Between my eye and your horizons – the Wall."

Yes, I thought. The Sun and the Songbird can still make it above, but the Donkey is equally doomed. We all focus on how the Wall has impacted the millions of humans inside. That is bad enough. The damage to the Land and the habitats of wildlife remains untold, unsung. In this perverse outcome of Solomon's judgment, with the clamor to divvy up land, the Land itself is disfigured beyond recognition.

Nearing Haifa, giant buildings boast the logos of tech companies like "Google" and "Facebook". Here is a First World hub that the rest of the world welcomes and does business with, satisfied that the Wall hides the ugly reality of Occupation that underlies Israeli technological growth.

Touring the organized, well-planned, orderly cities under their control – Haifa, Tel Aviv, even Jerusalem, it feels Israel deserves those places, when contrasting it with how we have managed Ramallah into today's chaos. At least, that's how someone unfamiliar with the history and the reality of the place may feel. Is this the message we want to send?

(On my subsequent visits to Ramallah, the mounds of trash only pile higher – on empty lots, outside remote villages. The Fig Tree Lot is now a trash dump, as the residents of the new Building behind my parents' house prefer to throw their trash bags out the window, than haul them up the long, steep ramp to the dumpster on the street. Whichever direction I look, I see trash. Whatever photo I take has a littered background. On a recent trip in 2019, I managed to photograph a perfect sunset on the outskirts of town, but only by tilting the camera up, above the silhouette of junk littering the field at my feet. Rusted carcasses of trucks and water tanks, interspersed with human refuse, strangled this thistly ground.)

The Wall and the population race create unnaturally crowded cities, and take a toll on land, water, and air. Ramallah has little breathing space, no wilderness. Qalqilya even less. They smothered the villages, penned us into urban prisons and shut the gates locked. People elsewhere in the world suffer from development. The difference is, they can visit parks, or take an excursion into the countryside. Here, our parks are small and crowded, and the countryside out of bounds.

Yet how much of it is complacency? Littering is perfectly within individual people's control. Cairo is as littered and as hectic as Ramallah though they supposedly have a government. People will not litter if they feel they own the public places. Some uncorrupted state authority is needed to preserve things like old cities and parks for the public benefit. In Ramallah, private property rules. Thinking of all those rooftop restaurants I enjoyed, it was only a matter of time before adjacent, taller buildings blocked their views. Without regulation on building heights, investment into one building evaporates once a new one comes up. I was green with envy ogling a housing development outside Haifa, on the slopes of Mt. Carmel. Built roughly to the same height, and appropriately spaced, every building had a clear view above the ones lower on the slope. Why can't we do that in Ramallah?

Two Weeks Later, Paris

Charlene met me in Cairo after my short flight from Amman. Or that was the plan. I left customs to find Zaher from JFP waiting for us at the airport. He was on vacation in Egypt and kindly offered to pick us up. We waited too long for Charlene. Concerned, I explained my predicament to the policeman guarding the exit from the secure area. "I want to help you, but", he said, indicating something. I slipped a few Egyptian bills, less than a dollar, into my passport. He returned the passport and waved me in. Wandering freely in the secure area, I found her. Apparently, she needed a visa in advance, never mind their embassy in DC telling us the contrary. I found an officer and asked if they were to send her back to America. He replied, "No, if God wills, she will enter Egypt today." Figuring "God" willed a few US dollars, I slipped the bills in her passport again and she was out in no time.

Leaving the airport, with recent memories of an "exploding" Ramallah, and an "overflowing" Amman, I was astounded at the scale and extent of Cairo. It was chaotic to the extreme. We were thankful to make it out of Cairo without getting in an accident. Few crosswalks, no pedestrian lights, and sometimes no sidewalks. The city was dusty and littered. Worst of all was the noise, and the constant, continuous, beeping. Fortunately, we got to spend a few days in Aswan. I wondered if chaos was a cultural trait, or the product of corruption?

Here was the age-old system of the Nile Valley: drive the masses of the poor to erect a Pyramid of corruption. I thought of the policemen at the airport and elsewhere. They earn meager salaries, insufficient for making a living. They look up, find everyone above raking in bribes, all the way to the top of the Pyramid. What's with a little tip for stamping a passport? I could well understand the sentiments, a few years later, when the "Arab Spring" erupted in Egypt and elsewhere. People crushed under the Pyramid's weight yearned for a decent life.

Experiencing Egypt, I also understood the trend of fundamentalism that took over the Arab world in recent decades. In a country where speech and other freedoms are suppressed, resistance movements build in the one place where assembly is allowed – the mosque. The rampant poverty and corruption spotlights the failure of the "isms" the country's founders had embraced – "nationalism," "socialism", "Arabism". The fundamentalists retreat into the safety of "traditions" and fantasies they attribute to Islam's "Golden Age". The very existence of their more cosmopolitan compatriots drives the fundamentalists even harder into their corners, as they see expressions of modernity as "dissolution" at the core of their society's failures.

> "A lot of mistakes were made with good intentions. Changes began with factories, agricultural villages, buildings, large foundations, and the human being was left until the end. ... Revolution is when the citizen reaches the level of the machine he runs."

Thus says a character in *Memory of the Flesh*, concerning the failure of de-colonized nations. In the context of Palestine today, I paraphrase:

"Peace happens when the ordinary human being is deemed as worthy as the kings and ideologies now holding sway."

Somewhere Above the Atlantic

Seeing how green Ramallah looked on this trip, compared to summer visits, I recalled a quote that popped up when I was monitoring book reviews on Amazon. A passage from Mark Twain's *The Innocents Abroad*, describing "Palestine" as a desolate desert, was used as "evidence" of Israel "making the desert green". I doubted, if Clemens was alive, that he'd approve of such misuse of his words. I was so upset, I read the book in its entirety to spite them. It was an apt and entertaining travel companion for my previous trip to Palestine and Italy. From the complaints about the heat, I thought perhaps Twain had visited in summer, and later verified he did indeed visit Palestine in August, the driest month. I also plotted his itinerary and found it mostly confined to the Jordan River Valley – a desert – and the West Bank hills, which appear dry and desertified in summer. He described the Jordan Valley as desolate, but writes of a green Mt. Tabor, fertile plains, and a Nablus of gardens. Not far off.

All that is beside the point, which those who quote the passage miss entirely. *The Innocents Abroad* is not simply a documentary travel journal. Rather, it's a spoof of a travel guide, a lampoon of the institution of "pilgrimage". Though one finds interjected some curious interpretations of Biblical passages and other such gems, mostly it's literary hilarity. The book pokes as much fun of the pilgrims as of the inhabitants of the lands visited. Contrasts are exaggerated for comic effect. More broadly, reading him and other travelers from that period, expectations matter. No greenery around the Mediterranean could impress someone who saw the Mississippi. Likewise, the real Jerusalem invariably faded next to the imagined one. Good travel writing often reveals more about the writer than the place. Written in the wake of the US Civil War, perhaps the "desolation" noted in the landscape echoed the writer's own feeling of devastation at home. At some level, I envied those writers' ability to travel freely and widely within the Middle East – at the time a region united under Ottoman rule. They traveled within Palestine more than I dream of doing today. I was reading the fine print on my Israeli permit earlier, when my mother told me how, in her childhood, her family could drive a car from Yafa to Beirut, have lunch there, then drive to Damascus for dinner, and back to Yafa in one day.

Thinking of the review writers, I wondered how they clung to that one tiny passage to support their historical lie. Pushing a false slogan, made up a century ago, along with a few others. Like "Land without a people …" Those slogans served their purpose, once, of instigating a gold rush for the Promised Land. Is clinging to those ideological fantasies a basis for building a better future?

I came back to the US seriously considering returning to Palestine. It was peaceful during my visit, and Ramallah appeared prospering. I could see myself making a living helping my father with his business. I could think of some projects, along the lines of advocating for the environment, or protecting historic houses from inevitable sacrifice to the stone gods. Charlene wasn't hot on the idea of moving to Palestine, though. Once our daughter was born, it became harder to relocate. My divorce arrested me geographically even more, as I cared to share custody. Ultimately, the trash, crowdedness, noise, and pollution in Ramallah magnified to intolerable levels. By 2015, I decidedly made up my mind I couldn't live there anymore. By 2019, my anguish inside that prison Wall was getting so elevated, I disdained even a short visit.

Memories of Palestine

the smell of fresh bread
rosy stone catching the sun on the Jericho Road
the peal of church bells
star flowers wild on the hills
flocks of sheep crossing the street, bells tingling
gunshots bursting the silence of a quiet afternoon
the *adhan* carried across the wind

reading on the balcony in morning sunshine
facing west on the veranda,
inhaling the salty sea breeze
Haifa in the morning, clamoring up and down the cable car
the glimmer of the rising sun skirting the ridge, (on the way to Nablus)
the dawn, little fluffy clouds blushing pink in the sun
the shadow of the peak slowly unrolling

Yafa, Akka, Beit Shemesh, Gaza, Beer Sabe'
I never saw al-Khalil
hide-and-seek in the vineyards of Latrun
Jerusalem in Easter – no Easter without it
where else celebrates *sabt an-nour*?

ants building tunnels and complexes, underneath a stone
lizards scurrying into the shadow
the bray of the donkey announcing the milkman

the Old City walls, its domes, and streets
beggars outside the church on Sundays
the nuns telling us what not to do

the ice cream boy walking the streets
while I comfortably idled my summers,
he toiled in hot afternoon sun
how many kids carried that loaded fridge,
only to be robbed – by the neighborhood bullies
I saw one beaten by the soldiers
(why do bullies always pick on the ice cream boy?
all he does is make children happy)

climbing the trees
waiting in spring, for fruits to emerge
the green almond, green plum, then cherry
the apple, grape, fig, and mulberry
the cactus pear
the guava and jujube ushering fall

what a bounty!
all under the concrete or barred by walls
hardly an open field, a hill, or a tree
the sea breeze, blocked
the rosy rocks of Jericho, out of the way
the churches of Jerusalem, beyond the Gate
and for sheep, nowhere to graze

The balcony is covered with dust
the verandah with bullet holes
Yafa, Haifa, Akka – not even in a dream
the village road all built up
the Sun peeking, every now and then,
between the high-rises

is the water still running?
(latest shortage lasted only three weeks)

the road to Jerusalem
so familiar
now so surreal
checkpoints and detours
sneaking, like a burglar breaking into –
his birthplace
child of the Land in a den of thieves

III

19

Full Circle

Ksenya.

    The bundle of joy and love.

    The irreversible change in my life.

    The gift entrusted to my care.

    She stopped crying when my fingertip soothed her cheek, awakened to the existence of something beyond the tortures of birth.

To leave the hospital, we needed to name her.

    I had long noticed how my family, in an effort to blend in, had given names from whatever culture held sway in Palestine at the time. The Greek names in the generation of new arrivals gave way to Arabic ones after the Egyptian invasion of the mid-1800s. By the turn of the century, my grandparents had Russian names. Born under the Mandate, my parents and their siblings were given British names. My brothers got Arabic ones again, to go with Jordanian rule. I was amused at my clan's short-sightedness, never anticipating so much change in one's lifetime.

    Admiring my truly multicultural family tree, I doubted the suitability of ethno-religious nation-states for such a diverse place. Instead of celebrating the richness of multiculturalism, the nation-state sees it a weakness, a fracture. In its attempt to impose a uniform "national" culture, this imported European system crushes minorities. The result, in the Fertile Crescent extending from Palestine to Iraq, was a century of warfare that devastated everyone and everything.

In celebration of our child's diverse heritage, and cognizant we now lived in a new world, Charlene and I decided on the Russian-Greek name we gave her.

I took family leave for a few months during her first year. Not wanting to repeat my own father's mistake of working all the time, I had promised myself to be present in her life. In between washing bottles and doing laundry while she slept, I started this book, awakening periodically from my reveries to her incessant famished cries. Her wide-opened eyes, when awake, took in the world without judgment. From her, I learned to observe.

Soon after, the Arab Spring erupted in Tunisia, then Egypt. Having walked down Tahrir Square just three years earlier, by the Egyptian Museum, Charlene and I were fixated to the nightly reports of the protests on TV. My social media feed was clogged by posts from Zaher and other Egyptian friends. It was a time of great hope, a time when all the corruption, and chaos, and backwardness was to be shaken. Watching the crowds chant "Long Live Egypt" felt like the welcome stir of a dear friend, long in a coma, and thought dead. The tanks evoked images of Tiananmen Square, but fortunately here, the poorly-paid soldiers staffing them were not prepared to lose their humanity for the sake of following a tyrant's order. Mubarak was toppled. Having seen his name more frequently engraved on Egyptian buildings than Ramses II, I never thought I'd live to see that day.

Sadly, the revolution was "contained". The fundamentalists who managed to organize enough votes proved that ideology alone cannot govern a country. Within a year, Egyptians pleaded for the return of the Pyramid. Or so we are told. The military took over again. I have not been back to witness the changes.

I was surprised at the US media's sudden fairness in reporting Middle East news, and its newfound positive view of Arabs. I saw Anderson Cooper pick up a tear gas canister from the streets of Cairo, pointing out the "Made in USA" sign, alarmed that they were "tear-gassing unarmed protesters." The role of US military aid to Egypt's repressive regime was questioned. No one had dared a similar report from the streets of Ramallah or Gaza, where tanks and airplanes "made in USA" were routinely used against civilians. Gaza had just endured another round of bombing on Christmas Day. I heard American commentators defending Egyptian protesters for throwing stones at the police: "With protest and assembly outlawed, throwing projectiles was the only way to keep the police from arresting everyone." A few days before the Arab Spring made the headlines, I noted in my diary that "another Palestinian was killed at a checkpoint today, for opening a bottle of soda the soldiers mistook for a weapon." Business as usual within the Wall.

Egyptians had struck a chord of empathy in mainstream Western media that is usually shut deaf to Palestinian protesters. The same struggle for basic freedom and human rights, on the other side of the Suez Canal, is distorted by the giant lens of admiration that Americans have cultivated for Israel. The dominant narrative in America, the product of decades of propaganda and a disregard of history, is of a heroic Israel, savior of Holocaust victims, refuge for wanderers in the desert, which Israel has now made bloom. The trampling of our existence by their project is a minor footnote, often hushed, diminished, and forgotten, if not denied. Palestinian protesters momentarily obscuring this spotlight are falsely perceived to be motivated by their hostility and "hatred" for Israel.

We saw Zaher shortly after, in New York City. Ksenya took a liking to him, entertained by the funny faces he made for her. He was teaching computer science at the university. For a while, he had been contributing a weekly online column in Arabic aimed at advancing scientific thought and progress in Egypt. We saw Razeen, too, who was teaching at another university. He created an online art project, Pal-Isra, a collection of cultural elements and insignia that unite Palestinians and Israelis into a common state. He thought of things from a flag and a national anthem to a language, a headdress, a prayer. His work made me think how people would rather cling to things that divide instead of those that unite.

2011

After a brief run-in with my parents in Michigan, at Hakeem's daughter Vivienne's wedding, Charlene and I took Ksenya to visit them in Palestine. For our first international trip with a baby, we were so rushed packing we forgot a small backpack at home. My Palestinian passport was inside it, but it was too late to go back, and I had the American one in my pocket. We got as far as Jordan, but I was stopped at the Bridge, where they required the missing passport, since I was born there. Luckily, a friend in the US with the house key helped me find it. By the time it arrived in Jordan, express, we had "lost" a week of the three-week trip, to my parents' agitation at their granddaughter's shortened stay.

Making do with circumstances, I spent time with Sandra's family and visited my other relatives in Jordan. We saw Aunt Andrea, who was still painting past her 90th year, her apartment an overcrowded gallery of her art. She told us the *saja'* poem she wrote lauding her eye doctor for a successful cataracts surgery. We also stopped at Aunt May's farm, surprisingly still the same. She came with us to visit the Roman ruins at Jerash and the Crusader castle at Ajlun. The castle grounds were Ksenya's first introduction to the pine cones and stones of the Eastern Mediterranean. We stood near the peak, admiring the full expanse of the land beneath. Amid the fine web of pine needles, we could see the sun setting over the hills of the West Bank. Nablus, perhaps, was on the other side of the valley. A day's walk at most, for us it was a cataclysmic divide.

Waiting, like Moses, to enter the Promised Land …

On this side of the river, pictures of Jordan's king greet us many times a day. All businesses display it, as do public places and government agencies. Love? Or intimidation? Dissent is stifled. People can sense that others share their grievances, but there is no telling who is who. The image gives the illusion of omnipresence, and hence, omniscience. You never know when the eyes and ears in the picture are busy recording. The equivalent of street cameras in East Jerusalem – the faceless electronic devices on the one hand, the familiar face of a friendly king on the other. Meanwhile in America, far more invasively than either camera or icon, we are invisibly tracked by the endless log of electronic data: our emails, social media posts, credit card transactions, medical records, and every website we browsed.

With a toddler, we opted for the VIP service on the Bridge. It was comfortable and, for the first time, the Israelis treated me nicely. You get what you pay for. Adding up the VIP fares, bridge taxes, Jordan visa, and ground transportation, the detour through Jordan can cost a family of three an extra $1000. By that point of our trip, we only cared about getting to Ramallah so Ksenya's grandparents could spend time with her.

The grandparents had a blast, of course. She was quick at grabbing grandma's glasses when she sat on her lap. She adored her grandpa, too, who took the time to play with her. After her birth, I became interested in learning the family tree, collecting interviews with everyone, including my father. The old, handwritten copy I had to start with listed only the names of the sons. I began a hunt for the missing daughters to rebuild the tree. Showing my father the draft, he objected to listing the names of females and their descendants. I challenged him, reinforced by the opinions of Sandra and two nieces – Olena and Amelia – who were visiting. It was time for a change, and besides, that was the tree *I* compiled, and Ksenya's name was to be on it. That settled, Dad actually helped remember more names of female relatives to fill it.

Sandra was there for Ksenya's baptism, which took place in the same church where mine was held. The priest folded her in half and dipped her under water entirely. She emerged gasping for breath. Then it was repeated again and again, the Greek concept of Trinity imposed on Christianity, the immersion in water echoing the legend of Achilles. I went back home guilty for putting her through that pagan ritual, where she emerged in tears. I could see how it symbolized a rebirth. Yet, Amelia (who likened it to waterboarding) and I scoured the New Testament to find references to baptism. Every Gospel spoke of the "baptism by water" being replaced by a baptism of fire, or holy spirit. Curious that, given how religious Adnan had always been, Amelia and his other children all turned out agnostic. She is a good debater, ultimately moving to Ottawa to work in Canadian politics and reporting. Olena was visiting with an American youth group. The only one on the bus born in Palestine, her presence caused the whole group difficulties at checkpoints.

Charlene got quickly bored of Ramallah and wanted to travel, but I had no permit this time. With Dad's car, I took her and Ksenya to drives around the countryside. Amelia joined us on one. I hadn't been to my childhood bike destination, Rafat, in ages, so I steered us there. Near the village, a new tunnel appeared underneath the Wall, connecting us with a pocket containing three villages that had been isolated for years. We drove through Bir Nabala, home of the finest olives in the world, stumbling into a section of Wall blocking the main access from the Jerusalem road. At the other side of town, we found the Gate that was the villages' only access before the tunnels. From al-Jib, Biblical Gibeon, we caught another tunnel, this time a long one under the stolenment of Giv'on. There, we accessed another "formerly" isolated pocket containing several villages including Qubeibah, home of the olive press I visited in childhood.

Amelia was stunned at the extent of the tunnel system, her first introduction to this 3-D segregation. They get the bridges, we get the tunnels, resembling the futuristic world of Well's *The Time Machine*.

At every visit, I find another inhumane barrier. This time, a permit to Jerusalem is not enough. I waste another day to get a "magnetic ID" card, a new requirement. Another 100 shekels to Israeli revenues. I willingly go to their office in Beth El, effectively legitimizing that stolenment. I voluntarily walk through a grated revolving metal door. There is no one to greet me – merely cameras. I voluntarily take off my belt and phone, then walk through the metal detector under the watchful eye of a big camera. After that, I walk through another revolving door, all this without encountering a single Israeli.

Then I stand in front of a tiny bullet-proof window and slip my documents through a narrow slit underneath. The Israeli soldier behind keys in my identification and hands me a number. I pass through the third revolving door to a waiting room. Two hours later, my number is called, directing me to a small room. By then, I know what to do from the example of those ahead, and the repeating video in the waiting room. I stand in front of another bullet-proof window, facing a camera trained at my retina. I voluntarily press my fingertips on the electronic pad. I consent to this invasion of my biometric privacy for the mere eligibility for a permit, with no guarantee of getting one. I wait another half hour before my name is called in broken Arabic to collect my magnetic ID.

The struggle is no longer against the Occupation soldiers, but against an inhuman system of cameras, walls, metal gates, and an oppressive load of documents. There is no Captain Ilan to ask me "Why!" I cannot escape the fact that I walked through there voluntarily. I did not have to get a magnetic ID. I could have functioned fine in the confines of Ramallah without it, but I wanted to access Jerusalem. Applying *to them* for the permit was another admission that Jerusalem was theirs.

"No one can make you feel inferior without your consent," said Eleanor Roosevelt. She never lived under Israeli occupation.

So what is the alternative? Abandon any plans to visit Jerusalem, leaving the city completely to them? Storm the checkpoints with a multitude of permit-less Palestinians demanding their right to visit the city? It is hard to organize against a system that so many of us buy into. The waiting room for the magnetic ID was full; the lines at Qalandia long; the VIP room at the Bridge crowded. Everyone who can afford it wants in. The sought-after "merchant permits" make it easier for storeowners to stock on Israeli products. The age-old divide-and-conquer strategy to further fracture us. We all became "collaborators" with the Occupation, at one level or another.

Inside the prison, nothing really changed. More buildings, worse littering. My new shoes turned white with construction dust. We breathe it in and see it floating in car headlights. The rainless Mediterranean summers are now anathema to clear skies. Every day was hazy and hot, and dusty.

Finally, my father managed, through his PA contacts, to get me a three-day permit to Jerusalem. We spent a day touring the Old City, not easy with a stroller. We visited all the religious places including the Western Wall, where we first passed through a metal detector. We also toured the Citadel, Jerusalem's castle near Hebron (Jaffa) Gate, renamed

"Tower of David" in Israel's scheme to place a thumbprint on every site in the city. Inside was a museum featuring Jerusalem's history. The movie at the entrance was missing about 1300 years, give or take, of the city's Arab timeline. The soundtrack accompanying the Hebrew narration was a creepy nihilistic track reminding me of Prokofiev, completely out of tune with the city outside. The reel ends with Jews returning to Jerusalem in a new Israel. It was painful to watch the Israel of Walls and Occupation portrayed as the culmination of history. The museum exit pours straight into the city wall walk, in the direction of the Western Wall.

I interviewed my parents before we left Palestine, and with the help of an online satellite-view map, pinned down the exact GPS coordinates of their childhood homes in Yafa and Ramleh, and my grandfather's land. We remember!

2013

Hearing I intended to visit Palestine, my friend Chris from Arizona and his wife, Amber, who were planning a trip to Europe, arranged to meet me there. They had the shortest stay of anyone I knew – just four days. Luckily, it was Eastertime, so my holiday permit was ready. Charlene was to arrive at Tel Aviv airport with Ksenya on the day of their departure. Meeting with Chris and Amber in London, I flew the red-eye to Jordan the night before, leaving the airport straight to the Bridge, while they flew direct to Tel Aviv in the morning, making it to Ramallah almost simultaneously.

My visitors liked Ramallah. I helped them find room at the renovated *al-Hambra Palace Hotel*, its historic building no longer student housing for Birzeit. With the spring rains, the air was so clear we could see the skyline of Tel Aviv from their balcony. We spent part of the time in Ramallah sampling *arghileh* places and restaurants. Showing them my old school on one of the drives, I noticed that the school's soccer field – Ramallah's only regulation-sized one – had disappeared to new construction.

I took them on a few village drives. We wandered about the ruins of a mosque in Kufr Ni'meh. Through the tunnel complex, we reached Qubeibah. The village walls were peppered with graffiti, signed by different, competing Palestinian factions. Hearing my translation of the inscriptions, Chris recalled the apt scene in Monty Python's *"Life of Brian"* about the "Judean People's Front". At Bir Nabala, they came up close with a section of the Wall behind the Jerusalem airport. They looked stunned by it, necks bent high upwards, searching for sky. Driving to Birzeit, I found the road studded with speed bumps, so I circled back to Ramallah through Jifna and Ein Sinia – more bumps. Reaching the main road near Beth El, we found it blocked with stones as a group of *shabab* gathered for a protest in front of the stolenment. I took a quick, prudent U-turn to the bumpy village roads.

We spent a day wandering in Jerusalem. Chris and Amber walked through the Qalandia Gate with me, experiencing the metal cages and turnstiles. We visited all the holy places. From the Western Wall, we walked through the Tunnel that instigated the protests of 1996. It ran under the Muslim Quarter, skirting the foundations of the Haram wall. Ambling underneath stores and houses, we experienced a rift in space-time as our assigned tour guide's narrative bore a wormhole through the solid rocks at arms' length, to a Temple a couple of millennia back. We emerged near the other entrance to the Haram, onto the via Dolorosa. With aching legs under the moonlight, we headed back to the bus stop at Damascus Gate.

Ksenya was now three years old. She learned the word "bump" on the Birzeit road. We took a drive down the steep valley to Ein Kinia ("Ein" means natural spring). Here and there, we saw ruins of stone towers for guarding vineyards. We passed farm animals with their newborns – horses, donkeys, sheep. It was a nice drive, but Ein Kinia itself was strangled by the stolenments noosing that water-rich valley. The Ramallah road was the only access. Trash was piled up at the village entrance.

There was little to do in Ramallah. We found one playground that was usually crowded. Ksenya loved it regardless. We met with my friends. Waheed had returned with a doctorate and was now working for the Qattan Foundation. Saleem, who had lived in Nicaragua ever since he was effectively deported during the Intifada days, was in town to evaluate the idea of moving back. A few months later, he abandoned the thought and returned with his family to Nicaragua. After their long absences from Ramallah, both friends were shocked at the high prices, across the board. The land prices were driving everything up. Apartments in the new buildings were out of reach. Ramallah's economy was floating on credit, the banks owning the town.

With the permit, I took Charlene and Ksenya to Yafa, where we spent time at the beach, then walked to the Old City. Ksenya loved the alleys and tunnels in this three-dimensional city, a perfect playground for hide-and-seek. Jerusalem was more daunting. She loved the maze of streets, but we still needed a stroller, and she was now heavier. At the Church of Holy Sepulchre, in addition to the Russians, we ran into Coptic Egyptians on pilgrimage for Easter. At the end of the day, we made it to the Mount of Olives, where Ksenya hid from the camel. Calling it a "monster", she did not enjoy her ride. She also found her first stalk of wheat in the garden behind the hotel. As I explained how bread comes from it, I thought how American city children miss that connection.

Reflecting, I saw a more entrenched Occupation – one with a smile. I had an easier time on the Bridge, a lengthy Jerusalem permit, and could drive on more Occupation roads in the West Bank. At the same time, the walls are higher, the borders more concrete, the stolenments fast expanding. Small favors, like permits, stifle dissent, muffling those kept invisible. Ramallah residents can sink into a microcosm of growth pumped by the influx of foreign aid. East Jerusalem, behind bars, is desolate. The hassle at the Qalandia checkpoint is their way of discouraging us from going. For that reason, I now think it better to go, even if it means tacitly accepting their permit system. Our being there is important.

My emotions on this trip? I feel like a stranger, a tourist, perhaps. Or a pilgrim, going there seeking my past, finding only the present reality, with its dust and thorns. Pilgrimage to my childhood home.

How do I describe it?

The Hills of my childhood are endangered species. The copious spring flowers are coated with dust. The night skies, no longer dark. Walls everywhere. Only the dust endures. I've seen that in Petra, and Jerash, and Rome, and Luxor. The pigeons nest in the ruins. They already populated the empty apartments in the Building behind, and the windowsills of my parents' house. Ruins. The fate of civilization. Buried in a stratum. Pondering these walls, future archeologists will perhaps theorize that we practice human sacrifice. Children of Baal. Aren't we all?

2015

By this time, Charlene and I parted ways. We agreed to divorce amicably and share custody. The challenges of single-parenting left me little time to dwell on the past. For a change, I took Ksenya to Ann Arbor, which hence became a favored destination for us. She loved the Arboretum and the Hands-On Museum. Waseem stayed there after his Ph.D., working in higher education, and starting a family after marrying a teacher from Ramallah. His workshop in the basement has the neatest robotics setup. Leroy also stayed, becoming an executive in the auto industry, yet subjected to the cyclic economy that wracked that state. We continued visiting the Arb, grabbing a bite at the *Cottage Inn*, or watching the occasional hockey game. I saw Moses a few times in Michigan before its bad economy drove him to Texas. Peter, likewise quit his career in auto and moved back to Ramallah, finding employment managing a large-scale development project. He lasted there about a year, returning disgusted with the corruption and rampant nepotism. I wondered if his love for travel rebelled against its locked horizons. He now runs his corner store in Ann Arbor, remotely, while he travels the world on adventure, scaling Kilimanjaro and Machu Picchu.

Roy remained in the DC area, halfway round the Beltway, reaching high up in government service. We still go hiking when we can. Chrissy had resigned from the foreign service during the buildup to the Iraq War. Ultimately, she settled opposite me on the Beltway, as well, founding her own company. Chris, I saw in Arizona after his Palestine trip. Something about the unnaturally verdant Phoenix, Albuquerque, or Los Angeles makes me uncomfortable in the American West. The Cartesian grid of streets imposed on a curvy natural world, the renamed locations, with hints of Native American languages, and Spanish, itself the language of conquerors. The LA freeways, overhanging the nonwhite city center, look no different to me than the Israeli-only road that flies over Bir Nabala. Chris once took me through the parched Gila River Reservation just outside Phoenix. Despite the absence of walls, my sense of being a "settler" there was disquieting.

Before 1847, San Francisco was called Yerba Buena. The Native name was probably neither – another instance of transforming the map to erase prior civilizations. Same with other places I know in America. Ann Arbor or Atlanta, Louisville or Aspen. The original names are lost. The official guide at the Cathedral of Mary Queen of Angels informed us that "the story of Los Angeles begins with the Spanish Missions." The Indians were "hunters-gatherers who denuded the landscape then moved on," until the missionaries "taught them how to farm." It irked me that he could spew this Catholic propaganda in the 21st century, while the unmarked graves of Native children are being unearthed in the yards of Canadian missions. Did any of the California Natives live to tell their side of the story? It seems "making the desert green" is the eternal theme of conquerors. (The guide's repetitive mention of the modern-day "Israel", in contexts unrelated, reminded me of Ernie. Then I learned that Israel purchased this publicity by "donating" $3 million-worth of "Jerusalem stone" for the Cathedral's fountain – stone forcefully extracted from occupied land.)

After my divorce, I met Helga. She lived in Lancaster, PA, so we visited each other on weekends free of custody. Her children were older, and I learned good parenting skills from her example. Having been a full-time mother for a few years, she went back to college for a degree in public relations, ultimately ending up working in nonprofits. I admired her determination to succeed against great odds. I also appreciated her kindness. Helga read more than half of this book and encouraged me to continue and publish it. She also educated herself about Palestine and joined a peace and justice group in her area.

I planned to take Ksenya to Palestine again in the summer. This would be our first time traveling there alone. I worried about the trip. Her safety solely my responsibility. A five-year-old girl, her age, was recently run over by a settler near Nablus. More realistic was the thought of getting separated in the throngs at the Bridge. I could take the VIP service going in, but not the other way. I asked Helga, who had traveled solo with her children before, for advice. Before we left, I gave Ksenya one rule. To stick to me and never lose sight while traveling, in airports, and on the Bridge. She was a trooper at keeping it.

For most of the trip we were locked in Ramallah enduring the intense heat waves of August. No holidays, so no permit. Homes still had no air conditioning, despite summer temperatures creeping higher each year, with crowded Ramallah warmer than its surroundings. Ksenya had a great time and became good friends with her grandfather. She loved the Hills. Giving her a choice to walk along the street or take the trail on the hills, she always picked the trail. I took her to one of the last empty lots on the street. Terraces dividing fields of thistles. She loved their exotic purple and yellow flowers, lost in her fascination with a natural world different from her home's.

The mounds of trash next to the Building disturbed me, more so that some of it flew into our backyard. I was so fed up one day, I drafted Ksenya to help me clean the backyard. She was a good soldier, together collecting six large trash bags of junk. Empty bottles, plastic bags, torn school notebooks. The most prevalent item was balls – basketballs, soccer balls, softballs. Without athletic fields or empty spaces, and with busy streets, the children next door have no place to play except the parking garage underneath the Building. Their shouts echo loudly in the enclosed space, the ball occasionally triggering a car alarm. Summers, the children seem to have no curfew, playing till midnight underneath our bedroom window while I fret over putting Ksenya to sleep.

Ksenya didn't like the playground when it was so packed. Parents smoked despite no-smoking signs. Fortunately, she loved the newly-opened memorial garden for poet Mahmoud Darwish, spacious enough to run around – a rarity in Ramallah. Being artistically-inclined, she also liked the gallery at the Sakakini Center, where we saw a photography exhibition featuring ruins from the depopulated villages.

My friends organized a reunion at a restaurant in Jifna. Rasheed was now working in internet services. Shadi had a gift shop. Najm had opened a swimming pool, which I found a real improvement to the city, cleaner and friendlier than the other pools in town. Sajid, Kareem, and

Waheed were also at the dinner. Almost everyone was married with children now. Abdul-Jabbar was in the hospital at his mother's side. She sadly passed away later that month. None of us could visit them in Jerusalem for want of permits.

The closest we got to Jerusalem yet was the hill at Ramallah's outskirts, where I took Ksenya to see it from above the Wall. She asked to visit the city. I explained that the Israelis, whom she had encountered at the Bridge, blocked us from going there. That night, before bedtime, she approached me whispering something. I leaned in, and asked her to repeat it.

She whispered again, with eyes as wide as when I told her about seeing a fox on the trail,

"Tell me more about the Israelis."

I immediately understood the weight of my undertaking. Her attitude toward them will be shaped by mine – not only what I tell her, but what tone I use, and how I behave. Am I angry? Or fearful? Vengeful, perhaps? Apathetic? Ignorant?

I want to tell her the truth, but how to stop its bloodied shadow from staining the course of her life? For it is *her* future that is foremost in my mind.

My first simplified attempt, I calmly told how Zionists came over from Europe wanting to build a new country. She asked, "Which country is Europe?" Telling her how they evicted her grandparents out of their homes, she said, "Like those photos we saw at the museum?" Nothing escapes her!

At the reunion, upon hearing of my frustrated desire to see Jerusalem, Sajid, who still worked at the PA, offered to help me get a permit. With everyone grumbling at the difficulty of getting one, I didn't think him serious, but gave him my ID number anyway. Next day, he was at my door with a one-day permit!

I walked through the Qalandia Gate while Ksenya rode through in a taxi with my dad. Over a certain age, he could do that. That spared her witnessing my dungeon-like entry point. My pedometer logged 20,000 steps at the end of the day, and, with shorter legs, she must have logged more. It was the hottest day yet, and the narrow streets of the Old City locked in the heat. This time she didn't fear the camel, and chose to ride by herself. Unused to such sights, she paused to stare when we passed armed Israeli soldiers patrolling the streets of the Old City.

The next day, at the Bridge, the thermometer read 48 degrees Celsius. I opened the car door to the rush of an oven, the hot, dry air lashing my face. We exhausted our water before reaching the Jordanian side. My hand was on Ksenya's as we navigated the crowded terminal. Done with the Israeli side, we came to the nerve-wracking part. Outside. In the heat. Multiple buses, crowds, and two long rows of luggage piled high, from which I had to fish our bags. Ours were nowhere in the nearest row, so I stepped behind to search the second, leaving her momentarily on the other side with the cart. That was my nightmare. I could not lose her. I kept an eye on her through the cracks of the stacked luggage wall. Soon as we loaded the bags on the bus, the door was closing, the driver asking people to take the next bus. Ksenya and I managed to sneak aboard at the last second.

2016

For the first time, I wasn't excited about an upcoming Palestine trip. The elections results had drained me. That people let such a person get so far was disheartening. My feelings rode successive waves: fixation on events and media; losing faith in America; then losing motivation. What was I working for? Paying taxes to fund what agenda exactly?

Basman had divorced. With his children almost adults, he decided to move back, close to my parents. His eldest son, Ziyad, was visiting for Christmas. His arrival coincided with ours at Amman Airport, together crossing the Bridge. It was a difficult time for my family. My father, strapped in debt, was attempting to hold his business together. Stressed over mother's ailing health, he had a short fuse, arguing with everyone, over things big and small. My mother was too sick to calm him down. I felt him increasingly strained, seething at the powerlessness and loss of control age had brought.

I tried to keep my head straight by staying active. Took Ksenya on long walks. She like the scenic views. She also enjoyed playing basketball and hanging out with her cousin. Ziyad had finished school and was torn between staying with his mom in the States, or staying here with his dad. Ksenya loved the new Garden of Nations and its playground, where she played with Aunt Sandra. Every new playground is welcome in that place. As the population multiplied, the few outdoor spaces left for their children's recreation were evaporating. A playground Ksenya enjoyed three years ago in Jerusalem was gone by our next visit. The terraced lot with the thistles she had loved the previous year was now a building one floor up and counting.

Like the last visit, I packed my running gear and went for a few runs, this time taking Basman with me. It was a challenge. The sidewalks are narrow, and frequently interrupted by trees, lamp posts, or dumpsters. Worst are the high steps bordering the frequent entrances and driveways. On weekdays, traffic gets dangerous after 7 AM. Not used to sharing a road with runners, drivers tend to honk in your ear. Add the altitude, the elevation (some 500 feet on runs down towards Ein Kinia), and steep slopes, and it's brutal training. My path on the map zigzags and weaves more than anywhere else.

In the middle of our stay, my mother's situation deteriorated and she was hospitalized. Fortunately, she recovered in a couple of days, but it was unnerving. I hardly saw anyone on this visit. Huda from JFP stopped by on our last day, with her husband. She was now living in Ramallah and teaching a Birzeit. Ziyad was happy he made new friends walking into an internet café and showing them what he knew about gaming.

Though we had permits during the whole stay, I had little interest in going to Jerusalem, dreading exposing six-year-old Ksenya to the treatment we got at the Gates. When I took her to Bethlehem Christmastime, I preferred the circuitous route via Hellfire Valley, my first time along that precipitous road. Full of twists and turns, it opened breathtaking views that Ksenya loved. She appreciated Bethlehem's Christmas decorations, and the low doorposts of the Church of the Nativity.

Enroute, at the junction to Jericho under the shadow of Ma'ale Adumim, we turned right to the infamous Valley road. Across from the stolenment lay the remains of an olive grove the Israelis had leveled during the Second Intifada, the stumps standing gravestones in a cemetery for Nature. I wondered what heinous crime an olive tree might commit to deserve this decapitation.

The VIP fee at the bridge was hiked to $150, but now it operates both ways. It occurred to me that Amman was the same distance from Ramallah that I regularly traveled to Lancaster. I wondered how Helga and I would fare as a couple if we endured a Bridge crossing for every visit.

Sandra's husband picked us up and took a surprise detour to the Dead Sea. On the way we passed tent cities for Syrian refugees. Starving and desperate, they approached cars begging for a chance to get out of that hell. Was this how we appeared in 1948?

2017

I wrote upon arrival back in the US:

"It's so quiet here. That's the most noticeable thing.

"Can finally breathe. Air over there so polluted, too many cars and unnecessary drives. It's unhealthy and oppressing everyone. Family oppressed by that building. Everyone was stressed to the limit, or over, with few exceptions.

"Dad most. Mom's health. Money. Us as well: Basman, Hakeem, my divorce.

"Basman worried over Ziyad, and his own future.

"Sandra a bundle of nerves, worried about everyone and everything.

"Myself, stressed out about my own future, about Mom. Plus, traveling with Ksenya a responsibility. Just a few days into our visit, they killed someone at a checkpoint.

"The exceptions were Mom, who didn't care what happened around her, too focused on her own pain. That, so uncharacteristic of her, scared me the most.

"And Ksenya. Too young to understand. Everything was there to be discovered. Good, or bad. She had fun. Looking for sheep, picking a chunk of salt from the Dead Sea. Going to Bethlehem. Seeing the birthplace of Jesus.

"I tried to disrupt things.

"My point was why be miserable? We might as well enjoy our time together. Why spend it arguing over trivial things? There is no reason to be miserable. Every turn of life should be celebrated, including death."

Adding, in a postscript,

"Gotta come to grips with that last one."

The Chair
He sat there –
   by the window,
      facing the street:
         watching,
         observing,
         greeting.

When we talked,
   He there sat,
      sipping the tea
         I had served him
         with a folded newspaper,
         searching for friends
         among the obituaries.

There, he sat.
How relieved I was,
   coming back,
      that the furniture was rearranged –
         particularly,
         that one,
         empty,
         chair.

Embassy Nakba
A photo-op.
For that, 50 people were murdered, on the first day alone.
Children of refugees, who languished in the Gaza camps for

generations. They marched to the border on the 70th anniversary of the Nakba, intending to walk through peacefully, unarmed, towards their family homes. Israeli snipers, hidden in fortifications, picked the protesters one at a time. A video in my social media feed showed a child get shot in the face. One moment he is standing, full of life, the next he collapses to the ground.

The ruthlessness of this shooting spree was amplified, on split-screen TV, by the ceremony in Jerusalem blessing Israel's claim to the city. The US imposter-president who won with a solid minority, corporate sponsorship, and foreign help, had outsourced Middle East policy to 666 Fifth Avenue. After all, human lives mattered less than the votes of radicals, who called themselves "Christians". This Embassy move is a fulfilment of prophecy, say their preachers to the gullible masses, the first step to Armageddon.

The utter disregard of the demons who occupied the White House to human life in Palestine was not surprising. On the other side of the world, those same demons were imprisoning children of refugees seeking asylum at their borders, while their police forces murdered non-white citizens with impunity. With a political system that hamstrung gun-control, and a morally broke imposter-president, nothing stopped the rampages of random shooters in schools, nightclubs, and public spaces.

Vegas and Gaza alike, the bodies fell.

Within a couple of years, the demons downplayed a raging pandemic to inflate the stock market, transmuting hundreds of thousands of human lives into net worths and bottom lines.

Throughout my life, the future of Palestine was a concern and a source of worry. Suddenly, America's future disturbed me. I joined protests, sometimes with Helga, sometimes taking Ksenya – to support immigrants, science, gun control, and black lives. Helga alerted me that local police forces in the USA were training in Israel. No wonder their brutality and disregard for human life.

In Jerusalem, murder of Palestinian children became a sport. Knives were planted on the victims afterwards, to facilitate a "self-defense" claim. In one video I cannot forget, a bunch of grown Israeli "adults" surround a child of about 12, on the ground and seriously bleeding from bullet wounds. Rather than offer medical help, the onlookers are loudly screaming at him in Arabic to "die, SOB". This is what Israeli society has become. Palestinian lives have no value to them. They never had, but with the fascists ruling America, it became no secret. Something to be proud of, rather. No need to impose a media blackout like Sharon did twenty years ago when he "cleaned up" Jenin. Now, they can shoot 50 Palestinians right in front of the camera, and suffer no consequences.

That summer, I deleted my social media accounts. I wanted to simplify my life. Friends who were close communicated outside social media anyways, while the rest – if we hadn't otherwise interacted for years, what was the point of keeping them in my feed? Besides, I didn't like the idea of sharing my personal information with companies that were selling it to unknown parties, especially not *that* company that gave the imposter-president fake advertising.

I said my goodbyes. People's lives diverge anyway. Social media is nice to let us re-connect and catch up, but at a time when our digital lives are unprotected, it's not worth the price. The Michigan crowd scattered far. Slava teaching literature in Korea. Zack an architect in NYC, and still fighting the power. Gabriel back in Lebanon. Sarab in Palestine, where I saw her on TV – as a news correspondent. Zaid, the joker of SAMAR, now a renowned surgeon. Will disappeared. After September 11, he was deeply affected and turned to religion, ironically after having preached atheism to me for years. His grandfather passed away but kept him out of his will.

2018

With the Gaza shootings so recent, I decided to stick to my plans of taking Ksenya to visit her grandma in the summer. She was missing her grandpa, telling me before the trip, "someone will not be there this time." For that reason, I chose to spend the entire time in Ramallah, so Ksenya could spend quality time with her grandma, and her aunt Sandra, who usually travelled to see us when we were there. Jerusalem was dangerous, and like last time, I didn't want to expose her to the Gate. We went for drives with her uncle Basman, visiting the few parks and playgrounds, the Sakakini center, the Darwish Memorial, and my old school. Basman took us to Mandela Square, the extended fist of the larger-than-life statue puncturing the pink sunset sky. We went for walks, rambling along the few remaining trails, repulsed at the piling mounds of garbage and junk. I could see her developing a connection to the place, landmarks she recognized, and favorite things. She liked the Arabic ice cream, climbing the smooth-barked fig trees, and picking fruits from the garden.

Passing the post office, I pointed to her the Language Institute building, where we took secret classes during the Intifada. I explained how back then, the Israelis had closed the schools, destroying any building used for education. Eight years old at the time, Ksenya responded enthusiastically:

"I know what to do! You could teach in tents. This way, when they pull them down, you can quickly put them back up."

I loved her problem-solving attitude.

The unbearable part of the visit was the constant beeping and the noise from the city. Parties that ran into the night. On Thursdays and Fridays, one nightclub nearby fired concert loudspeakers at maximum volume, from the early afternoon through well after midnight. They played electronica and genres I might have enjoyed, were it a hundred decibels less. The sick and aged were disturbed, and the bedtimes of the young were delayed. Concerned about Mom and Ksenya, twice I called the police on them. My sleep was suffering. I practiced running and yoga to keep my heart rate under control. Everyone's tempers were short. People bullied each other in traffic, with noise, and with littering and pollution. I had set up my laptop and workspace next to the only remaining window with a view. Twice a day, I wiped a thick layer of dust from every surface, blown from the construction site across the Big Gaping Hole. I wrote in my diary: "This country is not for me. I cannot take the bullying, the overcrowdedness, the lack of quiet, and the lack of breathing space. I cannot find one quiet moment for reflection."

Waheed stopped by. He was now opening a science museum, the first in Ramallah. Finally! I went out with a couple of classmates to watch a World Cup soccer game. They were talking about Maya. About ten years ago, I had found out from social media that she was living on the

West Coast, with a daughter. I had no idea she was married. It turned out her parents were opposed to the wedding because she was Christian and he was Muslim. The couple found it easier to live abroad. My two friends here disapproved of her. Having seen her happy in her new home, do conventions matter?

Cultural traits have developed over centuries, too slow to keep up with today's fast-changing world. Culture needs to adapt where it's not helping us. Back on the Bridge, we ran out of water. I held on to the empty plastic bottle as we climbed into the taxi to Amman. Offering to help me dispose of it, the driver tossed it straight out the window and into the verdant gorge beside us. My daughter, in the back seat, witnessed a culture that prided itself on disrespecting the Earth. Cultures are stubborn. Given the difficulty of changing other people's ingrained habits, the discontents among us reject their cultures altogether – emigrating, or remaining outcasts, sinking perhaps into an underground counter-culture. Ultimately, cultural change does happen, sometimes rapidly as in the First Intifada, but only through changes of outlook on the part of many individuals.

Reading E.M. Forster's *A Passage to India*, I understood its gist as "Colonialism requires a presumption of superiority." Precisely the reason Israelis put us down, treat us differently, and precisely why we must reject that inferior role. We have an unwritten caste system with regards to marriage, as well as profession, urbanization, and wealth. Our social divisions enabled the British and Israelis to exploit and colonize us. Only we can break the caste system, as India did, to liberate ourselves.

2019

This summer, Basman had bought a new car, which he was happy to employ taking us on excursions. We went to Nablus, mostly along winding, bumpy, village roads. Among the villages we passed, despite the neglect and age that clothed everything else, the mosques wore the wealthy glow of new construction. I wondered how many of those endowments had oil-stained dirhams and riyals constraining the message. The source was less my concern than the object. Why do people think it more important to expend wealth on stones than humans, on houses of worship rather than the multitudes quietly suffering inside?

We had a relaxing time at the Roman ruins in Sebastia, northwest of Nablus, going for a hike in the countryside amongst fig and olive trees. On the way back, Basman stopped at the peak of Mt. Ebal, one of the two mountains surrounding Nablus. We had dinner at an outdoor restaurant with an expansive panorama of the city. We were kept from enjoying our meal by the concert speakers beside our table, set at full volume for the live singer. The restaurant would not turn them down a notch, so finally we hurried out, our eardrums about to burst. I do not understand this phenomenon at all, forcing the whole city to hear distorted music from the mountaintop.

Basman also took us to Bethlehem, the long way. I got a migraine that night from the rapid pressure changes, quickly descending to near sea level then climbing 3000 feet, each way. We passed through an open Gate that could completely isolate the northern West Bank from the southern West Bank, and another elsewhere that could isolate Bethlehem from villages to the West. We had a nice hike amid fruit gardens and vineyards in one of those villages, Battir, where Ksenya was awestruck at a natural spring spewing out of the rock. From a nearby monastery, we also saw a new Israeli bridge connecting to the tunnel we took to escape Beit Jala in 2004. Underneath, the Wall looped in a narrow U-shape around the bridge's foundations.

On the way back to Bethlehem, similar to ones upon entering Ramallah, a red trilingual sign stood warning, *verbatim*:

> "This Road leads To Area 'A'
> Under the Palestinian Authority
> The Entrance For Israeli
> Citizens Is Forbidden,
> Dangerous To Your Lives
> And Is Against The Israeli Law"

It recalled whispers to "lock your car doors" in Detroit. I looked around for a "Do Not Feed The Animals" sign.

Basman toured us through a neighborhood of Bethlehem stuck against the Wall. For minutes we drove with a long section of Wall on one side of the street, right up to the curb. The guard towers peered into the Palestinian stores and houses on the other side. We slowed down to admire the murals left by international artists and activists on this largest canvas in the world. We ended our stay with a nice dinner at a "Wall-view" restaurant.

I relented from my distaste for Qalandia and took Ksenya to Jerusalem for a day. We waited our turn in the cages. The crossing was smooth. We walked to the Jerusalem airport's runway, now a bus station. She loved the bus ride, naturally. We wandered in the Old City, this time with her understanding the significance of the places we visited. She liked the nooks, dim alleys, and caves of the Old City and its churches. We visited the Haram, entering the Aqsa Mosque briefly before they closed it for prayer. She was more interested in the cats roaming the mosques' yards. We got back to Damascus Gate too exhausted to do anything but hop on the bus.

Ramallah was getting too constraining. Her favorite playgrounds were packed any time of day. Basman took us to a new park where we walked for a mile or so. The one thing saving her from boredom was the new fountain at the Town Hall park, which dances to music every hour through midnight. She wanted to go every evening, sometimes staying for more than one show. The place was crowded with children and families thirsting for recreation. We had a small reunion with Abdul-Jabbar, Sajid, and Veronica, whose visit overlapped with mine. Her children were graduating college now.

A new city council was responsible for the fountain. Though a definite improvement, little else in the city changed. The piles of trash grew higher. Someone lit the pile in the Fig Tree Lot near midnight, the suffocating smoke wafting through my bedroom window. I called the fire department, who put it out only after it burned the whole terrace yard and smoked out the neighborhood. Two more old houses at the end of the street were knocked down for new buildings. Flying a kite from the roof is a thing of the past, with those looming shadows. The whole society is paying for every new building, in the dwindling open spaces, rocketing prices, and neglect of cleanup and the environment. The lack of road expansion or public amenities, and the added crowdedness makes life stressful and unpleasant for all.

The chaos is still the same, and the noise. The only peace to be had is in the early morning, when I can drink coffee on the balcony to the songs of birds. By 8 AM, the street transforms into a main thoroughfare with a continuous stream of cars, mainly yellow "Fords" service taxis that must beep every few hundred feet for no reason. The honking gets on my nerves. On Thursdays and Fridays, the nightclub nearby still blasts its loudspeakers continuously, starting early afternoon. One night, fed up as the clock neared 1 AM, I called the police, hoping that would stop the racket. The music stopped, but for the next two hours the howl of drunken crowds alternated with police sirens urging them home. The dawn *adhan* (prayer call), now split into two portions, wakes me up, then a pack of stray dogs have a barking war with the neighbors dogs. Lucky if I get any sleep.

I was on the balcony sipping my coffee one morning, when the sound of repeated gunfire startled me. I went inside, waiting for it to stop, but it continued, all day, till midnight. There was no escape. The results of the *Tawjihi* high school exam were released and some of the students' families were celebrating with gunshots and fireworks. The explosions brought back recollections of real gunfire during the Intifada, triggering PTSD symptoms. Spent the day following Ksenya and warning her not to get too close to windows. The unstoppable noise gave me a headache.

Later that night, we went out with Basman to my childhood friend Nimer's new restaurant. There, we watched convoys of celebrants cruise up and down the street, each car packed with some six teenagers, their bodies stuck halfway out of windows and sunroofs. The parents were doing the driving, periodically skidding to the cheers of the thrill-riders. Some sunroofs had little children sticking out. We can't blame the Israelis for all our problems. No Israeli soldier pressed those parents at gunpoint to parade their child out of the sunroof. We oppress ourselves with our lack of concern for others or for public property, and sometimes with sheer stupidity.

"Freedom: the power not to abuse the choices we have."

So I wrote in 2016 in the wake of the US elections. The sentiment expressed in that 10-word story is equally applicable here. The "freedom" to fire guns in celebration, to toss plastic bottles into scenic gorges, or to not wear a mask during a pandemic, is a fictitious freedom because it ultimately destroys the society that fosters it. A suicidal type of freedom.

Upon returning to the US, I understood the source of the anguish I constantly experienced in Palestine. I grew up to love and respect the Earth. I spent my childhood roaming the hills. I dreamed up recycling paper before I ever knew it existed. I loved trees. I loved to hunt for unusual wildflowers and rocks. Such treasures are lost in the Ramallah of today. Worse, the explosive growth emits the constant sights, sounds, and smells of Earth's destruction. Rock being drilled to lay foundation for the next buildings. Mountains of trash lying about empty lands where sheep so recently roamed. The clamor of people and cars, and the prevalence of gasoline in the thin mountain air.

The sensory cacophony of Ramallah had become as painful as the sound of chainsaws felling the forest across the river for a new subdivision, the year before my divorce. I wrote in my diary back then:

"How can I sleep with the sound of trees weeping for their loved ones?"

Every restaurant in Ramallah had arghileh smoking, while few, if any, had non-smoking zones. On an adjacent table, a mother was smoking arghileh with a newborn in her lap. On our way out, a pregnant woman walked in. People no longer cared if they lived or died. You could see that in the reckless driving. I left Palestine concerned for Basman, who performed too many stunts for comfort while driving us to the Bridge along the twisting Taybeh road. People were on edge, short on tempers, bullying each other, wearing a captive, prison mentality. A collective suicide in slow motion.

I encouraged Basman to exercise. He thankfully fixed up his old bike. I carried my yoga mat on the next trip. Every corner of personal peace we can carve for ourselves, helps.

The Wall remains,
The knee of a policeman on the neck of a captive nation,
Crying to a world gone deaf,

"I CAN'T BREATHE!"

20

Olives and Cacti

A COMPUTER GAME I ONCE PLAYED was premised on someone going back in time to assassinate the young Hitler, changing the course of history. That idea got me thinking, what if someone time-traveled to assassinate Theodore Herzl, founder of Zionism? Or what if I woke up one day in a parallel universe, wherein Uganda (another early candidate) had become the Zionist state? What would the implications be, assuming Palestine remains free? Would I instead be living in Ramleh with my extended family? Would I have traveled as widely as I have? Would I have met the friends I have now? Even more fundamentally, would my parents have even met?

Stuck in Lydd or Ramleh, what would my reaction be to hearing about the poor "children of Uganda," driven by the Zionists into refugee camps? Would I care? Would I even hear about them?

In that alternate timeline where Israel never materializes, I have no illusions of a utopia. With meager resources and lacking the oil wealth of its neighbors, a nascent Palestine would have a difficult journey. I wonder if it could escape the fates and struggles of other countries in Asia, Africa, and Latin America: poverty, debt, corruption, economic disparity, and instability.

So, in a funny twist, were it not for Israel, I might not even have been born. Were it not for the Occupation, I might have had little reason to live abroad. Without emigrating, I would not have the friends I made in America, nor would I have married the person I did. My daughter would not be herself. I might have pursued a different career. For better or for worse, I would not be who I am today if I did not experience the exact circumstances I had endured.

For that reason, I reject the portrayal of Palestinians as victims. I gained strength from my experience there. I understood the universe from a vantage point few got to experience, and learned compassion. *Adversity is not a curse but a school.* Not to condone Israel's actions or spare it criticism, but seeing myself a victim takes me nowhere. Victimhood debilitates. A "victim" sees the monumental effort needed to get him out of the situation and feels it's beyond his reach, so does nothing.

For my own well-being, I need to reaffirm, I am NOT a victim.

"Survivor" is the wrong word either.

I choose not to be defined by my traumas. I am far greater, deeper, than that. The pain inflicted upon me by others binds me not.

The same applies collectively. Generations of Palestinians defined themselves by the conflict, or let themselves be defined by it. We are Palestinians because we have experienced a certain tragic history of loss and diaspora, a stigma no one else shares.

We have been portrayed in various ways: refugees in a war-torn land, fighters for freedom, and now, a hostage population imprisoned behind a Wall. Yet, we are greater than all that. We are resourceful and resilient. Despite losing our entire country, we refused to succumb to a life of destitution. We strove to rebuild, to work, to educate ourselves, even in the foreign countries we were condemned to wander. Our fate as a people never stopped us from striving for our individual dreams. Our national defeat never crushed our spirits.

By defining ourselves in terms of the conflict, we perpetuate the very myths used to vilify us. The Israeli government wants us to have no existence independent of "Hamas", "terrorism", "violence", or other such words of negative connotation. The deeper purpose of the Wall is to prevent Israelis from seeing who we really are.

We are not simply "anti-them". We must break out of the roles they set for us.

To be truly free is to be free to define ourselves as we want; to live our lives in the ways to which we each individually aspire.

Israelis, too, have been defining themselves by the conflict. They find it equally difficult to break out of their role. Generations of propaganda has entrapped them into a narrow vision of the world: the tiny state surrounded by enemies, forever on the brink of extinction – a vicious existence in which a minor lapse of vigilance can lead to another Holocaust. Israelis choose to live and relive their worst nightmares every day, in the name of preventing them.

I doubt they enjoy the part: the tough warriors, the militarized state, the security mindset. They vote for the paranoid and mistrustful Netanyahu not because they necessarily adore his empty vision. They vote for him, rather, because meaningful alternatives have not stepped forth. Olmert, who came into office promising peace, started two wars instead. Before him, Barak started a bloody Intifada.

Many leaders who identify themselves as the Israeli "Left" support peace for all the wrong reasons. They want to ditch the West Bank so that Israel can become more "Jewish", its religious or demographic purity unthreatened. It is not peaceful aspirations that drive them to peace, but a desire for more complete supremacy of one group over others. Ironically, their vision reinforces the nightmare of Israeli isolation – a purely Jewish state in a sea of Arabic-speaking Christians and Muslims.

How can such leaders inspire the average Israeli who has a genuine craving for peace – a thirst that he or she has long resigned to the category of hopeless dreams? The leaders encourage this resignation, shifting the blame over to Palestinians (or the Arabs, or Arafat, or Hamas) – "who don't want peace".

No people can live in peace unless they themselves overcome their fears and embrace peace.

My message to the average Israeli is to examine yourself, looking beyond the narrow minds of your leaders. Do you want to be known for who *you* truly are, your individual self? For your own contributions to the betterment of society and the world? Or do you want to remain known as the "soldier", the "settler", the tough guy, the ideologue, or the victim?

I sign my name "Sameer B.R. Zaitoun" because it contains two iconic symbols of Palestinian identity. *Zaitoun* in Arabic means olives. Olive trees are almost sacred, revered for their strength, stability and productivity. A tree continues to bear fruit for hundreds of years. It is handed down generations, producing fruit, oil, wood, and fragrance. Certain olive trees in Jerusalem are said to be living witnesses to Jesus's prayers underneath them. The richness of its produce made the olive branch a symbol of peace, brotherhood, and hope.

My initials spell the consonants of another Arabic word, *sahber* (pronounced *sub-err*), the cactus plant. The word also means 'patience', perhaps because much of it is needed to peel the prickly fruit. Villagers planted them as fences to protect their family farms from intruders. The plants became a symbol for persistence and endurance, as they kept growing back despite Israel's attempts to extract them from the destroyed villages' grounds. You can still see cactus plants when you drive throughout the Coast and the North, forever bearing witness to the Palestinian heritage of these now-depopulated sites.

Descended from that idea of "patience", is the concept of *Sumud*, steadfastness, staying put, enduring whatever hardships, but remaining committed to the cause and entrenched on one's land.

For people there, facing the daily difficulties Israel imposes, simply going on with one's life is *Sumud*. As an emigrant, however, I struggled with the concept.

Many Palestinians abroad, like my older brothers and some of my friends, cling to tradition. In their new country, they surround themselves with friends and family from the Arab world, speak Arabic everywhere they can, possibly go back to the "old country" to get married, and carry out traditions more faithfully than those at home. Are they unconsciously compensating for the guilt of what feels like abandoning *Sumud*? Of having left Palestine behind? I was more assimilated in American circles. Yet, were my years of activism my way of compensating?

One paradox nagged me. Israel has already interfered in my life plenty. No schools, no jobs, no opportunities, closed horizons, and I left, along with so many others. By dedicating so much of my time to activism, I allowed them to prolong their hold on me. Is true strength to ignore Israel altogether and pursue a normal life despite it? For someone on the ground in Palestine, that can be a sound resistance strategy. For someone thousands of miles overseas, it feels like cowardice and a shirking of responsibility, possibly because it is all too easy to ignore the millions left in the prison.

Then again, why should I let Israel influence my actions anymore? Perhaps the real struggle is to break free and leave the scars in the past; to achieve success and happiness despite the handicap of my origins?

These deeply personal questions are nagging because activism for Palestine can be a lifetime commitment, yet show little progress. If Palestine is to be free in five or ten years, it's a no-brainer. No one, however, myself included, can afford to be indefinitely controlled by external events, getting fired up at every Israeli atrocity. In this multi-generational struggle, mere continued existence on the land, against tremendous forces, is a victory.

I grappled with these questions in 2006. After all, I had a regular job, and a family to tend. I engaged in activism for a purpose, and needed to see results. So I tallied my activities in my diaries, from letter-writing to protests, and checked the payoff versus number of hours spent. Suffice it to say, it wasn't pretty.

The pertinent question is how to be more effective? How to integrate the long-term quest for justice in Palestine into my life, without it taking over?

I realized the need to be selective in my activism. Rather than being *re-active* to Israeli actions, be *pro-active*. Palestine-supporters need our own clear agenda to advance, regardless of Israeli *distr-actions*. I recognized I had a story to tell that wasn't often heard. When masked "gunmen" are often the image of choice for TV news when talking about Palestinians, the human face I can add is sorely missing. I decided to stop conventional activism and focus on what's important – writing the truth. I could not gather my thoughts to write a single coherent chapter if I kept frequenting downtown DC to protest the endless stream of Israeli offenses.

The basic struggle, one that colonized people the world over have grappled with, is how to emerge free from the clutches of a stronger industrial power, without losing who we are.

For proponents of Peace in Palestine, it is essential to develop our own answers. The -isms imported wholesale from abroad have failed us miserably – Nationalism, Communism, Arabism, Islamism, … A theory developed in industrial 19th c. England has nothing to do with the Palestinian economy. Same with Arabism and Islamism – diverting the energies of the Palestinian movement away to bigger and less accessible goals – a form of collective procrastination, so to speak. How much time and effort have our forebears squandered into these side-movements, away from the main and most urgent task of achieving liberty, equality, and a dignity of life for Palestinians?

There is no reason to suppose that importing a non-violent ideology serves us any better. The British were a minority in India, and had a home to return to. In the USA, African Americans are a minority. Neither is the case in Palestine, where the conflicting populations are of equal size, and most have no other home to go to. Palestine is tiny in comparison with India, South Africa, or the US, and suffers a scarcity of critical resources like water. Furthermore, the population race is putting an enormous toll on an already fragile environment. These are aspects particular to Palestine, and any path we hew to peace has to address them.

The Palestinian movement through much of its history looked to outward forms of liberation, such as protest, diplomacy, and armed struggle. Internally, however, we have done little to liberate our thoughts, or advance our society. Shouldn't we first clean up our cities, build the refugee camps, lift people out of poverty, develop and organize our society to point where we can win the uneven confrontation? Crushed by a sense of urgency, the movement instead kept launching wave after wave of ill-prepared attempts to regain what was lost, setting us further back.

The result of those failed attempts was the serious reverse mission creep besetting the movement, especially in recent years. Early in the British Mandate, when Palestinian "Arabs" comprised 90% of the population, the aim was to "Free Palestine" – end the mandate and gain independence. With the country threatened by growing Jewish immigration in the late 1930s, the slogan became "Palestine is Arabic". The Nakba made "*al-Awda*", or return of the refugees to their homes, the primary focus. The Occupation put us back further. By the time Oslo was negotiated in the 1990s, our objective shrunk to a "State" within the 1967 borders. After the second Intifada, it shifted in rapid succession to "End the Siege", "Stop the Wall", "Tear Down the Wall", and "Free Gaza". Scrawled on a wall in Ramallah in 2019, I read "Give us a Sea"!

By 2010, the most common rallying call for protests in support of Palestine was the demeaning "Let Gaza Live". Like "Black Lives Matter", I find it sad and shameful that we actually have to affirm something as basic as the right of a human being to life. (At least in the one case, "Black Lives" are the *subject* – they "matter". The defeatist "Let Gaza Live" puts "Gaza" as an *object*, acknowledging and accepting the power of the Occupier, whom the slogan addresses, over the lives of its people.) Whether inside or outside Palestine, I have not heard the words "Free Palestine" uttered publicly in a protest for a couple of decades. Perhaps the real impetus for Israeli-imposed hardships, like movement restrictions and the Wall, is precisely to distract us from "Free Palestine".

Individually, we have undergone similar mission creep. During the First Intifada, we were hopeful a free Palestinian state was soon to come. The dragging Oslo peace process slowly smothered those hopes. People's aspirations deflated to a time-limited permit to visit Jerusalem. Even with a permit, the cumbersome checkpoints plummeted people's conversations to which day of the week, or time of day, was best to avoid the crowds at Qalandia. Nobody talks freedom anymore.

We forget that a truly free Palestine has no checkpoints, and no Walls. Qalandia is back to being the village from which the old milkman has hailed, on his donkey. Jerusalem is open to all. So are the roads. There are no settlers, only citizens, equal under the law.

Peace plans crashed for ignoring the human dimension of politics, imposing provisions that infringed on the rights of individual human beings to a home, to citizenship, to equality, and to freedom of movement. True peace is woven by the people enmeshed in the conflict. Leave the political squabbles to the politicians. As an individual, I have little or no control over governments, not the PA, and certainly not the US government. I surmise many Israelis, too, feel they lack control over theirs. So far, we have been endlessly stuck in a deadlocked political maze of fear and animosity.

We – individual Palestinians and Israelis – have to change the conversation. We Americans, too, for let us not forget the fuel our tax dollars add to a fractured land. The relevant question is how we as individuals cope with the changing political realities (that are beyond our control). What those of us concerned citizens can do is lead the change. Ultimately, I believe, we win by becoming our best selves, modeling the society we dream of in our own personal lives. This is the only way forward.

Perhaps we can begin by looking at our commonalities. We both desire peace, a better future for our children, both want decent jobs and economic prosperity, and both want to live on the same land. That last one is the root of the problem, but we can make it the root of the solution, if we expand our horizons to include a shared state as an option. Can we begin to work together to protect and restore the environment we share? A recycling center, perhaps? Replanting trees?

Having lost faith in politics, activism, international law, and history, my thinking shifted to the personal and the psychological. How can I cope, and how can I change the *thinking* that perpetuates the conflict, *starting with myself?* These are not theoretical questions. At stake is what kind of world I hand my daughter, and what story to tell.

21

Gaining Altitude

I dream of a Jerusalem with no borders, a Palestine without Walls!

FLYING ABOVE, THE VISION grows clear. A slither of green winding through a parched valley; rugged heights suspending September clouds; the breathtaking expanse of the coast; a thin slanted line keeping the deep blue from washing over the land. I dare to imagine the faint glow of crumbling walls – the aura of tolerance and peace. A government that represents and serves everyone within its borders. A place anyone inside, of any identity, calls "home" and there finds equal justice.

Fortunately for me, the remove of continents and decades afforded me room to heal from, and reflect upon, the whirlpool of trauma that others call "The Holy Land." Those remaining inside the prison have no such luxury, accustomed as they are to the daily doses of fear, pain, frustration, and hopelessness. Recollections of my last visit haunt me: people slowly killing themselves, smoking *arghilehs* and playing Russian roulette with their cars. They see nothing on the horizon. A land in limbo, where only death awaits. With the Wall in place, they cannot even see a horizon!

Israeli society is not free from the clutches of that same whirlpool. The culture of strutting armed to the teeth reflects a deep-seated, multi-generational anxiety that predates Israel's founding. The Holocaust made Israel "necessary", we were told at the museum in Jerusalem's Citadel and elsewhere. The child of this Zionist experiment, 70 years later and deep into the 21st century, is a government exclusively favoring one part of the population within its borders, crushing everyone else. This arrangement entirely misses the point of one of the most tragic and horrifying chapters in human history. Using the past to muster fear only instigates and perpetuates conflict. Actually, the Holocaust is a stain on humanity, *all* of whom should be concerned with preventing the genocide or subjugation of *any group*.

Sadly, amid language of "self-defense", Israel has replicated the concentration camp, on an expansive, open-air scale, leaving those inside to slowly lose their will to live, or like myself, leave altogether.

To attain Peace, we must change our thinking, and our behavior: understand the psychology that perpetuates conflict, and replace it with healthier ideas. To this end, I found it insightful to regard the Occupation in the context of abuse. Like other colonized people, those growing within the Wall's shadow experienced chronic abuse. So have Israelis, who, in addition to the traumatic collective memories of injustice brought from Europe, fell victim to their own state's propaganda. Fed the founding myths of a "tiny country surrounded by enemies," they developed a sense of inferiority about their own strength.

Feeling powerless is a consequence of abuse. Others control the action: the Arab countries, Israel, the UN, the world powers. One feels the futility of doing anything, waiting instead for others to do things for us, or to us. That resignation certainly applied to the refugees of 1948, who fled for their lives after witnessing or hearing about gruesome massacres. They were too shell-shocked to do anything.

The formation of the PLO was a revolt against that powerlessness. Ghassan Kanafani, who was assassinated by Israel in the early 1970s, aimed his short stories at shattering the paralysis – highlighting characters who surprised everyone by confronting Israel against the odds. The First Intifada, igniting after 20 years of occupation, was another revolt against victimhood.

To the Jewish refugees escaping extreme anti-Semitism and genocide, Israel's creation was supposed to be an empowering rejection of victimhood. Any healing as such was thwarted by Israel's continued denial of the Nakba. Few Israelis who acknowledge the event show remorse. It was "necessary"; they "were forced" to do this; "needed the space urgently" to relocate Holocaust survivors ... Nobody is forced to go into a lone village throwing grenades through the windows, like they did at Deir Yassin. They *chose* to do this. They bear full responsibility. It's the deferral of responsibility that makes the conflict so intractable. When a whole society is indoctrinated to believe that the actions of their founders have been dictated by circumstances, that people have no choice, they are led to conform, to obey whatever their leaders tell them is "necessary" for their security. The way forward is for us to recognize that *we each have a choice*.

When "others control the action," it is easy to blame others for one's problems. Defensiveness and denial of responsibility follow from the mindset of victimhood.

Those who justify suicide bombing by the "dire conditions" under occupation are similarly deflecting responsibility. No one is forced to strap a bomb to their torso. They *chose* that route. They bear responsibility. Morally wrong, random attacks against innocents serve neither freedom nor peace, and have never helped our ultimate aims. The suicide attacks do point out one outcome of extreme abuse. Those who feel they have nothing left to lose stop caring about consequences. It is enough satisfaction to take it to one's abuser.

Heightened stress and anxiety are normal reactions to abuse. The constant smoking and short tempers plaguing the West Bank are symptoms. So is the self-censorship. People are afraid to write or speak their minds because Israel is powerful and has spies everywhere. I know Palestinians living abroad for years who continue to self-censor.

The self-esteem of the chronically abused is destroyed. They feel defeated, lose hope, sense that action is futile. They look down on the selves they detest, wish they are someone else who can stand up to the abuser. Or, like the "soldiers and *shabab*" game we played as children, everyone vied to be "Israelis". After all, they always won.

Sadly, abused persons often become abusers themselves. That is why child abuse is rampant in Occupied Palestine. A parent comes back home after getting harassed at the checkpoint, seething at their powerless situation. Their own child disobeying them adds to their sense of injury and loss of control, except unlike the Israeli soldiers, their child is within their reach. Sad, but real, and it doesn't stop there. From a young age, one is bullied at home, bullied at school, by certain teachers as well as other kids, and bullied on the streets. Tempers flare for the slightest things, like getting cut off in traffic. With the external control the Occupation imposes over their lives, people search for little things they can control.

Some bully *en masse,* parading their lack of respect, feeling, and empathy for others. Every trip home, I experience this self-bullying society: smoking in playgrounds and shared taxi rides; endangerment of lives with reckless driving; littering in public places. Audio bullying: music so loud you could hear in the other part of town, continual honking, shooting at weddings, and partying into the night. We're bullied by PA officials who exert their authority unfairly, bullied by money, bullied by store owners who overcharge, bullied by customers who haggle to death. We're bullied by real estate developers who destroy historical buildings and swallow open space to build high-rises that take light and trees from others, while trashing surrounding lands.

The abuse propagates down generations, unless someone grows enough awareness and determination to break that cycle. It is crucial that, as a society, we do. We cannot expect to thrive, let alone prevail in our quest for justice, when our children suffer from a demolished self-esteem brought about by a lifetime of being bullied. Child abuse perpetuates our greatest enemy for yet another generation: the victimhood perception that is standing in the way of our empowerment and fulfillment.

In Sun Zi's (Sun Tzu) *Art of War,* the number two most important principle for winning is to "know your enemy." Number one is to "know yourself." I can see my own self-censorship and defensive statements in earlier drafts of these chapters. It took decades of healing, while residing elsewhere in the world, to purge my writing of the scars of Occupation. Partially, anyway. Growth is the one "Process" that ought to never end.

Self-awareness is the first step to freedom. Are we taking action following a well-laid out plan, or are we responding instinctively with our programmed abuse response? True independence means not allowing anyone to push our buttons. Sharon succeeded in instigating the Second Intifada because he knew how we would react to his spiteful entry into the Aqsa mosque. We responded to the provocation by behaving exactly as predicted. We willingly fell into Sharon's trap. We were reactive, not proactive.

If our goal is independence, we don't have to wait until the USA or the UN or 150 countries recognize a Palestinian State. We can claim independence now by acting independently. We can surprise them by following our own agenda instead of fulfilling their expectations.

Life has taught me a few lessons in this regard:

We cannot change someone else or control their behavior. We can only change ourselves and can decide only our own actions.

Those believing they are powerless tend to patiently wait for others to change. Hence the inflated reverence for demagogues who claimed our cause, from Gamal Abd-el-Nasser to Saddam, and for inapplicable -isms where our liberation was made contingent on a whole sequence of world events. Naturally, others will act in their own best interest, not necessarily to our liking, so our waiting for them feeds into our sense of helplessness. Everything is seen to be going wrong, the whole world against us.

It is futile to wait for others to change their policies or actions. The way to rebuild our self-esteem, and demolish the myth of powerlessness, is to take what is beyond our control as a given. Accept the universe as it is, and work within our present capacity. Without diminishing our just aspirations, we must seek more effective strategies.

Israel can stop us from going to Haifa. A Wall, soldiers, checkpoints, and we are blocked from going there without their permit. However, they cannot stop us from making Ramallah more livable – cleaning up the trash, building responsibly and respecting city codes and neighbors, regulating our own traffic, or planting more trees. Doing these things does not mean abandoning our lands beyond the Wall. The idea is to build ourselves first. Set up a model society. By taking care of what we have, we further develop the ability to work with one another, to organize, and to stand united.

I was talking to Waheed on a recent visit. I have long admired how he dedicated his career to reforming the educational system in Palestine, precisely the right idea for effecting change. He therefore surprised me, when we got to the social ills of our society – the trash, the corruption, etc. – by saying that these were "secondary problems that we can solve when Palestine is free." I bluntly told him my opinion: if our society is like this, Palestine will never be liberated. How can we organize a campaign for freedom when we can't organize our own trash disposal? Even more fundamentally, what right can we claim to a land that we apparently don't respect? Our social ills are a reason Israel continues to win.

There is a point down the long list of grievances every Palestinian has, beyond which one can no longer justly blame Israel. For those problems, we have to look within, and be prepared to grow. Those who struggled to end segregation in America did so foremost by behaving as if segregation laws were null and void. Similarly, if we want Palestine to be free, we need to behave as if Palestine is already independent.

We cannot make a deal with Israel if it does not want to.

As long as Israel gloats in its power, and sees no value to making peace, negotiations are futile, at least at this point in time. To gain parity in negotiations, we need to transform ourselves, such that they will pursue us to negotiate. Thirty years of negotiations over a two-state solution have come to naught, so why negotiate if it's not going to restore our rights?

We have to choose our battles.

The tendency to challenge every provocation or falsehood can be exploited – by them – to distract us. They throw so much in our direction that we lose sight of the ball. The key is to identify our goal, choose our strategy, and firmly stick to it regardless of their actions. We should only pick the battles necessary to advance our goals.

Primary under this is that we cannot face them militarily at present. Israel and its settlers inflict considerable violence on us. Responding with violence does nothing to secure our freedom and human rights, while giving Israel undeserved international sympathy. It takes effort and ingenuity to inflict any minor damage on an adversary as militarized as Israel. However, it takes more strength and discipline to restrain ourselves not to respond at all.

Something that will advance our goals, and is within reach of individual supporters of Palestinian rights, is economic boycott and divestment. During the First Intifada, we succeeded in avoiding Israeli goods for years, until Oslo brought the illusion of "peace". Thirty years later, Israel still occupies, restricts movement, steals lands, and inflicts violence. It is perfectly within our power, as individuals, to say no.

I am more interested in individual actions that ordinary Palestinians and people of conscience worldwide can take, as opposed to national actions by the PA/PLO. Those entities are outside our control as individuals, and hence are irrelevant. Palestinian leaders, both inside and outside Palestine, were as surprised by the First Intifada as were the Israelis. A true grassroots effort does not wait for governments to act. We start with small actions that inspire others, organically forming nuclei of large-scale change. Initiative comes from the individual.

Healing ourselves from the abuse begins by rebuilding the damaged self-esteem. We simply have to believe in ourselves. There is no room for "bad luck" in the new world we want to be in. We are given what we are given, and it is up to us what do with it. "Fate" is a similarly useless concept. Fatalistic thinking is exactly that – fatal! We are here to grow, not remain stagnant. Similarly destructive thinking, so prevalent in Middle Eastern thought, is "divine intervention". Waiting for help to descend from the sky. The everyday Arabic language is peppered with phrases indicating, or promoting, such beliefs:

"Inshallah," if God wills, possibly the most used phrase in Arabic.
"Be'ein Allah," God will assist.
"Allah Bifrijhah," God will make things better.
"Allah Ysa'idkum," May God help you (i.e., don't count on me).
"Allah Yihmeek," May God protect you.

These phrases we need eliminate from the dictionary. If we want to be effective in our lives, we ought to leave the Creator alone and do our best with what God has given us, not wait for divine rescue.

Adding personal empowerment to our means of resistance, rejecting victimhood, and focusing on individual actions, a "Liberation Plan" emerges that anyone can participate in, and that can inspire and attract worldwide support:

- Foster personal growth and empowerment. Develop and support organizations that promote social work to advance Palestinian society. Rebuild individual self-esteem.
- Work on breaking the cycle of abuse. Support education and shelters for domestic violence and child abuse. Stop abuse in schools.
- Expand support networks by building bridges to everyone, not simply the Arab and Muslim audiences our parents' generation appealed to.
- Become good stewards of our environment.
- Support responsible growth and historical preservation of our heritage.
- Implement rigorous boycotts of Israeli products.

These are but a few of the avenues available to concerned individuals wanting to pave a path for a better future.

"I Am Still Here"

No matter how the Wall turns, how the Occupation is clothed, or from what camera angle the conflict is observed, one fact is inescapable. Millions of human beings, within the borders of historical Palestine, are being treated differently, simply because their declared religion is not that of the state currently in power.

Near the end of the movie "*Welcome to Marwen*," the main character, suffering from PTSD for years following a cruel beating, meets his attackers in the courtroom. They give him nasty looks, hoping the pain of his recollections would choke him from recounting the truth.

He does not falter. He is not afraid. His enemies can no longer hurt him, because, in his own words,

"I am still here."

If the trouble in Palestine was birthed from trauma meted out by the Nazis, so what? Hitler was dead for 75 years. Why are we enslaving ourselves, living people, to his legacy of violence? Why must we continue to fight?

The Here and Now

The current situation is unsustainable. At the same time we cannot expend our lives in endless struggle. The Nakba is over 70 years old, and the Occupation over 50. Most Palestinians within the Wall spent their entire lives under occupation, with no citizenship or identity. Millions of lives were put on hold for far too long. As individuals, we willingly suspended our dreams "until the Occupation ends," "until Palestine is free," or "until Peace reigns." We substituted the external peg of events beyond our control for our own personal responsibility to live our own lives, here and now.

"The only moment to be alive is the present moment."
— Thich Nhat Hanh, *Being Peace*

School could wait, work could wait. So we deferred, strike after strike. Especially so in the First Intifada, when the aroma of freedom was too alluring.

Success is to block the external cacophony from sabotaging our dreams.

Deferring the present is precisely the trouble with the Oslo Accords. Oslo was an Interim agreement, "interim" meaning *against* living in the present. Oslo's five-year "interim phase" is now nearing thirty. It was meant to be temporary, ephemeral, dangling a Palestinian state, but subject to negotiations – not quite there yet. The Oslo Accords had plenty of flaws, but the central one was in that very word "interim": *Oslo showed no respect for people's right to live their lives.* Every Palestinian in the West Bank and Gaza was expected to put up with this transience, constantly learning new ways to move across the multiplying borders, constantly paying attention to the news in case unpredictable events impacted their lives, all the while unable to plan a month ahead. The promise of "peace" lured many to place their lives on hold, "until the interim phase is over," an event never really meant to happen.

The increasing voices to "ditch Oslo" are a natural response to this tyranny. Rather than being partners to this "interim" charade, we can choose to live our lives in the here and now.

Thinking of Oslo in the context of the bullying and abuse, I suddenly saw it in a different light. Oslo is a codified version of Stockholm Syndrome, where hostages bond with their captors and associate their own survival with that of the hostage-takers. The same way the abused advances their abuser's agenda, the PA's raison d'être became to safeguard Israel's security. Regarding the Palestinians under Israel's control a hostage population, it is not surprising that Oslo was signed.

Empowerment and individual responsibility is the way to break out of that trap. We know well that the only viable answer is a government chosen by, accountable to, and serving the needs of *everyone* within its borders. This is what we should aim for and not let ourselves get distracted by interim phases and temporary agreements.

On my latest visit, I ran into one of my uncles. He and Dad had stopped speaking to each other after their disputes about splitting the family business, some forty years ago. I was walking with my daughter when I saw him looking at us, as if he'd noted some familiarity. I felt compelled, if only for her sake, to greet him, introducing myself. He met my olive branch with a lecture, blaming my late father for his own recent failures. It was a different story from what I knew, but never mind. What grabbed my attention was his lingering hostility towards my father, even years after the latter had gone to his grave.

My uncle seemed unwilling to take responsibility for his own life. Seeing him thus, I pitied him, not for the same reasons he pitied himself, but for his inability to let go. Bearing a grudge against anyone does them no harm, but rather consumes the bearer. Releasing my grudges does no one else a favor but myself.

The same day, my brother took me on a drive through the West Bank.

We took a roundabout detour on a decrepit Palestinian road to the nearby city of Nablus, adding an hour-and-a-half to what normally was an hour trip. We drove only briefly on the brand-new Israeli-only highway, where we could, then turned to a segment of the Palestinian road shared by settlers. The army, stationed at frequent embankments, heavily patrolled that stretch. At one point, young children were playing on the sidewalk, taking turns riding a bicycle. The soldiers, hiding behind their fortifications, had their guns pointed at the children.

It was a revolting scene.

Soldiers aiming guns at children, an immoral setup not new to me.

New was glimpsing Israel's invisible wall. As terrible as the Prison Wall they have erected around us, is the Wall of Fear they wrap around themselves!

I had a gun pointed at me twice before I was fifteen. It's hard, when the weapon is aimed at your face, to see the person behind the trigger. Now, forty years later, as an observer on the scene, I can look at the person behind the gun, and even while they are blind to my humanity, I can see theirs. In their faces, I spot the deep lines of perpetual fear, the price they exact from themselves to erect and maintain this system of tribal superiority. The absurdity of the entire Zionist project is highlighted by this reality: fully armored and equipped soldiers taking children for a mortal threat.

It was then that I understood, to be truly free, I have to forgive the Israelis. They live in their self-made fear-prison, and thus cannot escape the role they created for themselves. Without forgiveness, I'll remain entrapped in the role they created *for me*. I will continue to oppose the actions of their government, and to write down historical Truths, but there is no reason to carry angst and animosity. I have to, for my life goes forward from here. Burdening myself with bitterness only strengthens the power their past extends on my future. Forgiveness is the only gateway to true peace, at least to my own *personal peace*, and also the first step to empowerment, for only the strong are capable of forgiving. Despite the abuse and all the difficulties, obstacles, and walls they hurl in my path,

I am still here.

I stopped bothering about their harassments at border crossings. I now gracefully endure the exorbitant and unreasonable tax in time and money it takes to travel to, from, and within Palestine. It no longer upsets me.

"Give unto Caesar what is Caesar's." The Jordanian guards, the Israelis, or the unscrupulous usurers exploiting the situation – from taxi drivers to porters – can all have their micro-power trips, but their domain ends there. They impede the world, not make it go. In that, I pity them. They choose to mask their creative impotence flaunting an illusory power over people whose passports fall into their hands.

In the same spirit, I began greeting the Israeli soldiers at the Bridge. Quite disarming to be treated as human beings, especially when they put on their uniforms and insignia expressly to establish their authority over me. Even more disconcerting to them, by doing so, I am rejecting the subordinate role they assigned me, asserting instead my place as *an equal*. They claim authority to let me in, or bar entry. They can delay, search, hassle, or detain me. They are stuck in that role, but I don't have to be. Treating them like human beings, emphasizing my lack of animosity towards them as individuals, I am making my own statement of power. With their expecting hostility, my friendliness often gives them pause.

In the face of their attempts to dehumanize me, my best means of resistance is to assert my humanity!

I reject Israel's policies, but do I have any personal grudge against those individual soldiers manning the border? No. Similarly, the soldiers who knocked on the door, scaring the three-year-old me, didn't do so with that intention. They simply followed orders to knock on every door and search every home.

So back to my uncle and my dad. Neither could escape the hold my grandfather had on them, putting them together in the same business, favoring Isaac over Ishmael and Jacob over Esau. I had come to terms, and forgiven my dad for his mistakes in my regard. Perhaps it's time to take it a step further and forgive my grandfather (whom I've never met), and all his ancestors, back to our supposed "common ancestor", for all the craziness they bequeathed to us. Perhaps they didn't know any better, stumbling their way, striving to be as good parents as they knew how. All I can aim for is to do better myself – take my revenge by being the best parent I can be to my child.

Perhaps, if I get the chance to time-travel and meet Theodore Herzl, I will forgive him too.

I had to rush back to Palestine urgently at the beginning of 2020, just before the COVID pandemic. My mother was in the hospital again. She spent three weeks in the ICU. Sandra and all my brothers were there. At times it felt like we were pulling Mom from the jaws of death. Thankfully she made it. Each day during my stay, the Israelis cut off the power to different sections of Ramallah for a few hours at a time. The hospitals had their own generators, but we worried about keeping her medical equipment running at home. It was difficult to leave.

In the long hours in the waiting rooms, Hakeem and I got to chat, and he encouraged me to publish this book.

From him, I learned a curious fact about Ol' Granny, our ancient neighbor who perpetually argued with the shepherd when he let his goats at the Fig Tree. It turned out her land was on the *other* side of our house from the tree. In other words, the Fig Tree wasn't even hers!

When I was growing up, we not only tolerated their daily exchange, we came to expect it. The shepherd wouldn't be who he was if he didn't let his goats taste the fig leaves, and the old woman wouldn't be who she was if she didn't shout at him. It was their custom, their habit.

Habits can be changed. Not to change the habits of grannies or shepherds, but it seems that much of the seething animosity that underlies the conflict is a carryover by force of habit. The world stopped caring because the world is expecting us to keep fighting, till eternity. It is up to us to disappoint them!

We have to imagine a better world, for if we can't even imagine that, we must be truly doomed.

To be fair to Ol' Granny, she wasn't all curses to the shepherd. Sometimes when we played in the street, Danny and I overheard their exchanges. Once the shepherd called her "auntie", in an attempt to endear himself. It was then that she admonished him to use the proper Arabic term *khalti* for the imported word. Another time she spoke of the harm a fig tree incurs when the goats denude it. She extolled the tree's benefits. She loved the Land, saw the value of open space, and cared for the trees, hers or not. Tapping the wisdom that had built the *sanasel* and tended the Earth, she knew something ... if only more of us listened.

Ol' Granny has long passed away, the Fig Tree lives.

In its shadow, I looked for an escape from Ramallah's daytime shroud of dust and car horns. I yearned for a moment's peace to meditate, a special place isolated from all distractions. Having endured the encroachments of humans and goats and construction trucks, the Tree, kindly, communicated its secret. It waits not for cleaner air before it breathes, nor does it let the dust stop it from feeding on sunlight. The Tree sets no preconditions for its existence. It simply exists.

Peace cares less for an isolated garden. Neither is it secured by decades of negotiations and stipulations. Peace is to be found wherever you are, at any moment. Within.

Ultimately, I intuited the essential meaning of "Sumud", as it applies to myself:

"Sumud" is continuing to tell the story!

About the Author

Ramsey Hanhan, having come to America from Palestine in his teens, had experienced first-hand both the Israeli occupation of his country, and the immigrant journey of rebuilding life anew. In his former career, he was a physics professor noted for his computer models that describe and predict complexity in nature. Nowadays, you can find him on a jogging trail, deep in the forest, at an airport, or in a coffee shop. For his next titles, he is finishing a romantic novella and a collection of essays. Hanhan holds a Ph.D. in Engineering from the University of Michigan.

Fomite

Writing a review on social media sites for readers will help the progress of independent publishing. To submit a review, go to the book page on any of the sites and follow the links for reviews. Books from independent presses rely on reader-to-reader communications.

For more information or to order any of our books, visit:
http://www.fomitepress.com/our-books.html More novels from Fomite...

Joshua Amses — *During This, Our Nadir*
Joshua Amses — *Ghats*
Joshua Amses — *How They Became Birds*
Joshua Amses — *Raven or Crow*
Joshua Amses — *The Moment Before an Injury*
Charles Bell — *The Married Land*
Charles Bell — *The Half Gods*
Jaysinh Birjepatel — *Nothing Beside Remains*
Jaysinh Birjepatel — *The Good Muslim of Jackson Heights*
David Brizer — *Victor Rand*
L. M Brown — *Hinterland*
Paula Closson Buck — *Summer on the Cold War Planet*
Dan Chodorkoff — *Loisaida*
Dan Chodorkoff — *Sugaring Down*
David Adams Cleveland — *Time's Betrayal*
Paul Cody — *Sphyxia*
Jaimee Wriston Colbert — *Vanishing Acts*
Roger Coleman — *Skywreck Afternoons*
Stephen Downes — *The Hands of Pianists*
Marc Estrin — *Hyde*
Marc Estrin — *Kafka's Roach*
Marc Estrin — *Proceedings of the Hebrew Free Burial Society*
Marc Estrin — *Speckled Vanities*
Marc Estrin — *The Annotated Nose*
Zdravka Evtimova — *In the Town of Joy and Peace*
Zdravka Evtimova — *Sinfonia Bulgarica*
Zdravka Evtimova — *You Can Smile on Wednesdays*

Fomite

Daniel Forbes — *Derail This Train Wreck*
Peter Fortunato — *Carnevale*
Greg Guma — *Dons of Time*
Richard Hawley — *The Three Lives of Jonathan Force*
Lamar Herrin — *Father Figure*
Michael Horner — *Damage Control*
Ron Jacobs — *All the Sinners Saints*
Ron Jacobs — *Short Order Frame Up*
Ron Jacobs — *The Co-conspirator's Tale*
Scott Archer Jones — *And Throw Away the Skins*
Scott Archer Jones — *A Rising Tide of People Swept Away*
Julie Justicz — *Degrees of Difficulty*
Maggie Kast — *A Free Unsullied Land*
Darrell Kastin — *Shadowboxing with Bukowski*
Coleen Kearon — *#triggerwarning*
Coleen Kearon — *Feminist on Fire*
Jan English Leary — *Thicker Than Blood*
Diane Lefer — *Confessions of a Carnivore*
Diane Lefer — *Out of Place*
Rob Lenihan — *Born Speaking Lies*
Colin McGinnis — *Roadman*
Douglas W. Milliken — *Our Shadows' Voice*
Ilan Mochari — *Zinsky the Obscure*
Peter Nash — *Parsimony*
Peter Nash — *The Least of It*
Peter Nash — *The Perfection of Things*
George Ovitt — *Stillpoint*
George Ovitt — *Tribunal*
Gregory Papadoyiannis — *The Baby Jazz*
Pelham — *The Walking Poor*
Andy Potok — *My Father's Keeper*
Frederick Ramey — *Comes A Time*
Joseph Rathgeber — *Mixedbloods*
Kathryn Roberts — *Companion Plants*
Robert Rosenberg — *Isles of the Blind*

Fomite

Fred Russell — *Rafi's World*
Ron Savage — *Voyeur in Tangier*
David Schein — *The Adoption*
Charles Simpson — *Uncertain Harvest*
Lynn Sloan — *Principles of Navigation*
Lynn Sloan — *Midstream*
L.E. Smith — *The Consequence of Gesture*
L.E. Smith — *Travers' Inferno*
L.E. Smith — *Untimely RIPped*
Bob Sommer — *A Great Fullness*
Tom Walker — *A Day in the Life*
Susan V. Weiss — *My God, What Have We Done?*
Peter M. Wheelwright — *As It Is On Earth*
Peter M. Wheelwright — *The Door-Man*
Suzie Wizowaty — *The Return of Jason Green*

www.ingramcontent.com/pod-product-compliance
Lightning Source LLC
Chambersburg PA
CBHW022036220526
45357CB00059B/201